SHORT CUTS

Sam McColl

MCELLISONS

Edinburgh

First published in Great Britain in 2018 by
McEllisons, 4/6 Hillside Street,
Edinburgh, EH7 5HB

A CIP catalogue record of this book is available
from the British Library

ISBN 978-0-9957026-1-5

CONTENTS

I QUIT

THERE'S NOTHING UNUSUAL about waking through the slime of a dream about rape and loss and misery, but when I grope the pillow beside me for my fags, the first as yet unformed flutter of panic forces my eyes open.

It's true, then. A feeling as intense as the death of a loved one sweeps through me. Frozen, I stare at the wall and tell myself to calm down. Peter, my friend, is dying of lung cancer at the age of forty-nine and I decided a few weeks ago in a responsible manner, along with Sophie (flatmate and fellow puffer), to choose life. Since her mother died she's gone from a meagre five or six a day to over twenty. I smoke forty – at least. We planned this. We're going to do it. We applied our first nicotine patches at twenty-three hundred hours last night, smoked our last cigarette at twenty-three thirty hours and flushed our last smokes down the pan together at midnight.

The memory makes me feel a bit bitter – I mean better. I get out of bed and shower. The urge to call Sophie and see how she's doing nags at me, but she's on early shift – it'll go to voicemail.

Walking to work has got me through a lot of withdrawals, it'll get me through this one too. Amazingly, at this time of morning it's still cold enough to see my breath and for all of a minute I blow out great funnels of the stuff and smirk at the irony. I'd be on my third by now. There it is again, the death of another sibling – just for an instant. I try to reach back to it, grab it so I can spit in its face before mashing it, but it's the devil itself, and dances off gleefully, flicking at my gut, threatening unimaginable loss, forcing me to search for the early openers as I reach the beginning of Raeburn Place. First newsagent I come to I stop dead and stare at the small ads in the window. Do we need a washing machine? No. So I study the picture of someone's lost cat, Nov 2004 – be dead by now. A Ford Fiesta – no thanks. Between the ad for a twin buggy and a pair of budgies I can just see the rows of cigarettes. No harm in looking. I could ask about the twin buggy – one of the secretaries at work is expecting twins – it'd be quite natural to ask for a pen, take the number, no harm in going in …

The guy behind the counter looks up. I fear my jaw might be hanging open when he carefully lays his lit cigarette in the ashtray, which is balanced on an old safe next to the till. I am transfixed as I watch the lethal silver thread coil upwards in lazy nooses, willing one to come my way.

'Do you have a pen I could borrow?' I manage eventually. 'I want to take down a number from one of your ads, if that's okay.' I accept the pen, move back to the door and write the number on the back of my hand. My bravado of the night before was sheer lunacy, I'm not ready, I'm simply unprepared. I should have told everyone at the office for a start, I should have got sponsors, set it up. This is just typical of me – swept away by a crazy moment of empathy, bordering on the obsessive for Peter. Who on earth did I think I was? I'm only just coping with being off the booze. I'm far younger than Peter and most likely have years of healthy happy puffing ahead of me before I've even got to *think* of giving up. Even my motives are suspicious. Am I trying to rub it in – show him how together I am, prove I can succeed where he has failed? That I can choose life? Bollocks.

I pat my jacket pocket, the one I keep my wallet in. Something invisible takes a swing at me, but the pain's real enough. I swing back, flailing wildly for some strength of character, some resolve, and almost immediately it surges towards me on a wave of anger that extends rapidly and illogically to all the smokers of the world who kid themselves they're happy. 'Take away their fags,' it roars, 'take away the booze – see how chipper they are then!' Tell him, I say to myself, tell the idiot behind the counter – take them away, burn the lot of them!

Having avoided eye contact with the enemy till now, my anger makes me reckless and my gaze locks aggressively with a row of Marlboro. Contrary to my fears, I feel immediately calmer, reassured. I begin to see that even owning a packet might be enough, that it's partly the comforting bulge in my pocket that I miss.

As I hand back the pen, I drag my gaze off my seductress and search briefly in the stranger's face for a sign. Is he trying to give up too? Was that why he left his cigarette to smoke itself? Does he cough his guts up every morning and secretly despise himself for his weakness? The inch-long ash-worm drops silently to the floor. Its owner picks up the almost finished butt, takes one more suck and folds it over on itself, crushing the life out of it. I feel the pain of extinction too. I pull out my wallet, flip it open and offer the proprietor a look of acute despair.

'Thanks for the pen. Stupid, I've got no cash. I'll just find a cash—'

'We have a machine in the corner if you don't mind the charge.'

'Thank you.'

I feel trapped, confused, but take out my card anyway and wave it, hoping he hasn't seen the notes. I punch in my pin and draw out fifty quid.

'Marlboro, please.'

It works: the bulge in my breast pocket gives me comfort and courage. I set off at a pace and blow out again, this time owning the breath, this time acknowledging gratefully that it's steam – warm, damp air, not the effluent from an act of self-harm. Ha. I do it again, ignore the small collapse deep within, and for a few seconds, for a few golden seconds, I glimpse, no not glimpse, feel something, no, not feel so much as understand. Have I understood? Well no, not really – it wasn't really an understanding thing. Shit. And whatever it was has well and truly split while I was trying to glue meaning to the fucker. I grab at something else: there's not a smoker in the land who'd not, if they were man enough to be honest, rather be me. Ha, yes, this was true. I've nailed it.

Pale yellow sunlight spangles the glass on the flats opposite. I feel stupidly touched, emotional, close to tears, happy that I live in Edinburgh, didn't have a drink today, that I finally have a girlfriend, that she knows everything, that me and Sophie worked things out, that her mother is dead, that I have a job …

But I can't stay with it. A minute later any sense of triumph or conceit vanishes as the sordid implications of such a rash promise rush at me like a tsunami of wasted lives: hundreds of times a day – in fact every emotion, every thought, every breath I gasp, inhale or gulp is enhanced, punctuated or born by the actual or virtual link to my next cigarette. Without these small lifts, I realise, in a blink, my job would be untenable and I'd lose it. Then where would I be? I need to think seriously about giving up, and not just radically threaten so much stability for so many people for the sake of an unknown threat to my health. It is, in fact, I'm realising fast, intolerably, irresponsibly, selfish.

And so it goes on. I'm in a bad way – and I've only been up a couple of hours.

I know fine well that support at work will be weak – most of them smoke. As I walk up Broughton Street I notice a tramp being moved on by a policeman – that could be me in a few months' time. Something hardens up; I hung on by the skin of my teeth when I gave up drinking, made it through the vicarious underworld where nightmares are spawned and lived out – maybe I could again. With a bit of luck maybe I could.

'William's waiting for you.'

'Okay, give me a couple of minutes – get him a coffee, will you?'

I climb the two flights to my cubbyhole of an office mentally preparing myself for what lies beyond by inhaling deeply and holding my breath. I pick up the ashtray without looking down and shake the contents into the waste-paper basket which I leave in the passage for the cleaners. Then I open the window, stare down into the alleyway and up into the sky and leave it open. Ignoring the pull of the waste-paper basket's gaze through the wall, I pick up the phone and call down to the receptionist. 'Send him up.' But my coat's got its beady eye on me too. I snatch it off the door and jam it in the filing cabinet.

William knocks gently. 'Hello, Jack.'

'Come in,' I say, slamming the drawer shut and spinning round guiltily. 'Wow, you've got a lot of papers there. Is there a lot to go over?'

'No more than usual.' He looks around suspiciously. 'You okay, Jack? Something wrong? Something going on?'

'Nothing wrong, no. Or going on – it's our weekly catch-up, William,' I say, settling like a stranger in my chair. 'We're having it today, rather than tomorrow, because tomorrow you're wife's due to have a baby ...'

'Yes, yes, I know that, why else would I have this lot?' (He raises the tray of papers like a macabre toast.) 'But something's odd. Why's the window open? Why aren't I gasping for air? What are you up to?'

9

'Christ – can't I have a little fresh air without you waking the dead? Sorry, Sherlock, but can we get on, only I've got a very full morning.'

William dumps the tray on my desk, chooses the yellow vinyl chair and perches on its edge, folding his hands on top of his knees. It's hard to imagine him having a wife.

'Here are the papers for that house in Morningside. The owner's not happy that I'm not going to be around. You got it covered? Read up on the period pieces? It's a fabulous house, you know. No one's touched anything for a hundred years.'

'Yep. I was up there on Friday. All's good.' Having just sat down, I now get up, go to the window and close it.

'Are you okay, Jack – is this a bad time?'

'No. Well, yes, I have a lot on my plate at the moment. My sister's getting married – I've not written a speech, or, well, a million things. Would you like coffee or tea?'

'Thank you – tea please. Bonnie is it? Here in Edinburgh? I forgot you had that on.'

Without replying I almost run out the door. As soon as I'm in the passage I drop to my knees and stick my head inside the waste-paper basket. But the bitter-stale smell isn't enough. I pause hotly and shamefully before lifting it onto my knees and diving downward in guilty anticipation. I lean back against the wall and stare at a black-streaked butt about two inches in length, trying not to hyperventilate or giggle.

'Jack, what on earth's the matter?'

William must have opened the office door several seconds earlier.

'Nothing, absolutely nothing,' I say, waving it around. 'Got it in time – some idiot must have dropped this without stubbing it out properly. Tuh.' I tap my nose. I'm pretty sure it's the wrong gesture to make but William is used to my eccentricities and goes quiet.

'Now where was I? Tea?'

I rush to the tiny kitchen – slosh water into the kettle, grab the gas lighter and hold it to the butt when William's irritating little face peeks around the door jamb.

'Need a hand?'

I wave the dog-end around again for a second or two hoping he might bugger off, and then gloomily run it under the tap.

'Here we go,' I say, snatching up a tray, making the coffee and tea and taking them through to the office, William on my heels like a bloody spaniel.

'Now where were we?' I open my filing cabinet drawer, rummage under my coat, pull out some chocolate chip digestives and shake them onto my desk.

'Still taking sugar are you?' I ask, holding a spoon of the stuff above his cup. 'Only I know you were trying to give up …'

And then his face lights up like a fucking firework.

'My God, that's it! Give up, give up – you've given up smoking! I'm right aren't I? That's why you're so jumpy, why you were hugging the waste-paper basket, why the window was open! Congratulations Jack, this is wonderful news …'

'Actually I've not decided anything – I don't think I can do it – it's for a friend.'

He giggles and taps the side of his nose.

I sit on my hands.

'In the lap of the gods eh? This is just what you need, Jack – a challenge, choosing to live, setting an example. Please, take your hands out from under your backside and let me shake one of them.'

THE RIVER

LIAM TOOK THE KEY from under the bin and let himself in, but stayed only long enough to change into a dry hoody and sweats from the ironing pile and grab his waterproof off the backdoor hook. He was late, his mum would be home soon – he hadn't missed a day this week and had no intention of letting a little rain spoil his routine.

The swollen river was the colour of strong tea and the woods hissed with rain. He was hot and sweaty from the run and his stomach muscles hardened with anticipation. A few weeks ago he had stashed some dope in a jar beneath a fallen oak tree and the thought of getting high doubled the incentive to spend long afternoons and evenings at the river.

He squatted down against the log and pulled his hood up to make a rough shelter from the rain and rolled a one-skinner and lit it. Then, as though it wasn't raining at all he stretched out his legs and leaned back. He might have fallen asleep if a solid trickle of rain hadn't run off his hood and puddled on his belly. He folded over, hacked a lazy cough, stood up, shook out his top and stared at the river. A few seconds later, he stripped off down to his underpants, wrapped everything in his waterproof and rammed it all under a nearby root.

The way the water flowed into the shallow pools of his collarbones and wrapped around his neck sent a thrill right through him. He tried to make his breath steady and smooth, suppressing the occasional sharp gasp of hysteria. As he moved a little way from the bank the water picked up pace and needles of rain stung his face. He grabbed a twisted hazel branch above his head with both hands and wrestled with it until his arms ached. Trillions of tiny silver splashes steamed hypnotically and he half-closed his eyes. And then he let go and his feet lost their hold. He lunged up and back but the branch was out of reach. Over and again he kicked upwards searching for a handhold, but he was weak with dope, his eyes blinded by water and in the end there was nothing to do but go with it and paddle. The bank raced past, a low-slung branch caught his shoulder – he barely felt it. A row of those damned willow came and went, the oak with the rotten middle. Everything went spinning past. He began to urge his arms and legs to pull and push until at last some kind of regular pattern emerged. It felt like an hour, but it was only a few minutes before the river slowed into a broad pool. Standing at last, he pushed himself forward with long swaggering strides. He blew great plumes of water into the air and shook himself and saw it cascade off his skin and it was beautiful.

He pulled himself onto the bank, lay down, stuck his tongue out and caught the tingling rain.

He must do it again, go back, do it again. He stood up. His legs felt weird. He felt weird. He was changed. He could swim! He dropped into a press-up position and pumped: up down up down. And after a few burning minutes he rolled onto his back and started to giggle. It wasn't a wish anymore – it wasn't a hope. Sometimes over the past week he'd touched the bottom, just the faintest unacknowledged push, but now he remembered each and every cheat with the condescension of the expert. This time there was no hesitation – he walked back up the river and, with only the very smallest gasp, lowered himself into the water and found his hands and feet more than ready and eager to paddle and loop and kick.

As Liam heaved himself from the water a third time, Brian stepped up from behind a tree and offered him a hand. Liam stared, eyes widening. The other two were leaning casually against the crowding trees. Liam heard a camera shutter snap and the triumph of the previous moment transformed into humiliation: he knew what he had looked like in his underpants, a child taking his first struggling strokes, a prick.

Ignoring the hand he pulled himself onto the bank, twisting as he sprang up to face the river, feet still in the water, conscious now of the spots on his back and his exposing boxers.

Brian and Shawn and Dougie dropped tight beside him, ripped off their socks and shoes and flung them over their shoulders like grenades. The steady rain dripping from the trees popped and crackled like distant gunfire.

'Come on, guys, last in's a gay-boy.' All three sprang to their feet and tore off their clothes. Liam stood too, preparing to run, but Brian and Dougie snatched his arms and held him.

'Aw, come on, Liam, show us your doggie paddle.' And they pushed him hard and he fell sideways into the pool and swallowed water.

By the time he'd found his feet they were on him. Shawn and Dougie held one arm each. Brian nodded and placed his hands on the back of Liam's head and pushed forward and down.

Under the water and beyond the rushing of noise in his ears, he could hear them counting. They pulled him up after twenty. Liam gulped at the air. Brian pushed again. Liam began kicking with his legs as he felt his lungs spasm.

They were going to kill him.

After the fourth ducking, Liam's mind and lungs began to balloon and go soft and cave in. They dragged him up, words distant and slow. Liam hung from their grip like a doll.

'Come on, man.' They hauled him towards the bank.

'Let's go, Brian,' Shawn said. 'He's not worth it.'

'Fuck you! What's wrong with you guys – he's an idiot.'

Liam felt his arms released, but he was so weak that his head went easily down. When he surfaced, Brian grabbed his arm and twisted it behind his back, forced him over.

'Com'on, big man, stand up for yourself,' he said as he threw Liam forward in disgust, then waded after him, punched him hard in the kidneys, before turning to the bank where the other two were finding their scattered gear, silently pulling on their clothes. 'Com'on man.'

Brian batted the water again and spat and heaved himself out.

Liam folded over, coughing, clutching himself. When they were out of sight, he made it to the bank, gripped a root. A sleepy, post-adrenalin sludge was seeping through him but it was a long time before he managed to haul himself out and crawl to the knot of clothes jammed under the roots, and with his fingers numb and clumsy and his skin like glue, it took an age of damp pulling to judder his clothes back on. Desperate for a smoke, he first needed to make sure he was alone, so he tramped a few clumsy circles through the trees. They were gone – he was sure they were gone.

At last his wrinkled and fumbling fingers extracted a Rizla without it tearing and he laid it between two deep creases on the old oak's trunk. Then he crushed the heated hash and mixed it with tobacco and tipped it in the trough and eventually it all came trembling together. He sucked at it, hunched over the smoke as though it might warm him and, once it was done, he crumpled down onto his side and pulled his knees up, clamped his arms between his legs, waited for the nausea and shakes to pass and slept.

Later, in bed, he relived the near drowning. He could see it all – the way they'd crept up on him, commando-like, through the woods, the glint of a blade, Brian's muscular hands pushing his head down, he saw himself thrashing under the water and felt the collapse of his lungs …

But in the end he'd won, hadn't he, had shamed Shawn and Dougie and to hell with Brian; they had tried to drown a boy and the boy had been too strong for them and they had given up.

Closing his eyes, he heard the roar of the crowd as the gap closed between him and Brian, sought out his parents in the crowd and caught the pride in their smiles as he ducked to receive the medal around his neck, felt his fist raised in triumph … And all because – the boy could swim.

ANYONE FOR DARTS?

'TELL ME, ROSS,' the head teacher said as he deliberately and slowly squinted down the barrel of a pencil. 'Is there a reason for this sudden deterioration in your behaviour? I haven't been able to discuss this, this latest distraction, with Mr Hyslop due to him taking a few days' leave, so it looks like we'll have to muddle through – just the two of us.'

Aiming the wretched pencil directly at Ross's head, he shut one eye and flexed his forearm delicately and at a decreasing angle until it came to a threatening halt. He remained motionless and meditative for a few seconds and then, as if remembering where he was, he put the pencil down. 'Sorry, Ross. I've got a darts match tonight – was hoping to get away early for a practice ... So let's do this, shall we?'

Giving the pencil one more sly aim before opening a drawer in his desk, he dropped it inside.

Ross had made up his mind a long time ago that Mr Leadbetter was mad, the pencil confirmed it, and Ross begun to stand up, but the noise of a gun going off made him rethink. Only it wasn't a gun; it was the front legs of the head teacher's chair hitting the floorboards. But there was something in the force behind it, and the way Mr Leadbetter rammed his glasses down onto his nose, that made Ross sit up and pay attention. Mr Leadbetter didn't speak, though. Instead he lifted two A4 sheets of paper off his desk and hid his expression behind them for what seemed like an awkwardly long time.

'Sorry about that, Ross. I wanted to read back over the year. *A promising and intelligent boy. Well mannered and conscientious.*' He sat back and resettled his glasses onto his forehead. 'But sadly this has all changed over the last few months. Let me quote. *A bright young man heading for trouble. His attitude towards authority is challenging. Unable to focus on work, affecting apathy towards all subjects. Social difficulties.* You've already been excluded once and have a lot of unexplained absences.' He lowered the sheets and let them drop. 'Fair summary?'

Ross shrugged.

'Because,' Mr Leadbetter went on, patting the papers. 'Because, the thing is, Ross, if you keep this kind of behaviour up, your prospects of leaving school with some useful grades, and by useful I mean grades that might help you get into college or pick up an apprenticeship of some kind, will be compromised. Have you taken that pencil by the way?'

'You put it in the drawer, sir.'

'So I did. See? You're a bright lad and I don't want you to fail. Any ideas what I should do with you?'

'No, sir.'

'Anything going on at home I should know about? Any reason you're late most mornings?'

Briefly Ross felt the shame of his father leaving for the last time. It had been very sudden. He'd missed the bus, was hoping for a lift to school, sitting on a stack of blocks beside the garage, muttering under his breath in a range of emphasis and tones. 'Dad, can I get a lift?', or 'Dad, the bus was early and I missed it,' or even 'Dad, could you drop me at school on your way to work?' And when his father appeared through the front door, he'd stood up, and prepared to begin. But the withering look on his father's face erased the small speech and skewed his mouth into a frightened smile as he flattened out against the garage wall. And when his father climbed into the sleek black two-seater and Ross willed his legs to move, they wouldn't, so instead of running round the side of the car like any other boy would do, he'd stood like a dummy and watched the wheels bite the gravel and speed away. And that was the last time he'd seen him. Or heard from him or anything.

'Well?' Mr Leadbetter said.

'Sometimes I miss the bus. Then get a lift. Makes me late sometimes.'

'So that bus might be something you make an effort to catch. Got any idea of what you want to do when you leave school?'

'Nuh.' Ross shifted uneasily in his seat. The longest-term thing he'd ever pictured was moving in with his father, how to get money to score, and, of course, Abi ...

'Maybe it's time you did, because in no time at all you'll be asked to choose your subjects for Standard Grade; you need to get a picture of what you want to do in life. What does your father do, Ross?'

'He's the manager at the Soroba Hotel.'

'Hospitality. A very good career. Does that appeal to you at all?'

'Not thought about it, sir – maybe.'

The conversation ran along these lines, with the head teacher vividly describing some of his own less orthodox ambitions when he was a lad, until Ross, despite doing his best to remain numb, found his mind forming a daft picture of himself as Alan Sugar or a vet or a lawyer or the owner of a chain of hotels with a massive salary and a holiday home and at least one fast car ...

'But without qualifications, Ross,' Mr Leadbetter continued after a long pause, 'without keeping your focus and your emotions under control, you won't have any of that. In fact ...' He leaned forward in his seat. 'In fact, I'd say that, with the way things are looking right now, you're treading a very fine line, Ross. Because once you stop caring, once you actively start making the lives of your teachers hell, once that happens, it's very easy to slip through the net. And some do. We do our best, but a lot of young people are leaving school without a lot going for them. I'm sure your father would feel very disappointed if you became one of those boys.'

Ross stared down between his knees.

'Tell you what. We're going to arrange a meeting. I'll invite your parents and Mr Hyslop to it and we'll talk things over. We're only human, Ross, no one at this school wants you to fail, but we can't do this without your co-operation. You are the hinge, so to speak, on which the door to your future depends. As I said, I know you're a good lad at heart, and a bright one. But poor behaviour has consequences. Do we understand each other?'

Ross lifted his gaze briefly and found to his surprise that the head teacher's face was softer than he remembered, and a lot friendlier too. A painful lump gathered in his throat and he tried to clear it. 'Yes, sir.'

And along with the lump came the beginnings of a hazy picture in his mind of his parents sitting in this office or another one just like it: his father was shaking the head teacher's hand and smiling and wagging his head in tearful disbelief and approval ...

'Well, good. And because I'm a big softy I'm going to recommend that we don't exclude you this time. However, I want you to do something for me – I want you...' he said, holding up a pamphlet, 'I want you to take this booklet on careers and look through it, see if anything takes your fancy. And I want to talk again tomorrow. Okay? How does that sound?'

'Good.' Ross made eye contact for the first time. 'Thank you.'

'Good lad. In my opinion, there's nothing like seeing yourself in the future to find yourself in the present. At least, it helped me when I was your age. Now, Ross, I believe Mr Walters is waiting for you. You'll be wanting to apologise for today's outburst won't you, and complete the work you've missed in class?' He smiled. 'You can go now – unless there's something else you'd like to say.'

Over the course of the last fifteen minutes Ross had forgotten. But now he remembered and stood unsteadily.

'Nothing else, no,' he said.

He picked up the chair he'd been sitting on and threw it hard at the window.

SALT CUTS

BACK THEN, THERE was snow in winter, in the eighties – loads of it, and that Christmas holiday the cobbled streets of the Colonies were packed hard. Despite the weather many residents rode bikes to get around and the tyres cut dark salt gashes through the glassy pavements.

I lived at number 23 Bell Place with my brother, Jack, and my parents. I say Jack, because technically he lived with us, but it didn't feel like it. He'd been away a whole year, been awarded a scholarship to a posh boarding school in the middle of nowhere and we were all dead proud. At least we were meant to be. We were proper celebrities – no one in our street had been *away* to school before and for a bit it was exciting.

But that wore off soon enough. Jack kept writing, asking us to let him come home. Mum tried to be brave, tried to believe he'd get a better job in the end, like everyone said – be happier. But my life felt over. Jack was as much a part of me as the house was, or my room – or anything at all. Once he'd gone, I had no one to play with, no one to make apple-pie beds for and no one to share those secret looks, the ones that got us through tea, when Dad got all moody about something. And then we got a letter to say that he'd made a friend, and asked if he could bring him back for Christmas, and we were all chuffed to bits.

Gopal had never seen snow before – he came from a desert, he said, where there was only sand. But for me, in the beginning, the snow meant it was like living in my beloved Narnia and I would often pretend that Mr Tumnus was about to hop out from behind a lamp post or imagine I could hear the dreadful queen whooshing towards me in her sleigh.

But then it stopped snowing, froze at night and froze in the day and Edinburgh soon turned into some sort of snowman cemetery, or so Jack said, as he poked around in the dirty heaps.

Snow *body-parts*, we called them – of all shapes and sizes – discarded scarves, mittens and hats snaking through drifts or hanging from branches like funky snow fruit.

On sunny days we'd work the snow into slush and make ice balls, filling polythene bags with them, pelting unsuspecting passers-by from behind parked cars. One time, while Jack and me were replenishing stock in the back garden, Gopal chucked one at Dad just before he turned down our path – he hadn't seen him get out the van, didn't know his clumping walk, didn't recognise the great coat or his woolly hat pulled down hard. The nut of ice caught his cheekbone. Gopal rushed to apologise, but Dad barely looked at him, balled Jack out instead. Now of course it's easy to imagine what my father must have felt (an Enoch Powell fan) when this dark-skinned boy got off the train with his son, how humiliating it must have been – the whole street would have been mutterin' – and with the way things were, he most likely thought Jack had done it on purpose.

But whatever nastiness may have been lurking in the house that holiday, I felt none of it – not at the start. All I knew was that my brother was back from boarding school for a few weeks with his friend, who was unlike anyone I'd met before – a kind, funny, exotic prince, quite different from all the other hateful boys in the street.

Most days we would go to the park. Mum usually came with us, but that day we were alone. The coal-man was due and she needed to pay him. She gave us money for hot chocolate and told us to be good. The park was grim: butchered snow families were everywhere, making it look like one of them mass murder scenes from off the telly, except funny. For a bit we sat on the bench beside the swings, pushing our breath out in long funnels of smoke. The sky was heavy like lead or a humungous wave held back by the row of trees running along the top edge. We pictured it bursting through, gathering us up like so many dolls, splattering us against buildings, carrying us cartoon-like through the city and out into the Firth of Forth.

We were early. It could be a couple of hours before the local kids trickled in with their mates and probably not till after lunch before mums with pushchairs would swap a freezing hour in the cold for a little peace and a blether. To pass time, we built a body-part camp. In less than an hour we had a solid triangular fortress and a mountain of ammunition. We would wait for the enemy – any enemy, but none came.

We fooled about on the swings for a bit. Then I remembered the money Mum had given me, asked Jack if I could be the one to buy hot chocolate from the café on Dundas Street. I felt so made up; as I left the park they whistled at me, cheered and whooped and my heart nearly burst from the sheer joy of just being me and being part of them.

But that was then. I shift my weight to my other side, put my feet up on the stool. Been married four years now, about to drop my second baby.

I'm double the size with this one. If it's a boy, it'll be Jack, we've settled on that at least. Jack junior. It's almost five, his lordship will be home in an hour – I'll need to put the tea on. Ten more minutes, then I'll get up.

Seriously though, that was the last time I ever felt like that: so a part of everything, so, so complete. Even now, with a baby on the way, it never feels like that – most of the time it's all just one big hassle. Not that I think about it much – don't do deep, leave that sort of thing to Mum, but I can't help wondering, all the same, if that's when everyone gets their last taste of it, happiness that is, around ten or eleven – before all the shit starts to really sink in, before you clock stuff about life that drowns all that rubbish once and for all. Like an inevitable part of growing up.

I must have been about ten minutes getting the chocolate. Soon as I was through the gates I could hear shouting coming from behind the wall high above the side of the park that runs along Scotland Street. I couldn't see much because of the trees, just sprays of snowballs fanning out and crashing onto the grass, but instead of vanishing into the snow like our ones did, small stones rolled and bounced across the frozen ground.

I recognised some of the voices though: lads from school – lads Jack would have known in primary. Then Jack and Gopal streaked across the grass towards the camp, covering their heads with their arms to avoid the loaded snowballs and I sneaked over the path to see better, to reassure myself that this was still fun. It was then I saw Danny, just his profile, caught in the cobweb of bare branches.

Danny was about fourth oldest out of seven, eight maybe – still at school. I didn't know much about him, but I knew enough to be scared, too scared to do anything but edge closer into the fence and duck down behind some sort of evergreen bush. Nine faces I counted then, nine in all. I couldn't see the camp, not fully, where Jack and Gopal were, but I could see *them*, thugs, not boys anymore, as they filed out through the gap in the wall. Could see them swagger and hear them laugh, bulging poly bags thumping against their sides like a warning. Half way down the slope they bunched up. I couldn't make out much, but when they turned around, some of them were pinching their noses or bending over, hands on knees like they were steadying themselves against a strong wind, shouting and pushing each other down the icy cobbled path.

I squatted, pulled back deeper into the undergrowth and watched them pelting each other with snow, jamming great glupes of the stuff down their jumpers and shirt fronts, whooping and laughing, swearing like they owned the place.

'Cooeee, Jack?' That was Danny's voice.

I saw Jack wave – felt his blush. One of them, his hand fluttering against his mouth, began making Red Indian noises. They tiptoed towards the camp, exaggerated, trying not to giggle.

Heart thumping in my jaw I found myself preparing to sprint home, but my legs wouldn't work. One of the bigger lads stopped and kicked out at the fortress. Others joined in. Then Gopal stood up and gave them his beautiful brave smile. I shut my eyes then, covered my ears, tried to imagine myself invisible, but I couldn't shut out Jack's voice, yelling at them to stop – to leave him alone, nor could I shut out the chanting 'Pa-ki Pa-ki Pa-ki' over and over. Too frightened to look but looking anyway through a crack in my fingers, I saw some of the others turning away, coming straight for me, sniggering. And all the while behind the sniggering I could hear the choking and sobbing and then someone, probably Danny, issue orders to shut him up, and then a yelp. I wanted to run over but I was too scared. One of them started battering the camp wall again – taking a couple of quick-march steps my way and then turning back, putting the boot in, snow spluttering out, turning and turning again. But then others looked scared, I could tell, looking round like someone might see them …

I should have gone for help. If I'd gone as soon as I'd seen them coming down the hill, as soon as I saw Danny, I might have got back in time with my mum but I didn't, and now they were doing something bad, really bad …

I stood up, kicking over the bag of hot chocolates, now cold. Danny came out from behind the fort, laughing, doing up his fly, slapping his mates on the back, pushing them as they headed my way. I swung my scarf over my mouth and nose, pulled my hat down, jammed my fists into my pockets and made straight for the camp, right past them.

Jack and Gopal were sitting on the ground with their knees into their chests, staring down. I did the same.

'You okay – did they hurt you?'

They said they were fine.

'So tell me,' I said, going crazy with not knowing, looking for clues, bruises or cuts. But they just shrugged, said not to say anything to Mum, made me promise.

From then on I could tell they didn't want me around. They'd stay in Jack's room most days, Gopal teaching Jack the guitar. Mum never minded the racket, but come evenings or weekends, if I was in the front room reading I'd watch Dad's face. At first he'd look up with a shrug of tolerance, then he'd tut tut and shake his newspaper. A minute later and he'd leap out of his chair, grab the poker and bang on the ceiling, shout at them both to get out the house. My heart would quicken; perhaps they would take me with them this time – but they never did. They'd go quiet for a bit, that was all. Gopal still smiled at meal times, bobbed his head politely, but I soon saw it as pathetic rather than sweet. So that was it, really, something was over. The only time he'd go out was if we went as a family.

In the end I couldn't wait for them both to shove off back to school. You could tell they were pleased to be packing, and having them around was like having a cut that won't scab. When Mum heard me crying the night after they'd left, I told her I'd had a bad dream.

BLACK MOUNTAIN

IT IS 2016. I am an old man now, returning to what is left of my grandfather's house in the foothills of the Himalayas, near Lord Krishna's birth place.

I am sitting on a moss-covered stone slab that would have formed part of the grand stair before the house was gutted by fire and abandoned. There is much shade, many trees have grown where there were once rooms, but where I sit there is a patch of bright sunlight and it is warm.

Leaning back against a half-pillar, I shut my eyes and find myself thrown back thirty-one years to the mid-seventies when Ravi, my son, almost a year old, was taking his first unsteady steps.

It had been a hectic three days crammed with feasts, old friends and new faces. On the fourth, Sanya and I escaped the socialising and took a lift to Mathura, spent the day wandering through the market, sitting in chai shops, playing with Ravi, reading. Around tea time, wanting to eek out our time together, we decided to walk the few miles back to my parents' house rather than take a taxi. Ravi, like many small creatures, loved being high up, and sat on my shoulders like a tiny grinning Buddha. A faint tingle brushes my neck like an echo – even now I can feel his chubby thighs bouncing and rocking cowboy-style in rhythm with my steps.

It was early spring; a green fuzz was forcing its way through the cold soil, but still it would be a few weeks before a tangle of wild flowers cloaked the hillsides. The track curved steeply at first, giving us a long view of the river as it rose gently towards the falls. We must have been walking an hour when Sanya twisted her ankle. Although it wasn't a bad sprain – indeed, she could hobble reasonably well with the help of a short branch, but it was beginning to swell – it would not be strong enough to take her home. So we sat on the verge in the softening sunshine to wait for a lift. No cars came. The road petered out after my parents' house – there was still a link to the main Delhi road but it was seldom used. We knew Ravi would soon be tired and once the sun dipped behind the mountain it would be cold. I decided to return to Mathura – if I met a car, well and good, if I didn't I would be back with a taxi before dark.

Ravi waved the tiny fingers of one hand at me while he toyed with Sanya's breast proprietorially, putting her nipple between his teeth like the butt of a cigarette, wagging his face from side to side so it tickled the inside of his lips. I kissed his forehead and ran. It was steep in places and stony. I can still recall the giddy feeling of almost catapulting head over heels, my legs unable to keep up with the building momentum.

I found a cab on the outskirts of the village. The driver was lounging across the bonnet, smoking a bidi, and waved me away. He was waiting for a friend, he said, as he nodded towards a young blue-turbaned sheikh, carrying a food bag. After they'd eaten, he said, they were heading home to Delhi – couldn't wait to leave what he described as 'this hell-hole'. I pulled out my wallet and rifled through a wad of notes, taking out three times the normal fare. It wasn't far, I said, and they could join the back road to Delhi without doubling back. He agreed and I climbed into the back seat.

Sanya was sitting on a rock. The sun had left this side of the mountain and she was shivering. As I opened the car door and received a wriggling and delighted Ravi into my arms, I noticed how the sheikh eyed her up, saw the way he disapproved of the western bias of her dress.

At first we headed towards the house; then, with no warning, the driver swung a left into an old quarry, forced a gear-crunching three-point turn and roared back the way we'd come, accelerating dangerously while barking at me to shut the hell up. As we swung down the Delhi road I turned around, hoping to see a car or truck to whom I might signal for help, but all I could see was the glare from the sun reflected in a blizzard of orange sand. After a few miles, he threw a left. I was very scared by now – I knew this track led to a precipitous dead-end. I could feel Sanya shaking beside me and Ravi was beginning to whimper.

Then the road disappeared into vapour as the headlights beamed off into nothing. The driver slammed on the brakes, stopping just metres from the edge. Immediately he climbed from the car and sauntered to the door beside Sanya. I punched down the back locks. He pushed his face against the window to leer at Sanya. Ravi began to cry. Kicking the door in frustration he returned to the driver's seat, reached below it and pulled out a bottle of whisky.

'Shut the brat up, I'm warning you …' he shouted, gulping back the liquor.

Sanya and I locked eyes – she was near to tears, her hands shaking out of control as she unfastened her blouse for Ravi to suckle. 'What is it you want from us – money? Here, take everything I've got.' As I held out my wallet, I saw that the driver had small pointed ears, and his long greasy hair, coiled into a lazy noose on the top of his head, had begun to unwind. He took it, pushed the filthy strands from his eyes with feminine affectation and counted the notes, slipping them into his pocket before tossing the empty wallet back over the bench seat. Then he lurched towards Sanya and made a grab for her blouse. I pushed him off, snatched up the stick that Sanya had used, and raised it to threaten him.

'Steady up'. The man held up his hands as though offended – as though he hadn't meant anything by it. Then he began to giggle, slapping one hand over his mouth, while the other rammed the bottle up against his friend's chest. I was grateful that Sanya was bent over Ravi, unable to see the fear in the boy's eyes as he raised it to his mouth.

'Take us back. I'll kill you if you hurt her – take us back and we'll not say anything. The baby needs changing. Come on, take the money, man – take us home …' I pleaded.

But the driver just laughed and snatched the whisky from his friend. 'Shut the brat up, I'm warning you,' he mumbled, gulping at it. 'Why you so boring? The night is young. You've already made us late – we will have the party together, just the five of us. Here!' He thrust the bottle towards Sanya, but jerked it back, wagging his finger, tut tutting at her, laughing, drank more.

The turbaned one cracked lewd jokes – coaxing the other to think of the women in Delhi he could buy with the money they had.

But his friend was having none of it. The drink had focused his frustration, he wanted the girl first – once he'd had the girl he'd take us. It was simple, and to make sure everyone understood he got out of the car, dancing and booing at all the windows before lifting the bonnet to remove something from the engine. After he'd settled himself behind the wheel, he grinned toothlessly at us all and turned the key. An impotent whirring filled the car.

There are some moments in one's life, in most people's lives, when its continuation hangs in the balance. I believe this was one such moment: like the boy whose arm was caught between two rocks, or the climber who crashed through the ice into the void – there are times when the odds seem too heavily stacked. I saw in that moment, my wife raped, my son smashed against stone, and myself thrown over the precipice.

But the instinct to stay alive was strong: words we didn't think we knew bubbled up and soothed the madman. Or Ravi would stop crying and do something funny – the driver would throw his hands in the air, as if coming to his senses, pat his friend on the back, kiss him, shrug his shoulders, beg our forgiveness and climb out of the car. Each time we held our breath as we pictured him replacing whatever it was he'd removed beneath the bonnet, but time after time he came back grinning, wagging his finger at us as though we'd nearly tricked him, as though he'd almost fallen for it. He would shake the back door, start boxing his friend who would whimper and fold moth-like into the corner of the passenger seat – God knows what horrors he'd witnessed this man commit before. At times he cried and wept, either for himself or for us. Once he stretched out a hand to stroke Ravi ... but Sanya recoiled, just a fraction. He reared up and slapped her face, lunged to take Ravi from her until the turbaned one dragged him off. There were moments when everyone was crying, at others some sort of intimacy emerged as if raw emotions swithering around would slip into anyone who'd give them expression for a while. And then, out of the blue, after a long exhaustive slumbering silence, he announced he was taking us back. We sat up, wiped our filthy tear-stained faces as if preparing to meet someone important and watched, too tired for cynicism, too tired to really take it in, just a stirring of faint hope as we strained to see through the windscreen, building to a ripple of intoxicated expectation and childish eagerness as he got back behind the wheel and fired up. I gathered Ravi to my chest – the change of rhythm had woken him and I didn't want him to cry.

But instead of backing up he slammed his foot on the accelerator.

In a shattered second I flicked off the lock, flung the door open, pulled Sanya after me and started to run, Ravi's cries muffled against me. I didn't look back, couldn't look back. We just ran, ran for our lives up the black mountain – ran as though we had wings, ran forever …

MARTIN AND ME

WE'D BEEN IN Sea View on the Isle of Wight for almost two weeks and we were going home in a couple of days. Dad had been out late and had one of his headaches and he and Martin looked like they were about to kick off.

'I'm almost eleven – all the other lads are allowed,' my brother said, with that face on him. So maybe Dad wasn't looking – I dunno, but instead of going through the usual rant, he shrugged and walked off, turning at the bedroom door.

'Mind those tides,' he said, 'and take care of your sister. Anything happens to her and you won't what know what hit yer.' He would have though … He wasn't stupid, our Martin.

Rocks were stacked like tower blocks along the sea-front and we gauged our leaps from one to the other with care – one false move and we'd break our ankles. The beach would have been easier but neither of us wanted to brave

the sand, which hid invisible tar gnocchi like the
Italian sold in the High Street, and they oozed
between our toes like black treacle and wouldn't
ever come clean.

Priory Bay was wild and magic. It had none
of the hotels that our beach did. And no one
went there, not much anyway. It took us a good
hour to get round the headland, and we were
hungry and hot. We changed into our
swimmers, ate the bread and butter sandwiches
like half-starved wolf cubs and scooped water to
drink from the stream.

Scrub willows grew right up to the sand,
which was rippled with blue-green clay, and the
flat sea which went on forever was a marine
miracle, Martin said, groaning with shoals of
sleeping whales, or at least that's what we called
the sandbanks. We paddled from hump to hump
towards the horizon, where the only pucker in
the milky sheen was the tiny ticks of coloured
sails like butterfly wings.

We were so busy digging a network of
waterways on the fattest sandbank we never

noticed how the tide had rushed silently past and sunk the banks behind us. I was seized and paralysed by certain knowledge that I would drown. I knew this, because instead of twenty humps between us and the shore there was only this glassy sheen and I could barely see the strip of pale sand in the distance. Feeling sick I began to sob and run on the spot. Martin took my hand and began talking. I tried to snatch it back – if he thought I was going to follow him he had another thought coming, I would rather drown. Which of course I surely would if I stayed where I was, for my feet no longer thudded on the bank but splashed in water. In the end, all of a minute later, the irony of my words must have sunk in for I began to listen urgently.

'Look,' he said.

I looked at death by drowning.

'See the pale bands? We'll be able to stand in those places. It'll be just like swimming from the shallow end to the deep end and back to the shallow end again – it'll be fun,' he said, 'it'll be our adventure.' And as he was talking he was pulling me gently into the water, not once getting impatient or cross as I threw my head back in panic as soon as the sand dropped away – as I spluttered and gasped and choked as tiny waves began spilling into my open mouth.

I remember even now the tender coaxing he gave me: 'Kick. Come on, Jen. Kick. Pretend you're in the swimming pool – you're nearly at the shallow end, just a few more strokes.' But I couldn't get my feet up: I swam from bank to bank straight up like a sea horse, and as my toes skimmed the first ripples of sand I'd start choking again, but this time with relief and a rush of tears and the desperate struggle to get my breath back as we waded and pushed our way to the other side before slipping under again.

I recall it all now with longing not fear: a craving for a Martin I once knew.

Neither of us told our parents what had happened that day – we were too afraid of what they'd do.

Nor did we return to the island for several years. And by then the magic had gone – the giant world of boulders had shrunk to a straggle of rocks; Priory Bay was an exclusive resort with signs about the fast incoming tides and the dangers of wading too far out. And it wasn't just the boulders that had diminished and shrivelled, we all had somehow. It was over a year since Martin's first girlfriend had died of leukaemia. It had hit him hard and he'd taken up drinking in secret.

Dad caught him at least twice: heard him heaving into the flowerbeds outside his bedroom window the first time and a few days later in broad daylight with some local lads outside the Spar. The more enraged Dad became the less Martin seemed to care, completely ignored Dad's rules for getting in at night, treated him with scorn and condescension. The holiday divided us in two, Mum and me watching as Dad and Martin went at it, hardly stopping.

And that was how it was from then on. I don't know if they spoke about it. Mum seemed to accept Dad's ways, always smoothing things over, like everything was okay, like it might all go away. I don't think she should have – I don't think it was right; she should have got more involved. She should have done something.

HAPPY FAMILIES

I COULD KILL Sarah, I really could. As if having my crazy mother to stay isn't bad enough, she decides to dump Bruno on us for a month! My dog indeed. Yes, fair enough, he was my dog, but he became her dog a year ago when she begged us to leave him with her – when she said that her family was incomplete without a dog, and that he would remind her of her best friend, me, and all the happy times and laughs we've had training him.

Well thanks a lot. Best friend.

'God damn it! Get off will you, Bruno. No, Aiden, I have not lost my temper and I'm not in a mood – I just don't think Bruno should sit on my knee while I'm driving do you? No, well, so pull a bit harder will you? No, you can't take your belt off … I mean it, Aiden! Roz, could you just leave the radio alone? Classical is fine – it's what you wanted a moment ago. Please Roz, I'm really jagged just now, please, just leave it

58

alone! Thank you. Oh Christ. Don't cry. Roz, please don't cry. Okay, let's have the play, it's just that you said you didn't like it before, you said it was rubbish – but okay we'll try again, and yes the boring bit has probably gone. Aiden, I told you not to take your belt off—'

I grind to a stop, open the boot and grab some string, which I'd happily throttle him with – Bruno that is. I don't throttle him though, I remain cool, slip one end through the ring on his collar and the other through the grab handle above the door, cunningly winching his head in until it has only a few inches manoeuvrability. Then I refasten Aiden's seat belt and mutter a few banned words – at Sarah, whose ugly grinning mug has muscled its way into my brain. Aiden, my four year old, tells me calmly that he thinks I should take some deep breaths until I regain my sense of balance. Annoying little shit – always right. Precocious little jumped-up know-all. And I pray someone someday will bully him down to size, so that he can operate on a healthily neurotic level like the rest of us. Bruno looks contrite, I'm happy to say.

I climb back into the driver's seat and resist the urge to slap Roz's hand as she trawls through the channels, pausing at each for a few seconds, as though she's finally found what she's looking for. I can't stand this. I fumble below the dash for a few moments until I locate the wires, pray they're not part of the engine and pull one. Silence.

I flex my hands, stretch out my neck and glance at Roz who is fiddling happily with the silent radio. In the rear-view mirror I catch Bruno's look of pathetic self-pity as well as Aiden's silent pout, acknowledge a brief but precious tingle of triumph and turn on the ignition.

The Proposal

THE EAST WIND has washed the early dusting of snow off the trees and a few hours ago there was soft winter sunshine, but it has failed to warm the air.

I can see Leah. She's early for once, blowing into her gloves, glancing at her watch. I wave and she smiles and hurries towards me and we link arms and go through the park gates and walk briskly, heads down.

It is spotting rain now, but more than anything I'm struck by an odd sharpness to the air − not cold sharp, though it is cold, bitterly cold, but it's not that, it's more of an electric tension felt on the scalp as if something is waiting to happen. I remember yesterday, how the pines glowed lime-green against a yellowing sky; today they are blue, blue-green and fernlike, a child's painting on deep mauve brushstrokes.

I listen. I'm all ears. If there is sound, I can't hear it: no birds, none of the usual kids' voices. I am reminded of a stage where the curtains have gone up and no actors have appeared, and I'm sure she feels it too. I tug my glove off and hold her hand tight. I am so glad I have hands so I can hold hers, and for some time I'm simply glad for everything in my life that has led me to Leah. Countless 'what-ifs', hundreds of coincidences, have tripped me along blindly until I've arrived. I am in love – in love! Could it be she doesn't know? Could it be that she's in some doubt – doesn't understand that she's the pivot upon which my fragile universe depends? She might not. Honestly. She might not know that unless she's with me till I die – I'll die? How would she?

I pull her around. The air is charged with electricity, no mistaking it now, fizzing with it. I take centre stage, remove my other glove, clasp my hands together, bend a knee and wobble ungraciously to the ground.

She looks around – probably for help.

'Leah, will you marry me, be my wife, my best friend and mentor. Please will you? Will you promise to continue to be my reason for getting up in the morning and my reason for going to bed?' A low rumble – God's orchestra probably, shakes the ground beneath our feet. Several people stop feeding the ducks, check out the sky and turn towards us. Some move away, imagining the rumble is a storm warning. But I don't care – I have just been moved to ask the most important question in my life and all of a sudden I don't feel anything but confidence and joy and excitement.

At the margin of my vision a rabble of ducks is heading our way. I've always found ducks to be a bit threatening and persistent once you start feeding them, especially en masse; any pause and they switch to automatic, robotically padding towards the food source. Their bodies may be little, but there's something unmanageable and hardcore and pushy about them. And if pushy moves to attack and you grab them, feathers, like alien limbs, come away in your hands. Gives me the willies. But right now all they do is unnerve me, to such an extent that whatever entrenched patterns I ignored thirty seconds ago slam into my brain and almost knock me over. My knees are aching: rheumatoid arthritis, most likely, and it occurs to me that I am already married. Okay, okay, only legally, but still, these things matter don't they, when you ask someone to marry you. And even if it didn't, *matter*, this is merely the winciest pothole when compared to some of the massive roadblocks that are erupting like mines on the long desolate highway to hell, which for a few pathetic moments I had somehow smudged clean away ...

Breathe man, breathe.

God – how could I forget, how could I do anything so dumb. My past races in front of my eyes, along with a lightning flash, I swear, lightning – real as you like – as with horrific clarity I relive my most poignant moments: I place her in impossible positions, make lunatic demands on her time and sympathy, virtually ignore the grief she is going through while demanding full attention to my own trail of unhappy dramas. I withhold secrets, misread our relationship almost entirely and without compromise, behave like a selfish prig and blame her for my depression. Pictures and snippets whiz by. While avoiding looking at Leah, I prepare to bolt from the ducks who are barely six feet away and sneak a glance at the faces of our loyal but misguided audience, and it's blindingly obvious that they are already feeling terribly sorry for me.

I can't stand now anyway, my knees have frozen solid – how the hell did I get down here? I can't look at her, because now I'm convinced she's enjoying this, that her beautiful face has become a disbelieving sneer – and it's all my fault. From now on, this place and winter and gloves and even my knees will forever be associated with humiliation and shame … Oh God—

'I'd love to.'

Relieved claps from the crowd, and Julia Roberts bends down to pick up the now prostrate Hugh Grant, who has fainted, but despite being quite unconscious, is still babbling on like a complete idiot. 'I'm sorry. I should never … I mean, I don't know what came … Oh Christ, I'm a bastard, what an impossible position. Please, just forget I ever—'

'Oh do shut up, Nathan. I will, I'd love to. I'm thrilled you asked me – you left it long enough.'

I'm on my feet now, kicking wildly at the earth, trying to get my head around it. Giant blobs of sleet hide my tears and the ducks flutter about in feigned panic.

'Come on, you lunatic. It's about to turn nasty, I'm starving, and you're already late for work.' She wraps me in a hug and for a blissful moment we rock and turn circles under an opening sky. Thank you, God.

Thanks so much for buying and reading *Short Cuts*. If you enjoyed it, I'd be grateful if you left a review on Goodreads or Amazon or both.

By the Same Author

Call Billy 07899 232007

Call Abi (due for publication in 2020)

Contact

I'd love to hear from you.
sam@sammccoll.co.uk
www.sammccoll.co.uk

TOUR HEAD

I WAS AN ACID FUELED TEENAGE DEAD FIEND!

NORDY

TOUR HEAD PRESS
PORTLAND, OR

TOUR HEAD

Tour Head Press.
Portland, Oregon.
www.deadtourhead.com

Acknowledgements appear on page 389.

print ISBN 978-1-73766-800-8
ebook ISBN: 978-1-73766-801-5

Covers designed by Nordy and Farrell Timlake.
Graphics by Scott Underwood.
Front cover painting by Andrew Bobrek @andrewbobrek.com.
Front cover photograph for artist by Maegen Gentry 2020.
Back cover photographs by Mark Rockwell. 1987-2019

Printed in the United States of America.

-TOO ALL MY FRIENDS!!
FROM TOUR TO TOKYO TO CHARLIES!
HERE'S TO YEARS!

-FOR NAOMI YOSPE. FOR BEING EVERY-
THING TO ME,
LOVING ME, AND PUTTING UP WITH MY
CRAZY SHIT.

FOREWORD

By Far-L Timlake

November 2021

How many people say something along the lines of "I met my best friend" or "I met my future wife" in line for tickets to a Grateful Dead concert? More than we will ever know I am sure of that. Like, I reckon the line of people who could claim the same stretches pretty far out there.

Perhaps farther than all those freeway miles we rode, and wider than every parking lot we hung out in combined.

Because in those days when you actually had to line up to get tickets, before everything became just a click away, the endless line to get tickets, truth be told, was all part of the show. And it was a sacred space, a place where strangers actually stopped strangers just to shake their hand.

Since being in line was no guarantee to get tickets, no worries. You were still set regardless. Your recent acquaintance and future best friend became then and there a front row ticket to a thousand memories shared from that day forward.

In each and every line for a Dead show existed a chance to connect with a kindred spirit. Realizing from that point on, you were each bound to a shared adventure of epic proportions. If you embarked on that sublime journey together, sometimes mundane yet often otherworldly, then a line could be drawn from that exact point, where you stood shoulder to shoulder hoping for the opportunity of a lifetime. To get to the next show. To experience the here and now. To make each moment a lifetime of great memories.

Then, together in mind, body, and spirit, or at least the best of two out of three, you could both look toward a bright and clear future of magic, kismet, and serendipity. Or weather a gale force storm of misfortunes together. Who knew what the weather might bring?

You could look out and it could extend far across a galaxy of colorful, actually psychedelically so, adventures both grand and weird, wonderful and terrible, and always worth the wait in line.

Because no matter what...

We could always look back and say, "Remember when we met in that line for the show?"

The funny part is, looking back to that halcyon time of way back when, you may even disagree which show you were actually in line for. When you have been tight that long, sometimes a few of the details slur into memories fuzzier than a few dancing bears spinning on the head of a pin.

You look at each other, neither positive of your own recollection, nor doubting the others' collection of reminiscences. Because at the end of the day, all that really matters is that you both know you met in line for the Good Ol' Grateful Dead. And it was worth the wait. And you would do it all over again in a heartbeat.

The bond is eternal. It is a boundary around a wonderful lifetime of shared experience. And it creates a line which can never be crossed. Nordy and I met so many years ago and we are still tight to this day. And we are still in line together. Having shared the good, the bad, and the ugly and still able to smile, smile, smile respectively, we stand.

I remember meeting somewhere in a line for the US Festival, but he remembers differently. We both agree we officially met as part of that great colorful, trippy, regal procession to get back on the bus for the Dead. The Grateful Dead may not be around, but for us, the music definitely never stopped. So, we are still waiting to see what tomorrow may bring and seeking the harmonies of a song that never ends, just like our friendship.

1.
PULLED OVER ON ACID IN UTAH!
9/8/1985.

How it came to be that a Utah State Patrol Officer was sternly rebuking my driving speed after pulling us over while we were high on acid.

I felt the LSD starting to creep into my brain as we sped over the top of a hill in the middle of nowhere, speeding along in Dan's little gold Tercel at 68 mph, with the late afternoon sun burning in our eyes. We each took a hit of fresh blotter acid at the last gas stop. We needed to get someplace fast, with no delay, and this was standard practice for us. We had been on Grateful Dead Tour for three weeks and we still had to drive one thousand and six miles from Red Rocks in Colorado, all the way back to Claremont, California, by the next day. We would sadly be missing three shows in Oakland, out of twelve on this tour. I was a week late for my delivery job (after getting a *paid* week off already) and Dan was leaving for college in Europe for a year. We really had to move!

LSD usually takes an hour or so before it starts kicking in and it was coming on sweet and mellow. The sun was vivid and gorgeous as we cruised along, and as you can imagine, we were fully absorbed in our music and conversation.

The 1985 Grateful Dead Southwest Tour had been amazing. It was an incredible trip. So far.

As we crested the hill, I saw the hat first! Flat brim, beehive top, sharp and shining in the yellow-orange sunlight. It was a Utah State Trooper standing on the side of the highway holding a radar gun in one hand and a potential prison sentence in the other. We had acid on us, and we were *on* acid! Oh fuck. My heart jumped and started pounding, but

3

my brain somehow told me to stay cool. I'm not that high yet. Yet? How high will I be when I get to jail?

Everything was hidden, and we hadn't smoked weed in the car for obvious reasons. We drove right on by him as he pointed his radar gun at us, with absolutely no expression on his big cop face. A quarter mile past him, and The Hat turned into six more Hats with Utah State patrolmen under them, waving five cars over at a time in a huge speed trap. People often use the term, "I was tripping" to describe something crazy, but I really was "tripping," and I had to pull over into a sea of huge cops with a car full of everything. Acid, mushrooms, weed, bong, pipes.

We were caravanning. Far-L and Sue had gotten caught in the same radar net right in front of us, with a car full of everything also. Plus, they had a triple beam scale.

Do not freak out. Smile and say, "Yes sir." Think to yourself, *You got this! You're an actor on a stage now.*

Dan and I had been on the road for years and knew what was up. I looked slowly around at all the cops. No dogs. That was huge in our favor. Unless they performed a rip the car apart piece by piece search, we should get out of this okay. But if they did, it was over for us.

One of the biggest Hats was on us in a second, probably sniffing for weed smoke. He had a big voice!

"License and Registration. You know how fast you were going son? We do not like speeding in Utah." He looked about nine feet tall. The shadow of his hat stretched all the way through the window across Dan and I in the front seats. "Where you boys going in such a hurry? Sign says 55, son. My radar says 68. I expect you to slow down next time you're in the great state of Utah."

I was using all my practiced cop tricks. Don't move around, hands on the wheel or your lap, do not touch your face, don't mess with your hair, look straight ahead, squeeze the steering wheel to kill the nervousness, look directly at the officer when he talks to you. Make eye contact!

Dan was sitting stock upright, looking straight ahead too. But then Big Hat's face softened ever so slightly and said he would be right back, and we each knew we would be on our way soon. Big Hat and his giant shadow came back with a ticket for going 68 in a 55. I never paid that ticket (still have it) and subsequently got a seven-year warrant as a result. I barely signed my name on the line and off we went, by the skin of our asses, into the Utah sunset. Far-L and Sue drove away unscathed as well. About a mile later, Dan and I freaked out and cheered and high fived. No Utah jail for us! It could have been so much worse. Dan had been arrested on Dead Tour in Ohio a few years before for a *tiny* bit of weed and a bong, and had he been driving and his record came up, that total search we had been fearing would have been on in full effect, and we would've gone down. We slipped the noose on that one, but didn't learn a damn thing.

We traded drivers and Dan got back behind the wheel. He started driving 90 mph like he always did. There was nothing I could say about it. That's just Dan. He would have said something funny like, "Shut up you little weasel, I'm driving now!"

So I sat listening to Jerry, watching the darkening, Utah on LSD landscape float by from the dusty and comfortable tour car passenger seat, as we headed west toward the smog of Los Angeles.

2.
FUCK MOVING!
VIRGINIA TO CONNECTICUT 1974

"**Fuck!** Fuck!! Fuck!!! Fuck that moving truck, fuck Connecticut, fuck you!" I was young and I knew the power of this word and it felt right to use it at this time, so I screamed it out in the woods by our house. My small roots I had planted over the two short years I had lived in Virginia were being yanked up, yet again. Another sudden move, another promotion for Pops! A result of my dad's kick ass approach to whatever he does in life. This time we're going to Bethel, Connecticut. I had been moved three times already. This would be the fourth state I had lived in during my short life. I was only nine years old. Moving was the end of the world to a kid like me. I hated it. But I adapted.

It was uncomfortable at first, but Connecticut turned out to be okay and soon I had new friends. My neighborhood was full of families and kids. We all had Huffy bikes and Grentec GT and Nash skateboards, and everyone played together. It turned out to be a good place to be a kid, and as the years went by, as we all became young teenagers.

3.

FIRST WEED. FIRST GRATEFUL DEAD FREDERICKSBURG, VA. 1978

As I make my first encounter with marijuana and the Grateful Dead all in one fateful spring evening.

My folks, my little sister, and me, are headed south to Florida. Disneyland in Orlando for her and The Longwood Pipeline Skate Track, as it was called, for me. We had kept in contact with our old neighbors in Virginia and stopped in to visit and spend the night. It had been about four years since we moved, but the neighborhood looked the same. I skated straight over to my old friend Keith's house, and he was home, but he wasn't the same kid I remembered. He was older and cooler now and had learned some stuff about life I hadn't figured out quite yet. He seemed happy to see me, and I thought that was super cool!

He wanted to go to 7-Eleven to play pinball, but before we went in to play, we went out back because he wanted to smoke a joint with me. My first! I was eager to be a cool kid, so I acted like I knew and smoked it like a cig, which I had been smoking for a year or so already. I subsequently hacked my little kid lungs out, as Keith laughed at me.

It was a fat joint of shitty pot rolled up in a strawberry flavored paper (I remember the rolling paper tasting better than the weed), but it worked well and did its job on me. I was virgin stoned! A joint rolled in a strawberry paper took my weed cherry!

Pinball was a whole new game now! The 7-Eleven seemed different, and my skateboard ride back was a life changing cruise of carved turns and cutbacks. I liked it! A lot!!!

Now, keep in mind I'm barely thirteen at the time, so I had to be back soon. I tried very unsuccessfully to sober up for the first time in my life, and skated back to the house to see the family and friends. I got lucky. They had been drinking and reminiscing and after I said hi, they forgot about me downstairs in front of the TV. I was glad to get away from them for some *new* reason. I watched TV for a few hours, marveling at the effects of THC, and soon SNL came on! One of my favorite shows! Thirteen years old and high as hell on one hit of Columbian weed!

The show was now even funnier than before! SNL had a musical guest that night I had heard of but had never seen or listened to before.

4.

THE GRATEFUL DEAD.

Super cool name! Sounds heavy. I couldn't wait to see them!

Are they like KISS, or Aerosmith, or Led Zeppelin, or Black Sabbath? Bands I knew all about and loved already. Uh, nope. No way. Not even close. Miles and miles apart.

The Grateful Dead got on stage and didn't do anything! Nothing. They just stood there. No theatrics, no pyro, no smoking guitars, no dripping blood, and no drums rising.

They just did the normal, nothing thing they do, and I was instantly infected. I fell into The Grateful Dead like a drug habit starts. Innocent, excited and interested.

5.
MEETING MILLER AND ROCKWELL.

My dad had car-guy friends who would have picnics, and during one of these outings, I met a wild and hyper kid named Scott Miller and his older brother Ken. I liked them right away. Scott and I ran around, had fun that day, and a year later Scott and Ken moved to my town. Scott was down for any adventure. Our little kid crew was gravitating together.

We were grouped alphabetically in sixth grade and Mark Rockwell sat next to me. He brought the fantastic KISS *Alive* double album into class with him, and promptly opened it up so you could see the whole band onstage on the cover. Then he proudly displayed it on the book ledge in the back of the class. I thought that was so cool! He brought this record in just to add a little rock and roll to the stuffy classroom. I was youthfully impressed. I had heard and liked KISS and knew right then I had to hear more of them.

Our parents met at some school function, and soon afterwards, I started to sleepover at Mark's house some weekends. That's when we started to saturate our young brains with rock and roll! Music had been an interest. Now it became a passion.

6.
MEETING GEORGE.

George Jurdy lived across the street from Mark. The first day I met him it was winter and bitter cold outside.

George's mother Irene was a super nice woman, that doted over George, and was *always* cool to us. George wanted to go across the street to Mark's, but he had just gotten over a bad cold. Irene wanted him to put on more layers so he wouldn't catch cold again when he went outside. George said he had enough layers, but Irene insisted he didn't. George took his jacket, his sisters' jackets, and his dad's jacket, and five or six hats. He put all of them on, plus a pair of snow pants and two or three pairs of mittens on his hands.

We were out in Mark's yard and this super chubby kid comes waddling down this long-ass driveway. I can see he's having a hard timing walking. His arms are sort of sticking out to the sides and he is kind of lurching along. Mark starts laughing as George sneers at me for the first time and says, "Who's this kid?" I was thinking to myself, "Who, the heck is this round, over bundled kid asking me who I am? Look at you! Who are you?"

We went inside and George started to peel his layers off, one by one, and a huge pile resulted. He ended up being a skinny kid. We were cracking up as he was telling us how Irene would not stop bitching at him about going outside until he put on another layer.

So he put on everything he could fit into, went outside, and stiffly and sarcastically waved at her from the driveway and bumbled off. I remember thinking, *Who the hell does this to their mother? I guess this kid does, huh?*

That was my introduction to George and his distinct sense of humor. Always creative, sometimes vindictive, and always full of laughs.

The next day George took out a silver metal weed pipe. I tried to be cool and smoke it, but I didn't breathe it in hard enough and the weed just burned on the top. I had never used a pipe and I was scared and nervous. George got mad and quickly took the bowl away from me. He turned to Mark and said, "I'm not going to give him any if he's going to waste it." Then he took a big fat hit, blew it right in my face and said, "That's how you do it."

Needless to say, I didn't get to take another toke attempt that day. My next attempt would yield far different results, however.

7.

SECOND WEED. GLEN.

Glen was another good friend who was musically influential to me and one of my first stoner buddies.

I was with Glen when I bought three of my first records. Grateful Dead *Skeletons from the Closet*, The Doors *American Prayer*, and Todd Rundgren *Road to Utopia*.

Glen had two older brothers, Jeff, and Ray, and they had tons of cool records we always listened to. Glen would air drum dramatically to Styx and other bands of the time.

One day, Glen liberated some weed from Ray's stash, and brought a skinny little joint to sixth grade class. He said, "I have this bone (East Coast term for a joint) and you and I are going to smoke it after school." I said, "Okay," although I was scared. I had only been stoned once, a year before, and that was fun. But I had heard stories since then of getting too high on drugs and was equating that to weed. I didn't know shit about any sort of drugs back then and weed was as bad as heroin as far as the news was concerned. I knew in the back of my head it would be fun again, but I still had beginner nervousness, like I did with the metal pipe hit.

The school bell rang promptly at 2:30 and I had a bit of anticipation in my stomach and head already. Glen and I walked behind Bethel Middle School and out through Consolidated Corp. parking lot. We ended up in the woods behind Cawley Ave. Glen had the joint hidden inside a blue and white plastic pen with the ink center removed. He slowly unscrewed it, took the skinny little bone out, and smiled at me. Then he lit it up with a match. I watched the flame touch the end of the joint and flare up. I watched how Glen hit the joint. I copied him and smoked it less like a cig and more like a joint this time. Small puffs.

We sat on a big rock in the corner of the woods and smoked the whole bone. Whooooaa! This time I got high as fuck! I was truly wasted. Glen and I sat in the woods for another few hours, talking and laughing. It was great and memorable. The sun, the sky, the trees! All so beautiful, so alive, and so vibrant.

I had made an excuse to stay after school and secretly smoke out with Glen. I didn't take the bus home and my mom was going to pick me up at some point. After Glen went home, I went to wait for my mom. I was so stoned I just lay on the grass in front of the school, face down. *I don't look obvious do I,* my head asked my head? Perhaps my first little battle with the weed paranoia creeping in, as I'm wondering if I'm going to look high to my mom. She didn't notice (at that point she had no clue), and I was high until about seven that night. It started to wear off during dinner, so I started assessing my day's weed adventure.

It was incredibly fun! I decided I liked it. I liked the smell, the taste, and the effect, and I wanted more. Thus, began a lifelong (for better or worse) love affair with the little green bud.

8.
MEETING ERNEST.

I hit seventh grade at Bethel Middle School, and I got lucky! I was put in the amazing Mr. Jackson's class, *and* I met Scott Ernest. Scott would become one of my best friends.

Scott's dad was out of the picture and his mom was at work all day. We ran around constantly doing crazy shit. Skipping school was high priority for Scott and me, and we got away with it often. When we got caught, we would get stoned before we had to be in detention after school, and ride it out together. We loved *Skateboarder* magazine, Marlboro's, and U.S. Bong hits. That slipped into Dead records, nitrous oxide, acid and U.S. Bong hits.

The only time I ever saw his dad, he surprised us, and I had to toss the red four chamber bong down into the woods on the side of the house. E, as he is known, lived on a super steep hill covered with trees and rocks, and the bong bounced down and out of site. Miraculously, his dad didn't notice, and didn't smell the smoke. We barely squeaked past him. I was running out the back door as he was coming in the front. When I went to retrieve the bong, which I expected to be destroyed after its fifty-foot tumble, it was just-fine. I wiped some leaves off, rinsed out the stinky spilled water, filled it back up and took a fat hit. U.S. four chamber in the color of red! You couldn't get a better bong then! Built to last baby!

Scott's mom refused to come up the stairs after he was about 14, and his room became our rock and roll, weed and cigarette cave. One time, we had an entire tank of nitrous in his room, loud as fuck, while his mother was just below us in her own room. We kept trying to fill balloons super slowly to keep the noise down, but it was not working. E took a fat hit while he was standing up, passed out, and shook the whole fucking house when he hit the floor. We were exploring and it was fantastic!

The KISS posters fell, and the Dead posters took their places. We skipped rungs on the short ladder of life and naturally tried to be older and wiser, while we were still truly just kids. Super stoned kids, but still just kids none the less. Growing up way too fucking fast and loving every minute of it! This was also the same time that Scott Miller moved to Bethel, and we reunited as young friends.

9.
LIVE GRATEFUL DEAD.

I was 14 and I was staying overnight at Mark's house. George had been off at boarding school. He came back during spring-break with new albums. Amazing stuff! Frank Zappa, Overnight Sensation, Apostrophe and live Grateful Dead, Skull and Roses and Europe '72. George was the first kid who had Zappa and Grateful Dead records, and at the time, was our most musically influential friend. George went to a private boarding school called Kingswood Oxford. He got a scholarship and was very smart, almost too smart, and a bit conniving, even at a young age. He mixed Oxford and the street knowledge he was learning and created his own unique persona, even as a kid. George was cool, yet shifty, but it all seemed cool to us at the time. He learned all about rock groups from his fellow students, who had cool parents who had gone to various live shows. Then he brought it all back to Mark and me.

He eventually got kicked out of boarding school for multiple shenanigans, and ended up back home in Newtown, Connecticut. He tried to go to Newtown High but bailed out shortly after. Going back to Newtown High after Kingswood Oxford just wasn't going to happen. It was easy to not fit in at school back then, and no one really judged you at that time if you just dropped out and got a job. Which George did and didn't do? He dropped out but not many jobs followed. So then he went back and finally graduated.

He always listened to the best music and knew so much about rock and roll, that you couldn't help looking up to him and wanting to be a part of what he had going on. Rock and roll, weed, acid and most importantly live concerts! Live shows are the best thing ever if you really like the band you go to see. Life changing and forever! Thank you, George. You gave this to me! But you also gave me other things that I found out later I could do without.

10.

NEIL.

Neil was the prime musical influence on George, in conjunction with school at Kingswood Oxford. His band knowledge also bled onto us. Neil was the first cool cat, the first different one, the first stand out in my eyes as cool.

We all idolized him, but he didn't want any of it. If you told him something was cool that he created or made, he would often give it to you or change it by the next day.

I always liked this small red and black wire tree sculpture he made (still have it), and he gave it to me. I said I liked the tie dye he had sewn onto the back of his jean jacket, and it was off the coat the next time I saw him. Neil turned us on to Hawkwind and Tangerine Dream and inspired music to live in us, like it lived in him.

11.
MEETING KURT.

Kurt Ogrinc moved to Bethel from Norwalk, Connecticut in my freshman year. We met right away because my last name starts with N and his starts with O, so we got desks next to each other and became instant hooligan friends. He had a rock and roll attitude and the best record collection ever, way back then. Kurt turned me on to so many bands I had not heard of before. I loved heavy bands and Kurt was way ahead of the new, coolest music curve. I think we connected over Thin Lizzy at first. Who knows? He knew all the new, heavy bands. He opened us up to acts like Rush, and most importantly Van fucking Halen! He had *Fly by Night* and *2112*! Van Halen *One* and the best standards like Zeppelin and Sabbath! It was epic. We would all end up at Kurt's house after school, since both his parents worked, and we would smoke weed and listen to all his insane records. It was a music defining and life affirming time for me. It opened my mind and made my brain sponge even more ready to absorb more new sounds and tones!

12.
KID BULLSHIT

When I was 14-15, I was going through a ton of adolescent bullshit everyone goes through, even though I thought in my young brain it was just me. I would run away from home often. It was confused kid stuff and lack of having the amount of freedom I felt I deserved. I basically wanted to do whatever I wanted to do, without anyone saying anything about it.

But that was never going to happen, so I ran off for a day or two thinking this would give me some leverage in the situation with my folks. It did not. I just got in more trouble, got grounded longer and ultimately had less freedom.

After about ten times, George had gotten sick of me running away to his house. One of the last times, I was over at his house and my folks were calling on the phone. I didn't want to go home, and I made George swear he wouldn't tell them I was there. I was in the sunroom and George called me into the master bedroom. He was holding the phone receiver up to me. What? Fuck you!! He had called my mom himself to come get me, so I would be forced go home and stop bugging him. Asshole!

I reluctantly took the phone to speak to my mom, and George started in on "Cosmic Charlie" singing, "Go on home, your mama's calling you!" over and over with a smirk on his smug face. Bastard.

My mom kept me on the phone so I wouldn't bail out, as my dad drove over to retrieve me. I was the short-term teen runaway.

13.
LSD AND MESCALINE!

Bring on the psychedelics!

I had gotten my first psychedelics and it forced the last runaway situation of my youth. Someone had this mescaline that looked like a piece of pressboard with several colors of purple in it. I took some with a friend, and spent the afternoon with a much older ex-con, who we barely knew from Rogers Park, the local park where we bought our weed. We stumbled upon him as we were walking down the road headed into the woods to trip. He had rented a room in our town. We went fishing with a line and a bobber. No rod. I was all into it until ex-con caught a fish. Then I was bummed and almost had a bad trip. I freaked out a bit and ended up wandering away from the fish death scene.

Day turned to night, and I wasn't coming down. Not even close. Getting higher. I found out later that's just how mescaline is. In and out. Heavy and mellow.

I ended up in the big tree we would climb by Kurt's house, smoking cig after cig and thinking to myself, *I know. Now, I know. I understand now.* I honestly wasn't sure what I knew, but the drug made me feel like I had made some breakthroughs in how to perceive the world. And it really had. I saw everything in its real form. The bark of the tree for instance. It was alive and a part of the tree's wellbeing. The dirt the tree was growing in was also a part of the whole scheme of everything. "I," "everything" and "all" now had completely new meanings to me, and have ever since that trippy day.

I finally started to come down well past midnight and went home. My mom was up, insanely worried, and ultimately pissed off. I have no idea what my excuse was, but because of the drug I was coming off, I saw my mother's pain in her eyes and on her face a bit more clearly than before. Then I saw the love she had for me when she knew I was safe and not gone for good. That moment changed me, and I didn't runaway anymore. I was close to leaving home and not coming back until I was older, but I decided against it on that high as fuck night, way back then, when I actually saw the stress I was causing my wonderful mother.

14.
JACK'S CLASS ON MESCALINE.

E and I had been flagged as *problematic* in our high school and had been assigned to a counselor named Jack Leonard. Jack's class was clearly known as your last chance before being permanently expelled from school. Kurt Ogrinc, Mark Rockwell, Scott Miller, Scott Ernest and I had to attend Jack's class daily for third period. This was the second go round at ninth grade for all five of us. In a few short months it became just Ernest and me. Mark and Kurt got shipped off to V-Tam reform school and Miller got expelled and banned from the school grounds.

Jack's class had some true benefits. All class cut slips and any problems went to him and not Frank Forrester the vice-principal. It helped us *not* get expelled as quick and we had our own smoking area. It was cool!

Jack was away one day, so E and I decided to skip the last few classes and hitchhike to George's house. As soon as we got our thumbs leveled and out, Jack takes a left in front of us headed back to school. He just beeped his horn, waved, and laughed at us. We could never get away with shit when Jack Leonard was around. But we never got in trouble, and he would talk to us and help us out, instead of crushing us with penalties for being a rowdy teenager.

Jack's program changed me as a person. I got a different perspective about life from him and as I saw my friends get sent away, I tried to absorb more of Jack's influence. I turned my shit around and did good in school for the first time in years. But, not without a few more hijinks thrown in for good measure.

In Jack's class we had privileges like a private smoking area out back. One day I had bought a hit of that purple mescaline, and it was in the pocket of my tan corduroy Levi's jacket. I had eaten mescaline in school before, but it was a super weak hit and I barely felt it. This time I ate the whole pill in the early part of my second period class. I went to Jack's third period class thinking I would be fine like the last time. Wrong!! I started to feel it quickly. I thought it was okay for about ten minutes and then started to realize it was going to be heavy. Scott and I went out back to smoke a cig and ended up smoking a bowl. We never smoked weed in Jack's class. Ever! We would be instantly expelled if he caught us, but I was getting so high that Jack had sort of disappeared for a moment.

We went back in, and Jack started in on his daily motivational speech to us. I tried to drink hot chocolate, but the little marshmallows were bobbing up and down even though the mug was on a flat table. We had a big globe and a large rubber tree plant in the room. Somehow the two blended together. On the end of every leaf of the rubber tree plant I saw the leaf tip blow up into a globe, then deflate back to a rubber tree leaf, then blow back up into globe repeatedly like Christmas lights blinking on and off. Jack must have known, but he didn't say anything.

The bell rang really-loudly, and I walked out into the basement hallway of our school. My next class was biology on the third floor. I was having a hard time focusing. I started to climb the stairs. Students from the art classes had painted ten-foot-tall cartoonish renditions of students walking down the stairs on the walls. I was walking up the stairway next to these giants that were walking down. I felt like they were trying to push me back down the stairs. They looked huge to me. It seemed so hard to go up the stairs.

I finally got up to my proper floor and sat in my seat at a science style table with three other students. The teacher said we had a film strip to watch that day about waves and currents. My brain was already experiencing waves and currents and as luck would have it, the seat I sat in that electric day was the seat the person who turns the filmstrip sits in. The seemingly simple task of turning a dial and advancing a filmstrip one frame at a time, even when prompted by a beep, was beyond my phys-ical means. I was so lit, that it took several students going, "Hey," "Hey," each time I missed the beep and didn't turn the slide, for me to do it. The projection screen with the waves and currents on it had become a stormy sea and the little arrows that show water direction were poking out like real arrows.

I got through it somehow. As soon as the insanely bright classroom lights came on, I got up and approached Mr. James' desk, and in a strained voice said that I needed to go to the nurse's office. I wasn't feeling well. He said, "All right," and handed me a little yellow square to fill out. It was a hall-pass, which was standard issue to have with you if you were in the hall during class time. I could not focus on it and the pen felt very strange. I scratched something on the pass and shoved it back at him. He looked at me, said nothing, and signed it.

I grabbed it and out the door I went. Then I started running! I ran down the hall, took a right down a few flights of stairs and flew right out the front doors of the school during fourth period. Ten classrooms can see out the front, so I wasn't being discreet at all. I was running in a drug induced fear, away from Bethel High School as fast as I possibly could. I ran up the stairs, through the parking lot, across the street, past Berry Elementary and straight into the woods alongside the playground. I stopped to breathe and calm down, but it didn't work. I took the path through the woods and got onto Judd Avenue. I ducked behind trees and cars thinking the school had called the cops and they were looking for me.

I dodged and weaved all the way to downtown Bethel, and Scott Miller's mom's apartment. Scott was already expelled so I knew he would be home, and his mom would be at work at the fire station. I knocked on his window and woke him up. Scott was born a grumpy old man, so he didn't take kindly to being woken up by a crazy mescaline fueled truant who needed a place to ride it out.

"What the fuck did you come *here* for? I'm sleeping," he com-plained, but he let me in anyway. He put on some Dead, we smoked ciga-rettes, and I watched the room breathe and flex.

I was having a hard time indoors, so we went up the street and into the woods of Overlook Park. This old town park was always empty and perfect for doing fun stuff to make me not overload and freak out anymore. We spent the day wandering, but I eventually had to walk back a few miles to school and catch the bus home.

I again dodged and weaved and snuck into the parking lot, crouched next to a car, and waited for the last bell to ring. The car fender was raising up and going down like it was on a slow hydraulic jack, and the smoke from my Marlboro looked silver in the winter sunlight. I got past my second period teacher who was the daily bus monitor, without getting popped, and jumped on my bus home. The inside of the bus was a cacophony of squeaky kids voices in a big metal cocoon.

I got off in my neighborhood and went straight back into the woods to finish the ride I was on in my mind, as I finished the pack of smokes in my pocket.

15.
LAURIE K AND MY FIRST LIVE CONCERT.

I had a good friend named Laurie for many years in Connecticut. Our moms went to church and worked church groups together. Laurie and I always had to attend these church group functions. It was weekend retreats and Wednesday night CCD (Catholic bible class) meetings.

It's funny because the local priest and all the volunteer moms were trying to show us a new light and an inspirational way of looking at the world. What we used it for was to get stoned, make out, and learn how to have beginner's touchy-feely sort of fun. We all smoked cigarettes and drank smuggled booze from the parents' liquor cabinets and the mothers never seemed to know.

Since our moms knew each other well, when Laurie asked if we could go to a concert and have her older brother Ed chaperone us, they said sure. Ed was looked on as a solid kid. He had his own car and was responsible in our parent's eyes.

The show bill consisted of three bands. The Little River Band, Heart and The Eagles with Joe Walsh. This was 1979! Heart and The Eagles were huge, huge bands! The venue was the Yale Bowl. A huge outdoor stadium that holds 70,000 people in New Haven, Connecticut. I had seen Thin Lizzy or Golden Earring (not sure which) as a kid at the Minnesota State Fair from a far distance, and only for a few songs, and that wasn't really a show. This was going to be a real event for me. Not just a kid watching from the sidelines of the beer garden with his uncle Stan.

It was a daytime concert, so we had to leave early. My mom dropped me off and we hopped into Ed's car, and off we went. We didn't even get a mile down the road when Ed turns and hands us a joint. He lights one for him and his girl and says, "That one is for you two. Those Miller beers in the cooler are yours and the Michelobs are mine." And so, it began. We knew Ed was cool and would do exactly what he did, but our parents didn't, and we knew that also. It was a perfect scenario of a young teen adventure into a new musical jungle. It was beyond exciting!

Laurie and I were smoking a joint on the wooden stadium benches in the warm summer sunshine. I knew I was going to hear LOUD-LOUD-LOUD rock and roll, and I sure as-fuck did! "Barracuda" hit me so hard I felt it in my entire body. The bass guitar thumping and throbbing in my chest was the coolest feeling ever! They did "Dog and Butterfly" and it sounded so clear and crisp and clean. I was completely hooked on live music from that moment on. My life was changing forever. I knew it and I felt it.

These thoughts are all happening in my head before the Eagles came on! When they did, I was even more blown away. Joe Walsh climbed out of an equipment crate they rolled out on stage and was already playing his guitar inside of it. The whole band was going off!

"Life in the Fastlane" was by far the raddest song of the afternoon, and a live version of "Hotel California" lived up to its dreamlike album quality. Those incredible tunes on that sun splashed afternoon acted like a sledgehammer, driving a live music spike deep into my young brain, where it has stayed permanently embedded ever since.

16.
FIRST GRATEFUL DEAD SHOW.

"As my adventure really begins" "It's show time!"

Hartford Civic Center,

Hartford, CT

3/14/81

My best friend E and I got out of his mom's car a block or two from the Hartford Civic Center. Our very first Grateful Dead show and our mothers drove us because they didn't trust George. He was the older, bad influence. George had no family rules at home and our moms hated him, but we thought he was the shit!!! He had been seeing the Dead for three years already, and that was as cool as you could get in our young eyes.

We made plans to meet our moms later and pretty much ran up the street to the Civic. It was amazing, crazy, and very circus like. Several thousand Dead Heads all in one place and now I am one of them! It was truly surreal.

First thing we did was buy our first bootleg Dead shirt *and* some acid from the same guy! Of course, the T-shirt guy sold acid too, it was a Dead Show, after all. Homemade Jerry shirt and some real good hallucinogens (with a few extra hits to sell back home) were quickly checked off the list. Then we smoked a few bowls to get ready! We had teenage goals and we were accomplishing them in short order.

I remember thinking when we bought our doses and shirts (and saw the fat wad of money this travel dirty Dead Head had) that I could also do this and see a hell of a lot more shows. I remember watching cops, walking around and thinking, *just make sure you don't get caught*.

We met up with George and ML (as Scott Miller is known), who had also seen a few shows, and had the inside line on the gig. "Just follow me," ML said, in his normal gruff tone, and in we went.

We got killer seats (Section 103, Row C, Seat 4) about halfway back and up one riser. We couldn't see that great, but it was perfect for sound! And it sounded fucking amazing! I knew all the songs and I could sing along! Now I was a real Dead Head, about to be dancing and tripping with all the other Dead Heads! I finally made it to where I wanted to be for years! Right in the middle of a Grateful Dead show!

The band came onstage, started playing, and the acid really started to kick in! I had that *here we go* acid feeling when it starts to work and consequently, there I went! They played two extra full sets. The "Feel like a Stranger" opener got it all going and by the "One More Saturday Night" encore, I had been completely changed for life! I needed to devote whatever it took to see this band and be a part of this scene! It was mandatory to me. No way to explain it. I was getting on that bus!

But, before I got on that bus, I still had to get in Scott's mom's car, high as fuck on acid, and face my mom. We must have had Visine and Grape Bubble Yum gum with us, because somehow, we pulled it off.

It was not an easy 60-mile ride home. Watching the back of the front seat "breathing," trying to make sense of and answer our mother's rapid fire mom questions, having spontaneous fits of laughter, then long quiet spells. The worst of it all was trying to hold it together when they took us to McDonald's on the way home for being good young men who stayed out of trouble! The Grimace, creepy ass Ronald, The Hamburglar, that green character, Mayor McShake or whatever the fuck they had back then, all staring at you from the ads in the window. All the while tripping balls with our moms right there in the front seat!

"You want fries with that?"

"Huh? What? Yes. I mean no." It was almost too much, and about to be a bad trip, but we got back on the road and held it together, and soon got home with our first show firmly stuck in our high little heads.

17.
ALL THINGS DEAD.

New Haven Coliseum

New Haven, CT

5/14/1981

I remember the songs but not the show or anything about it. I know I got another ride with parents, but my acid must have been stronger at this show because my memory fails me. I have a vague recollection of Kelly and the rest of us helping a girl who was too high on acid, but like I said that's all I got for that one.

18.
A DEAD IDENTITY.

Back at school I was fanatical, drawing Dead logos on my book covers, making flyers, and immersing myself in everything Grateful Dead.

After my first show, I felt I needed a shirt of my own that I could wear that had my personal patches and old cut up shirts sewn onto it. Not a simple Dead T-Shirt. I wanted a long sleeve that had room to add stuff to. I had to have my own identity in the Dead scene. It was super important to me to fit in. It still is because it's MY scene. It's OUR scene. It made a huge difference in my growing identity and how I felt about myself, to define my musical likes so everyone could see them. The crowd at a Dead shows always had a unique outfit thing going on, and I wanted that as well. Badly!

And so, I did it. I got a denim looking shirt I thought was cool (1981) and added a handmade Skull and Roses patch to the left front pocket first. Then I sewed on a part of a *Blues for Allah* shirt on the front lower side. I cut it out, so it fit the seam and the edge. I then drew a *Steal Your Face* on the back and colored it in with these old fabric paint pens my mother had. It was really starting to look cool to me by then. I was as stoked as a young Dead Head could be. DIY stood for Dead It Yourself, way back then. And we did. Always.

The last thing I did before I had a growing episode that made my creation unwearable, was to make a handmade stencil of Jerry from the *Pink Birds* cover, and spray paint it in a black silhouette on the very bottom of the back of the shirt. I loved it. But I grew and it went in the closet where it has been living ever since. Always save your Dead stuff! All of it. It means so much more for the memory factor if you can look at things from your past. Save those things to remember, who, what, when, where and well, you already know why.

19.
THE DEAD SHIRT GAMES!

We loved and lived for our Dead shirts. We each had a few unique ones in the early days that we got at various shows or head shops, and we were super proud to wear them. We did not care if people didn't like the Dead, we *liked* the fact that they didn't like them. It made it even cooler in our eyes to like a different and unique band. But, as much as we loved our shirts, we would still take risks with them.

My friends and I would bet our Dead shirts against each other in games of pool and pinball. George owned the pool table and the pinball machine, so he was naturally better than us and usually won our shirts right off our backs. I remember him wearing his Dead shirt with one of mine over it, one of ML's shirts over mine, and finally a huge shirt of E's.

He layered them over one another just to taunt us that he was the Dead Shirt, pool tourney champion. The rest of us were decent players, so George didn't always win. Once in a while, the tables were turned and he was unshirted!

We used to come up with fucked-up ways to get our shirts back if we kept losing at the games. One of them, that was cruelly thought up, was to put a tablespoon of baker's chocolate in your mouth for two minutes. We also did this with tablespoons of salt, pepper, and tabasco. It was almost impossible to keep these things in your mouth for two minutes. Each one has its own fucked-up way it chokes you or gags you until you're forced to spit it out.

Those few minutes of agony for the person who wanted the shirt back resulted in days of hysterical laughs for the rest of us witnessing it. But it sure did suck when it was your turn to try to get your shirt back. It was brutal. Choking and spitting and coughing. If you miraculously lasted the two minutes and won, you felt so good. And then it got even better when you took your Dead shirt back from George and told him to fuck-off.

20.
PRANKS AND PENALTIES.

We did other fucked up little things to each other all the time. It seems brutal to me now, but at the time it was hilarious.

George and his family had a nice big house in Newtown his dad had built. George had his own phone in his room, and his mom had the phone line downstairs by the room ML lived in one winter. ML and George had a little prank war going, while ML roomed at George's for a few months.

It started out with the two separate phone lines. ML thought it was funny to call George from downstairs early in the mornings. George would answer after twenty rings or so and ML would say, "What are you doing up?" and hang up on him. George would do it to ML as well. Ring the phone forty or fifty times at 7 am and go back to bed. You didn't have a way to turn off the ringer on some phones back then, if you're wondering why they didn't turn them off. Nothing was tech back then. Phones were connected by real, actual wires.

After a million rings, ML would jump out of bed and scream "WHAT!?" into the phone, as George said something like, "Get in that bed!" to him. This went on and on. One time, George got a ridiculously long phone cord, stretched it out, and put his phone at the bottom of the stairs by ML's room. When ML tried to ring-wake George, George's phone just rang in ML's ear. Then it got ugly.

George let it go for a week or two, so ML was off guard. He snuck down the stairs one night and put thumb tacks (not the newer push pins, old school tacks are flat sided and can lay point up) all over the floor, from the bedroom door all the way to the phone. About ten feet. There was no place to step to avoid them.

George laid his trap, then he waited until morning and started ringing the downstairs phone. He let it ring. A lot. Over fifty times until it drove ML crazy, and he came jumping out of bed to answer it, swearing! Every step he took with his nice warm, just out of bed feet, he stepped on at least two tacks, if not three or four in each foot. Every step he took, more tacks would stick in his soft under foot. He naturally ran forward to get away from the tacks, but George did an extra thorough job with his placement and spread them wide! ML was sitting on the floor screaming "FUCK YOU!" over and over as he pulled all the tacks out of the tender soles of his feet. Of course, George was still upstairs relentlessly ringing the phone all this while. ML finally got off the floor, hobbled over to the phone and answered it only to have George say, "Sorry, wrong number," as he hung up on him. It was gnarly!

ML exacted his revenge for that one though. He put tacks all over the forward part of the floor of the shower that George had in his bathroom upstairs. He even put in a dimmer light bulb, so George didn't see them. George got two full steps into the shower and bang, here comes the tack foot revenge! It was so rough!

Yet another time, ML had a bet with George, with ML's shoes at stake. If ML lost the bet, he would have to hitchhike all the way home, in the winter, wearing old boxing gloves on his feet instead of his shoes.

ML lost the bet, and he scraped off down the street with his cold heels hanging out the back of the boxing gloves where your wrists normally go!

21.
TEEN DEAD HEAD LIFE.

Our lives as young teenagers in the early '80s were crazy. There was nothing to do in Bethel, Connecticut back then, so we got by, creating our own way of doing what we wanted to do. I had lots of rules at home, but I learned how to get around them and get what I wanted also.

We all started smoking cigarettes at around 11 or 12 years old, and as you have read, by the time we hit 13 or 14 we were all about weed. It had such a unique edge to it. It made you listen more intently to the music, but not necessarily to your teacher in school. It has its up-sides and down-sides, and we figured those sides out as we went along.

We would sit in George's room and play records and smoke cigs and bowls. We would go to the head shop and make ridiculous ten-inch long, triple chamber pot pipes out of all the parts you used to be able to buy. We would go to Record Broker in Danbury and buy our Dead buttons for our jackets. Looking back, it was all time! I miss those days!

22.
GRATEFUL DEAD TICKETS
BY ANY MEANS.

When tickets were going on sale, we would get a spot in the line at Ticketron, in Bethel, and wait in shifts for two or three days to get our tickets. I remember being too young to go to a show at first (parents had rules) but still waiting in line with ML and George for their tickets, not even my own yet, just to be part of the scene. Sleeping bags, BBQ's and weed. Trading shifts so we could go to school or skipping school to cover your shift.

George and ML did the night shift because they had no rules to follow and had already dropped out of school. They overwhelmed their single mothers, and their moms had no choice but to let them do whatever they wanted. I was so jealous of their freedom, but I still had an old school dad to fear and had to come home at night, or suffer the consequences.

It got to the point where so many people would be camped in line that they had to move the Ticketron office down the street from the covered spot next to the old Spinella Dentist office inside the travel agency, to the Mr. Donuts strip mall. We liked the old, covered spot in Bethel, but it got blown out so badly the other businesses in the shared building could not handle it. The new ticket line was fully exposed to rain and winter weather, and we knew they did it like that on purpose to try and discourage us from camping out for our golden tickets.

It was solely because of us. No other fans camped out for tickets except Dead Heads and Mets fans back then. The town plan backfired. Everyone got tents and made it even crazier. Now you had room for a way longer line with more Heads and everyone was *still* camping out. You made a great effort Bethel, Connecticut. It just did not work. Dead Heads were growing at an incredible humping rabbit like rate and your little town ticket office got ran the fuck over by the tour bus.

23.
DEAD MEMBER FAVORITES!

All of us has one certain band member as our favorite, outside of Jerry because Jerry was officially everyone's favorite, all the time anyway. I love Phil. For me, it has always been Phil. I love the bass! E always loved Keith. ML, of course, always takes his fanaticism to the extreme. Bobby, was and is, ML's favorite and he let us know it constantly.

He would queue up his tapes at home, so they would start with a Bobby song when we got in the car. He would fast forward through a Donna song to get to the next Bobby song, and he even made a full 90-minute cassette with all his favorite versions of "Looks Like Rain" back-to-back. ML is Bobby's biggest fan, and he will be that way forever! He used to exclaim, "I am Bob Weir" in the way people say, "I am The Trail Blazers," or "I am The Mets!" and start laughing. That shit runs deep with ML.

24.
JUMP KEYS AND THE FRONT FUCKING SEAT.

George was the first one to get a license to drive. He would always get his mom to lend him the car, and of course, we all wanted to ride with him in the front seat. We would all run to the passenger door and push each other out of the way to get that coveted front seat spot. George got sick of this quick and started tossing the keys out into the yard to see who scrambled fast enough to get them.

When George got sick of that game, he invented a new one he called jump keys. Just like basketball, he would line us up to jump, and toss the keys up, normally in the direction of whoever *he* wanted to sit up front that day anyway. If George was sick of driving and you were at his house expecting a ride, he would look at you and ask, "How you getting home?" That was it. If you heard that, he's not giving you a ride. If you complained, he would say, "Can't do it." Better bundle up and stick out your thumb because that's all you got.

If you wanted one of his smokes, he would toss it up on top of an exceptionally tall bookshelf behind this ornamental metal piece. Cigarette behind the pan, as it became known, was a bitch to get down since the shelves were nine feet tall. That one sucked. Teenage pranks!

25.
HEATHER, KELLY AND OTHER MUSIC.

I was starting to see a few other bands at the time. I was always into all kinds of music, not just the Dead. My good friend Kelly, and my awesome girlfriend of the time Heather, and I went to see shows and check out different bands. We saw the legendary Frank Zappa together, as well as Genesis before they got more mainstream. We also went to my second and third Dead shows, and the last ones for me on the East Coast for many years.

Kelly, Heather, and I were a little inseparable team for a few years. Heather had her gold Dodge Swinger, and the three of us would sit on the bench seat and drive everywhere smoking cigs and drinking Tango. We all went to the same school, we all worked at Consolidated Control, and we partied together all the time. Heather's car was our haven, our island. It represented freedom at that youthful time, and we took full advantage of it. I consider it one of the best eras of my life.

26.
I SEE FRANK ZAPPA
AND GAIN MY FREEDOM.

I had seen three Dead shows and got dropped off by parents. My next show would be Zappa in New Haven where my folks also dropped me off. I was at the point where I was just about to gain my freedom to go on my own, but they still worried about me driving myself or with friends. They knew we had discovered booze and drugs, and they were just trying to keep me safe.

My girlfriend Heather drove to Zappa with Kelly and E. We saw the show together. They heckled me about my folks giving me a ride, and left me on the street waiting for my dad, as they drove off safe and sound. I hated having to have a parental escort then, and as I look back, I still hate it now. But I still got to go! I was still at the show after all, and I'll always have the memories!

The Grateful Dead had a different sort of show than other bands. They came out late and played two long sets. Zappa, on the other hand, started on time, played his show, and it was over. The Dead had a parking lot scene that everyone hung out at before and after the show, Zappa did not.

Suddenly I was out in a big city at night by myself. The crowd was long gone. We had no cell phones in 1981, so I couldn't call my folks and tell them the show was long over, and I'm standing out in New Haven, Connecticut, by myself, getting fucked with by city kids out to hustle me. It was 9:30 and my folks were not picking me up until 11:30.

My meeting spot by the parking garage was not close to the Civic Center. It was a dark side street with lots of shady motherfuckers cruising around asking me, "What you need?" and "Why you here?" Some guy, with a car full of obviously drunk passengers, drove right through the parking garage, wooden gate arm, where you pay, and splintered it into a thousand pieces, almost hitting me with the debris. The attendant in the little glass booth about shit his pants, then came running out screaming trying to see the car license plate number. A woman I assumed was a hooker, stopped and smoked a cig by me, until a car pulled up with its window down, and off she went. I was a little nervous out in the city like that. I had already spent my money on a Zappa shirt so I was broke, except for my smokes, and I couldn't have been robbed for much anyway.

My dad and mom eventually pulled up a little early, which was fine by me, and I gladly hopped into the warm Chevy. I immediately started to make and prove my point of how it's way worse for me to stand around in a dark, dangerous city, than it is to drive myself, or go with my friends. My dad looked around at the city night life and knew I was right. That was the last time my folks drove me to a show. I proved my point and won my case.

Now it was on! I had unsupervised concert access and a burning desire to get on with it. I had no idea then it would get as crazy, and in depth, as it did in the future. But things sure fucking did!

I wanted to see more shows, but the folks were not having it. Jerry in NYC and Dead shows on the Fall Tour, but it was not to be. Afterall, I was barely in eleventh grade.

27.

OTHERS BECOME DEAD HEADS. ITS SPREADING!

Meanwhile, Jeanne Kennedy, Pete Rasato and Rich Manone started feeling the Dead vibe. Around the time I moved to SoCal, Pete, Rich and Jeanne and a few others began to see shows with ML, George, and E. The wheel was turning!

28.

FUCK MOVING PART TWO.

Bethel, Connecticut to Chino, California

Spring 1982

Here we go again. Moving away. This time kissing my amazing girlfriend Heather goodbye, and saying farewell to all my friends, as I unwillingly left Connecticut for California at 17 years old. Certainly not by choice, but as I look back on it, it seems a destiny choice was made for me in some cosmic way.

My dad received yet another job promotion, like he always did, and off we went for the fifth time in my life to yet another state, another school district, and a whole new set of friends. I was *way* into to my life in Connecticut. I was leaving all my great friends and my girlfriend behind and that was a huge downer.

The move did have one positive side. Just one. I was going to California, the home of the Grateful Dead and all the mythic venues I had heard so many bootlegged shows from. Fillmore West, Oakland Auditorium, The Hollywood Bowl, WinterLand Arena! "Estimated Prophet" was ringing around in my head, and I couldn't wait to get to Berkeley or to walk down Haight Street, but it didn't turn out like I dreamt it would. I ended up in SoCal in a cow town called Chino, right up the road from the Chino State Penitentiary.

Not one fucking person I met liked the Dead, most hadn't even heard of them. It was a brutal shock. I was blown away that the music scene I was so accustomed to didn't even exist here. I was lost and wasn't sure what the fuck to do, so I filled my time with cars and refined my skills at body work and auto painting. I also found a few shows to attend to pass the time and hopefully meet some Dead Heads, eventually.

29.
MY SISTER AMY AND DAVID LEE ROTH.

Peace Sunday

Anaheim, CA

6/6/1982

The first West Coast show I saw was the Peace Sunday concert at the Rose Bowl in Anaheim, California. I had no idea it was going to be as big as it was. It was an insane show with Gil Scott Heron, Jesse Colin Young, Graham Nash, Bonnie Raitt, Donovan, Timothy B. Schmidt and Don Felder, Crosby, Stills & Nash, Taj Mahal, Joan Baez, Bob Dylan, Dan Fogelberg, Stevie Nicks, Linda Ronstadt, Bette Midler, Jackson Browne, Garry U.S. Bonds, Tom Petty and Stevie Fucking Wonder! He was incredible on that day! The total attendance was huge, with over 85,000 people turning up to listen to the music.

My sister Amy (who got her worst sunburn ever) and I went in my dad's company car, and as we were walking in the parking lot, we saw Diamond David Lee Roth, in all is early '80s rock star glory, park his chopper and strut his way to the backstage VIP entrance. DLR! Fuck yeah!

I remember hearing many famous songs from groups I had heard of and hearing some new stuff I really liked. I also got a strong newfound feeling for counterculture, and global awareness. I was much more enlightened to what was happening politically and globally after that show. Glad we went Amy!

30.
MEETING GREG.

I was not especially ready for SoCal in early '82. Punk rock had not hit Bethel High back in Connecticut quite yet, but it was in full spikes and boots mode when I got to Don Antonio Lugo High School in Chino, California.

My new closest friend was a hardcore punker from Arizona name Greg McNeil. He had a classy triple mohawk and a chicken bone earring (that looked more like a human finger bone). He proudly sported a torn dress shirt with the sleeves ripped off, dirty hole filled jeans, black boots with chains and faded bandanas around the ankles. Serious punker. 1000% *not* into the Grateful Dead.

Greg was extremely smart, cool, and unique. We sat next to each other in several classes and answered every question the teacher asked, just for a laugh. We came from different states, and we had already learned the same shit in our former schools (California was way behind the rest of the country), so we sailed through class and became friends from then on. Greg was all about music and lived for it. He had all the early punk shit, and a big variety of other records. He slept on a mattress on the floor in a tiny room he shared with his punker brother Don, surrounded by 45s and albums. I was already way into everything semi mainstream like Bowie, but he flipped the Bowie card, and on the other side was Iggy. Greg is an amazing, musically knowledgeable guy. He'd say, "Oh, you like this band, cool, me too! Now check this group out!" I loved it! He opened so many doors for me in music, just like so many others had before him.

Greg played drums and had his own bands that I loved. The Scooperheads at first, and then President Joe. Incidentally, the irony of our President being named Joe as I finish writing this book is not lost on me.

Jeff, Shawn Tracey, Ed, Audra Molachek and Tracy were the key players in his bands of the time. I would watch them practice and half-ass roadie for them with my dad's car at a few of the local shows they scored.

31.
WEED CLOUDING MY DAD IN RUSH HOUR TRAFFIC!

President Joe got a gig playing at a little restaurant bar spot in downtown Chino. My dad would normally let me borrow his company car if my own car needed some parts or repair. He lent me his car, and I picked up Greg, Jeff, and Shawn at Greg's house, and brought them and their gear to the bar about five miles away. They played for free to about ten people max, including staff, and we packed up and split.

It was still only about 10 pm so, we decided to smoke a joint, and go back to the warehouse to drop off the gear, and have a beer or five. We drove out of the parking lot in my dad's car as I pushed in the car lighter to blaze up a fat joint. I remember it not lighting to well, so someone gave me a lighter and I lit it up that way instead. We smoked out, ended up at the warehouse, and did our thing for the rest of the night.

I eventually drove home and parked my dad's car. I checked it over to make sure we didn't leave any empty beer cans, and crept in so my mom wouldn't accost me and ask mom questions. Then I went to bed.

So, here's where it gets fucked up for me. My dad still smoked cigarettes at the time. I did too. Everybody did it seemed like. My dad got into his car at 7 am to go to work. This is the car his company pays for, and he lets me drive, very graciously, and often. He pushed in the cigarette lighter to have a smoke while he's commuting to Santa Ana, California, in heavy morning traffic. As he pulled the lighter out to stoke up his smoke, the end of the joint that wouldn't light, from the night before, was still stuck to the element of the lighter. It smoked and flared up in his face. My dad never smoked weed before and it totally clouded him out on the Santa Ana freeway. I hotboxed my dad in his own car! He was so pissed off! My dad can get super-mad, and I saw it that time way more than other times!

I knew nothing until he got home from work that night. Then the shit hit the fan. My dad's ultra-loud yelling voice was the first thing I heard, and I had absolutely no excuse. It was my weed, and I couldn't deny it. No car for a while for me, and my mom checking for red eyes every-time I went someplace is what I ended up with. I learned a lesson though. Clean up better, don't fuck with my dad's cars, and don't make him inadvertently smoke my weed in rush hour traffic on the way to his corporate job at 7:18 in the morning!

32.
ACID AND A LOT OF US!

The US Festival #1
Glen Helen, CA
9/3-4-5/1982
Dead ON 9/5

I walked into the early morning US Festival Dead Show by myself. I drove two town locals I knew, but we soon got separated. The Dead wasn't on until the third day.

We arrived in the middle of the night between the first and second day and saw a ton of other incredible bands of the time. They played one after another, all through the day and late into the night. We hung out the first night in a beer and acid haze, but after that I lost them in the 300,000 person crowd. We left notes in the dust on the car. "Fuck yeah bro." "I'm so wasted." "Where aren't you?" "Meet me at?" Stoner stuff like that.

It was way too easy to get lost in that event. It was massive! You hopped a bus in from a poorly marked desert parking lot, got dropped off into a sea of people, and wandered through it all towards the gates and this huge distant colorful stage.

When you got to the entrances, the ticket checkers had taken away all the booze that 300,000 people had tried to bring in, and piled it up right there. No one bothered to read the *no alcohol* small print on their tickets, so they left it behind, and it was a booze free-for-all just outside the gates. Wasted people sitting on cases of abandoned beer, slugging them down. People passing around whiskey and tequila. You had your ticket and wrist band, therefore you had re-entry, so you could go out and have a drink at the "free bars." So that's what I did, and that's where I found a sheet of acid for cheap. 100 hits.

My resale margin back in town was high, and I didn't like my dish-washing job of the time that much anyway. I sold it all to an older biker friend back home and tripled my money! I needed that extra cash to do what I really wanted to do! See more Dead shows!

This particular show had a crazy time slot. The band had filled in as a late addition to the lineup. The Dead played at 9:30 in the *morning*. I had barely slept for two days and woke up on the hood of my dad's company car, parched and getting roasted by the sun. I got up, got stoned, grabbed my sunscreen, got a warm beer, and walked to the makeshift bus stop. I split a half a hit of blotter on the shuttle bus with some stranger (I offered, he accepted) as we drove through the hot, red, dust clouds. The bus was full of weed smoke and clearly the hired driver didn't give a fuck.

I remember it feeling good to sit in a normal seat. I couldn't sleep in my dad's car because it was so dusty. I couldn't leave the windows open because I didn't want to clean the car later, and it was too hot to keep them shut if I was inside. I had been sitting on the ground, sleeping on the car hood, or standing for two days.

I stopped at the free bar, which seemed to have been recently restocked, and had a few semi-cold beers from the pile. Thousands of people swarming by, almost swimming by in dusty waves.

The beers and lack of food sped up my acid trip and I was getting super high outside the gates. It's about 8:45 am at this time, so I scrambled inside and made my way to my favorite spot of that era. Dead center, about 50 people back. I can see great, and it sounds the best. It got crowded quick and it was hella hot, even that early in the day. They played damn good considering the early hour (rumor has it the band did not sleep the night before) and the 100+ degree heat. The "Playing in the Band" opener into "Shakedown Street" was sweet and tight with a sick jam! The "China Cat"-"Know You Rider" was fuckin' killer also, still one of my favorites! Jerry blazing through the guitar licks! The "U.S. Blues" encore got me so hyped up that I didn't want it to stop!

And then it was over. It felt very, very strange. I just saw a full, two set Dead show, but it's only noon and they are done for the day. It was like an acid jet lag of sorts. Time wasn't in the right order. I couldn't wrap my head around it being midday and having seen a whole show before I would normally even eat lunch.

I walked out to the free bar and drank a few hot cans of beer, as my head got a little more focused. After two days, I was burnt out. I wandered around tripping, and vaguely remember Jackson Browne playing, but I cut out before Fleetwood Mac came on.

Never did find the guys I came with, and I don't remember seeing them around town again after that.

I was tired and worn out. My folks were out of town, and I knew the house would be quiet. I drove the short drive back home in the late afternoon sun, and washed a half inch of dust off my old man's car he had graciously lent me. I sat around for a little while, letting the last of the acid get replaced by my natural need for sleep, and I finally crashed out after one hell of an US Festival weekend!

33.
SMALL AND TIGHT SHOWS. ALONE!

Bobby and the Midnites

Reseda, CA

11/15/82

I went by myself to Reseda. This was a time when the only Dead Head I knew, was myself, and so it became a one man show. I just kept going to shows, knowing I'd meet someone near my area one of these days.

I ended up seeing more Jerry Band and Bobby and the Midnites shows than Grateful Dead shows for a few years during this time.

34.
COLLEGE KIDS!
REAL DEAD HEADS AGAIN!

The Claremont Grateful Dead connection I finally forged presented itself via a cool Head named Melissa. I met her early one morning waiting in line for tickets, at a Ticketron, for the Aladdin show on 3/26/83, and Irvine Meadows show 3/27. This was in Pomona, at Sears off Garey Ave., right by the old Pomona Pipe and Pool Skatepark, which was one of the last five '70s cement skateparks left in SoCal at that time. I was so stoked! I saw everyone wearing Dead shirts, I smelled good weed, and I knew I was in the right place again. Finally!

Violent Femmes fans were also waiting for tickets that morning. They were super cool to wait in line with! I had never heard of Violent Femmes, but I had been getting into a lot of new music via Greg McNeil, and they sounded cool just from the name. We hung out in line for several hours until the ticket office opened, and I ended up getting Melissa's number to trade tapes and hang out. She was a college student attending Pitzer College in Claremont. Pitzer is on a huge campus, tucked up against Mt. Baldy, that has five colleges on the grounds.

I eventually gravitated up to Claremont to hang out with the college kids who had a lot more knowledge and exposure to the music I was into. I needed to have West Coast friends who loved the Dead like I did. I missed that special bond. I had to get it back, and Melissa was one of the first people I met in California who made me feel that way again.

Back then you used to have to wait outside in a line for tickets at the actual box office, sometimes camping out for days. Later, mail order and online sales changed all that.

It felt good to be back in the Dead Head zone. I also met my lifelong friend Farrell Timlake (Far-L as he is known) in line that morning, although we may disagree on the fact! Melissa lived on campus. We exchanged numbers, and soon I was going up to Pitzer College with a box of bootlegs and a box of blanks.

I didn't start to hang out with Far-L until Kahoutek, the annual Pitzer College music fair the following year. During this time, I met Randy Baker, Matt Brandt, Mike Simpson, Tor Perkin, Steve Guillford, Stevo Prime, Dan Stein, Chris Peck, Barrows Worm, Gayle Ellet, Sue Higgins, Alex, Mary Nueberger and Naomi Bendiner, to name just a few. This was a time in my life that was opening up to new possibilities and new options for adventure. It's crazy how a simple spot in a ticket line, next to newly met people, realigned my Grateful Dead course in life.

Having met all these great people changed me forever, and I hope all the friends I have not seen in years are all doing all right!

35.
DODGING LIONS!!!

Irvine Meadows Amphitheatre

Irvine, CA

3/27/1983

In spring of 1983, Irvine Meadows was basically a sprawling parking lot with a 15,000-seat amphitheater connected to it. It was built next to an equally sprawling wild animal park. I was up on the lawn in the way back at this show. The lawn area was steep and sat over on the far side of the venue, opposite where you come in. That far fence butted up against the Lion Country Safari, which had been open since 1974, and would close in November of the next year.

I was smoking out, sitting on the steep grass, when I saw three guys creep up on the outside of the fence. They tossed a blanket up over the barbed wire on top, quickly climbed up, and jumped into the lawn area. The last guy somehow pulled the blanket off the sharp wire when he jumped down, and they quickly disappeared into the crowd. I discussed the fact with some random Head that they had clearly just went through the Lion Country Safari to get into the show. Neither of us could believe they took that risk. All the animals lived in separate, wide-open areas so they could roam around. They had to cross several different animal zones just to get to the back fence of the venue without becoming dinner. This was the first sneak-in attempt I had seen, and even though it isn't cool to sneak in, this was a damn good one. Lions and tigers and hippies! Oh my!

36.
OTHER ROCK AND ROLL BANDS!

Greg and I went to see other bands in SoCal. Some I had heard of and some I had not. We saw The Specials with Fishbone at Pomona College, and the incredible Ramones at Rissmiller's (4/24/83) in Reseda.

At the Ramones, I sat in the upstairs seats, discretely smoking weed and watching Belinda Carlisle pour whiskey from her flask into her cup she had with her. It was her and another one of The Go-Go's, finding a mellow spot away from security to get their cheap drink on. I sat next to them for six or seven songs, maybe 12-14 minutes, and then went back to the floor and into the pit. I got right up front, and it was super cool to see Joey, Johnny and DeeDee that close. Richie was on drums then. I believe Marky had taken a boozy time-out from the drum seat after five years.

I dipped out of the front and tried to smoke some weed over on the side of the crowd, and a security guy nearly threw me out. I can't remember what I said, but he let me stay inside, luckily. The Ramones were ripping it up, and 20 minutes later they were done. Fast and hard. They performed thirty-plus songs, but it was still over in an hour, since every single Ramones song ever, is a two-minute ear blaster!

37.
GRADUATING TO MY LIFE!

I was about to graduate from Don Antonio Lugo High School in June 1983, and still I didn't have any friends in my school who liked the Dead. Not one single one.

During my graduation ceremony I was daydreaming, and I looked up into the crowd of families sitting way up in the bleachers. Some guy I did not know had on a light blue *Steal Your Face* shirt. That guy and his Dead shirt inspired me to make it to more shows. The shirt that random guy wore that night, made me feel like I was graduating high school and graduating onto Grateful Dead Tour all at the same time.

38.
VENTURA ALL ALONE, BUT NOT REALLY!

Ventura County Fairgrounds

Ventura, CA

7/30-31/1983

I drove myself both days because I had to come back home at night. My folks would not let me camp in the parking lot. They heard some bad media stories about the Dead after party that went down, and put a nix on my camping plans. I drove, parked, dosed, drank beer, got stoned and danced in the sun. I did it all anyway, even if I couldn't camp. It was epic! I still saw a few friends like Melissa, and I had a blast regardless. I got home at midnight, and was gone by 8 am the next morning to do it all over again!

The summertime beach scene that I envisioned Ventura as being (wide, sandy Huntington Beach style), turned out to be a huge, dusty parking lot, with the stage set up in a dirt rodeo corral, and the Pacific Ocean as a western border. It was perfect for us!

I watched a girl dancing against a girder beam, stripper, sexy style, as I was looking at the ocean from the stands. Everyone was gyrating around. It was very primal. The dust was billowing up from the dancing crowd, eventually covering everything in a tannish dirt layer, leaving a gritty orange haze in the sky.

I was in traffic after the Sunday show and I remember wanting my hair longer, and my journeys to move ahead a little quicker. Reality check! Hair only grows so fast, and my freedoms still had parental reigns on them, holding me back from what I really wanted from my life.

As I was daydreaming about longer hair and more shows, a car next to me slow-speed rear ended another car with Dead Heads in both. Radiator steam immediately erupted from the grill, and the trunk popped open on the car that got hit. I felt bad for them. I remember thinking, not a great way to end your awesome weekend, and hoping that they did not get swooped up by the cops.

39.
MEETING ALAN!

Jerry Garcia Band
Palomino Station Bar
Riverside, CA
10/03/1983

I had been looking for more Dead Heads in my area. The college that Far-L and Melissa attended was 25 miles away, and it wasn't always easy to get over that way. A Jerry Garcia Band show was coming up and it was surprisingly close to my house. I got a ticket and headed to the show, hoping to make some friends who might be a little closer to where I lived.

The show was at an old cowboy bar called The Palomino Station, in Riverside. This is where I met my lifelong friend and future ex-insurance agent, Alan. This tall, skinny, mustachioed guy with Peter Frampton hair had a camera with him and was snapping pics of Jerry. I thought that was super cool, and I remember thinking I wanted to buy or trade a photo of his if I could. He discreetly lit a joint and I wanted a hit. Killer weed was hard to come by in Chino in 1983. That joint smelled exceptionally good, so I said hello. He was super friendly and more than willing to share. We got stoned, talked Grateful Dead, and got super up-close to Jerry. I seem to remember him playing on floor level or on a real low stage. He was right there in front of us. The show wasn't crowded, and someone put a long-stemmed red rose on the mic stand.

At one point, Jerry's glasses slipped so far down his nose while he was jamming, that they fell off and got caught in his guitar strings. Alan got some amazing photos of a fairly skinny Jerry and his mic rose! It was awesome! I found out later that he tried to shoot the pic of Jerry's glasses stuck in his strings, but he shot his last frame just before they dropped off. No digital then!

He went and grabbed beers for us, and no one said shit about me drinking at 18. We listened to Jerry, partied, and I got Al's number so I could get that photo I wanted (still have it), and trade some tapes. Turns out Alan lived a short six miles away from me, which enabled us to hang out often. I was stoked. Another Dead Head besides the transplant college kids *did* exist in SoCal after all.

Jerry played great that night, even though it wasn't a long show, and meeting Alan that evening, once again redirected my Grateful Dead world. I didn't know it then, but this was the first of many shows and many crazy adventures Alan and I had in store for us in the future!

40.
TAPE TRADING AND MORE DEAD HEADS!

I went to visit my new pal Al, about a week after the Jerry show in Riverside. He had an apartment in Pomona at the Son Risa Village. It was all college kids, and it was going off all the time, unless it was finals week.

The place had its own coke dealer, and a party spilling out into the court-yard pool and hot tub area was a nightly occurrence.

I went to his place with a dozen bootleg cassettes so that he and I could do some trading. He had a bunch of shows I had never heard and vice versa. I walked into his ground floor apartment and met Joey Vargas and Liz, Al's old friends. Joey was noodling on his guitar (as always, I would find out) when I arrived, and Liz was looking cute (as always, I would find out), sitting on the couch. Al opened his silver film can and removed his infamous triangle pipe. He loaded it up and started passing it around as fast as we could smoke. We played some of our favorite shows on Al's cassette deck and a lifelong friendship got its roots that very night!

41.
MY FIRST NEW YEAR'S EVE SHOWS!

Civic Center

San Francisco, CA

12/27-28, 30-31/1983

I was super excited because I was going to my first New Year's Eve run of shows! Four in total at the San Francisco Civic Center. Melissa had gotten tickets for us via the Grateful Dead Ticket Sales mail order, and we drove up to Oakland where her folks lived, with a car full of college girls, and me.

I brought a six pack of beer in the car for the ride and promptly drank all of them. Pretty soon I had to take a wiz, but I held it in and didn't say anything, until one of the girls said they needed to go. I had never held my piss in that long before, and I was ready to burst when we stopped at a gas station to fill up.

I hobbled off to the restroom trying desperately to not pee my pants before I made it. I was undoing my zipper as I was opening the door to the men's room, and barely made it into the urinal with my stream. I was breathing kind of hard, and it took forever to get it all out of me. As soon as I was finally done, I felt dizzy, and the room got dark around the edges of my eyes. I remember thinking, is this a stroke? Is this how you die? I took a step back and went black.

I woke up on the floor of the men's room with my dick sticking out of my pants, and a bump on the back of my head. Luckily, I wasn't bleeding. I had held my pee for so long that when I finally pissed, I blacked out and fell backwards into the wall behind me.

Everything slowly faded back in. I'm not sure now how long I laid there. Probably only a minute, but it really freaked me out. I got up as quick as I could, tucked my cock back in and zipped up.

No one came in while I was on the floor, and I was thankful for that. I did not need to make a scene and jeopardize seeing the shows. I looked in the mirror and splashed some water on my pale face. I felt okay at that point, and got in the back seat and we drove on. I didn't tell anyone because I was freaked out and slightly embarrassed as well. We eventually got up to Oakland, with no more blackouts on my part.

42.
OAKLAND AND SAN FRANCISCO.

I vaguely remember our parents talking on the phone and me getting the go ahead to stay at Melissa's family house in Oakland. This was one of my first freedom trips. Melissa's family was fantastic, and I thank them to this day for letting me stay over that week.

We did everything! We went to Melissa's friend's salon and had an after party. We ate at the amazingly bare bones Shem's Restaurant in Berkeley. Shem was an incredible Asian cook. His restaurant was in an old house that had all the sheetrock removed from the walls in between the rooms, so you could see everyone who was in the house as you ate. Shem let you bring in your own beer and booze and he let us smoke joints, bowls, and bong hits semi-freely at the tables. Although, he did warn me one night with my bong to, "keep it low."

The entire place was full of Heads eating, talking, smoking, and drinking. It was a unique spot that later got closed, not for food or health codes, but for being too loose, and pushing the envelope of what we should be able to consider normal, good times.

43.

LEAVING THIS WORLD ON NITROUS OXIDE.

After shows and Shem's, we were riding back to Melissa's house, and I took a big nitrous hit off a balloon. That was normal and nothing new, but this time I went someplace in my mind I have never been before on any drug *ever*.

People speak of reaching the other side. I reached it and it was crystal clear. I went to another entire dimension. It was the most bizarre realm. It was another world that did not look anything like our world. It was massive and dark, but not frightening at all.

I've had plenty of hallucinations and this was *not* one. This was going past the boundary of our world, and when I came back from there, I knew I crossed over. To where, I had no idea.

Ironically enough, we had just heard the first "Mind Left Body" jam since 1974, and that's exactly what happened to me! I think perhaps that may be the feeling of dying, or of death itself. I always wonder if I was about to die at that moment and did not. Nitrous *is* a sedative, after all. I was shook-up from this little excursion to the next world, and it has been an unsettling thought in my mind for 40-plus years, and shall remain with me for life. On a positive note, if that's what it's like to die, at least I'll recognize the place when I arrive!

Now, how can I kill a skateboard so it's waiting for me when I get there? I'll need time to ponder that question.

44.
GRATEFUL DEAD TOURIST.

The next day we cruised around in Melissa's blue Chevy Citation to see the sites. I did the Grateful Dead Tourist stuff (go see the 710 Ashbury house, walk up and down the Haight etc.) for the very first time! I was stoked to see things in person I had only seen through books and magazines.

Then we went downtown to the Civic. The weather was perfect, as it often is in San Francisco in the winter, and we spent our days wandering around the Shakedown (it wasn't even called Shakedown yet) set up beside the fountains in the park in front of City Hall.

45.
INSIDE NEW YEAR'S EVE.

We went into the shows each night and all of them were spectacular. The marque out front said GRATEFUL DEAD, on top, HAPPY NEW YEAR below it and SOLD OUT on each side. That gave me a real, honest, insider feeling. I'm part of this! I got my tickets and it's sold out. Only so many people can get in and I made it! I initially got a rejection letter for my attempt at mail order, which I still have. Melissa got me extras somehow!

I was on the floor at midnight as several thousand balloons came down from the ceiling. The balloons covered everyone, and it got hot underneath of them really quick. I was super high under the multi-colored balloon ceiling that forms over your head! We had to pop most of them just to see the stage again.

It is so fun to be in the middle of all that, all that stoke, at the stroke of midnight. So many fantastic things are going on. Bill Graham is dressed as Father Time, floating around the arena in a huge earth globe, waving a *Steal Your Face* flag and throwing long stem roses down to the crowd. Wavy Gravy is Baby New Year as per tradition. Dancers are on stage in costumes. The entire crowd is jumping up and down screaming at the top of their lungs. Then you hear the band start to play, and it *really* goes crazy. The whole room gets elevated to a different place, and we all go there happily and willingly. It's something you want to do repeatedly because it's such high energy, and everyone's on the same emotional upward trajectory. It's a fun fucking way to spend your New Year's Eve. Every single time, it never fails! This was my first time participating, and it has had a lifetime effect on my love for celebrating New Year's Eve with live music.

I was high and all over the place at these shows, and while I was processing everything on the spot, it took me a while to realize what insanely good music I was seeing. "Big Boss Man" and the only "Good Night, Irene" the band ever played? Wow! This set of incredible shows had yet another life changing effect on me!

46.
BAD EXPOSURES.

Bobby and the Midnites
Country Club
Reseda, CA
1/15/84

Al was so high on acid he took an entire roll of photos and not one turned out! He thought he was the getting them all perfectly. I kept hearing him say, "Oh yeah," to himself like he was the new Annie Liebowitz. Every single slide was blurry and black.

47.
AL, CRAIG, AND THE KID HIT THE VEGAS STRIP.

Aladdin Theatre

Las Vegas, NV

4/06/1984

Alan, his old friend Craig Benson, and I grabbed some beer and some whiskey at a liquor store in Pomona, and drove back to the Son Risa apartments. We started drinking and smoking, and decided it would be cool to lay out all our tickets and use Alan's camera to take pics of them. Dead tickets are cool and came embossed with Dead images and glitter in the ink. The photos got put away for forty years, and when I saw them recently, all sorts of fun memories came back to me.

We had gotten up early and quickly got ready to go. Three of us. Two show veterans, eight years, and four years older, and me. The "kid" as they called me back then. We piled into Alan's infamous '63 VW Bug and headed out I-15 to Las Vegas referencing Hunter S. Thompson and smoking bowls out of Al's triangle pipe.

We drove into Vegas and hit up a long since torn down motel on the strip. We got into the room, got a bit more loaded, just to add fuel to our fire, and walked down the strip to the Aladdin Theatre and Casino. This was the old school, original Aladdin that was torn down in 1998. Fortunately, they did keep and remodel the stylish theater and built a new hotel around it. It had a cool old school charm to it, and we took full advantage of all the fun things they had going on there.

We would play nickel slots to get free drinks. We would run around drinking and sneaking key bumps of cocaine in the hallways with tour friends Elizabeth and Martin. We would get into the elevator and push all the buttons for every floor, and everyone just laughed and went with it. We would see the elevator coming to the floor we were on, then each take a big hit of weed and hold it in. The elevator doors would open, and it would be packed full of about 90% Dead Heads and 10% civilians. The three of us would get on, the doors would close, and we would all slowly let our weed hits out inside the elevator. This cracked everybody up except the straight people, but the uneasiness on their part was part of our fun. When the doors opened for the next floor, we would all jump out just as fast as we had all jumped in!

What a strange scenario! Having all the Dead Heads mixed in with the gamblers at the card tables and the old claw armed ladies at the slot machines, all gumbo'd together with the Las Vegas glitz and glimmer. A bizarre match up indeed, but one that worked fine for us.

Everyone was making cow and sheep noises while we were herded into the show lines. "Moooo!" and "Baaaaaahh!" It was super crowded, and the animal noises had everyone laughing.

This went on and on until we finally got into the theater to see the show. We sat in the upper balcony in Section 8, Row W, Seat 7. I remember the place being big and fancy. We had a fantastic show together and danced all night.

48.

LSD EXPLORERS UNDER NEON LIGHTS.

When we got out of the show, after the band was packed and gone, we were all still super high on acid, so we took it upon ourselves to go on an adventure in night-time Las Vegas.

We slowly started walking up the strip, absorbing the madness. We could see the lights on the Tropicana spilling down like a waterfall off the top of the building to the ground. Craig said he wanted to see where the lights came from, or something to that effect, and we walked into the casino below the luminescent cascade. We made our way up the elevator to the top floor and entered a stairwell. We went up the last set of stairs and suddenly we realized we were right at the point where the lights start the descent down the building. The façade on the outside of the Tropicana had big decorative holes cut in it, and we could stick our heads out of these holes, and be right next to the top of the light waterfall. It was so cool to be up there looking down, as the lights spilled past your head on the way down to the ground.

We hung around up there, and no one said a thing. If security saw us on camera, they obviously didn't care, and we eventually went back down to the casino for a fresh beer. We hit the strip again and wandered into the Flamingo. Once again, Craig wanted to explore, so we went through an empty banquet room and out a side door into the closed pool area.

The old Flamingo was lush, and it had tons of vegetation around a huge array of old school pools and architecture. It was surreal to be out in it at night. All the lights were off, and you could only see a bit, from the brightness inside the hotel.

I was worried we were going to get busted by security, but none came right away. We felt like we were exploring a jungle. We wandered around laughing, while stumbling over lawn chairs and trying not to fall in the darkened pools. I'm not sure how long we were out there, but eventually a security guard magically appeared out of a bush and gave us the boot.

We cut out quickly, walked back down to the Aladdin, and joined back in with the mad reverie that always follows a Grateful Dead show.

49.

BLACKED OUT KID.

We hopped in the clay-colored VW Bug and drove across the desert to Son Risa, to pick up Joe Vargas to take him to Irvine with us. I have no memory of driving back from Vegas or the Irvine Meadows show the next day. Alan had to remind me we picked Joe up. I was gapped out. Chances are, I just dosed again all day that day.

50.

SPOT THE PUNKER
SPIKES STICKING UP!!

Jerry Garcia Band

Irvine Meadows Amphitheatre

Irvine, CA

5/18/1984

This show was fun and funny as hell, due mainly to the fact that I brought my two hard core punker friends, Greg and Jeff with me. They sported all the proper punk gear of the day! Dirty faded Levi's full of holes, black eyeliner, and spiked up dyed hair. Jeans tucked in with chains, and bandanas on their tall black motorcycle boots. It was super funny seeing them walking around the parking lot talking to all the Heads, eating veggie burritos, and looking at tie dyes. I bought some weed for us and a sheet of acid to sell to the biker guy back home and went in by myself.

My punker buddies just wanted to party in the parking lot, so they didn't bother getting tickets. I had convinced them to go just to check out the scene and they said all right.

The show was good. It was a warm spring night and I liked Irvine Meadows. It sounded good there and it was only an hour or so from my place. They had a giant parking area, and you could do pretty much whatever you wanted. Jerry did five songs in the first set featuring a hot "Rhapsody in Red," and three songs in the second set, ending with a "Harder They Come" into a ripping "Tangled Up in Blue." I wandered around inside for a bit, to take it all in.

I went out soon after, and hunted for my missing friends. They were easy to find considering how they were dressed compared to everyone else there. Just look for the Mohawks! They were ready to go, and as soon as we got in the car, they took over my silver boombox.

All the way home they played hard-core punk cassettes because they had heard enough hippy shit, as they called it, for one day. I just laughed, shut off my ears, and thought about how good the show was that I had just seen, and how long it will be until I can see another one. I went back to work and school, wishing I could go on tour. A real full-on tour. Every show, every town, every place kind of tour!

51.
ACID EQUALS MORE SHOWS!

I sold my acid to the biker and used my profits to buy tickets to the Ventura County Fairgrounds shows. Two days on the summertime beach with The Grateful Dead was an incredible party the previous year, and I couldn't wait to do it all over again that approaching summer!

52.
ME AND AL, ROAD DOGGING IT!

Cal Expo
Sacramento, CA
6/9-10/1984

With Alan once again, and I made up another story I told my folks to be able to go. This one may have been helping someone move. We headed up I-5 driving the tan Bug as usual, and smoking fat joints.

As Ventura Fairgrounds is dirty, Cal Expo is clean. Nice, flat asphalt parking lots, with no parking attendants to herd you where you don't want to be parked. Trash did pile up, but that was from dirty Heads.

We camped with a variety of friends from the previous shows we had seen this year. I was getting a set of *Tour* friends and I loved it. Elizabeth and Martin, our camp mates, knew how to do it right. They rolled out several Oriental rugs to cover the asphalt and set up living room style lights on end tables. They brought a high-quality home stereo, tables, chairs, string lights and ran it all ran on a generator tucked away some place. Modern day Glamping originated on the Dead Lot, if you ask me.

Sacramento is close to being a desert, and Cal Expo is hot. All during the killer show, we kept going over to the water they were spraying on people to try to cool down. The sun set and the party kicked in. Heads went crazy in the parking lot all the way until the sun rose. I backed off about 3 am and fell asleep on a nice Oriental rug using a pair of blue jeans for a pillow.

53.
DUCK WALKING FOR TICKETS.

Morning was overcast and burned off about 10 am. I went and found the cold outdoor showers, and took one to clear my "morning after" acid head

I realized I was super sunburnt, as Elizabeth pointed out when the sun popped through the haze, but I shrugged it off. Liz had warned me the day before I was getting burned, but I never listened! I had to find a ticket for the show and time was slipping by. The camping parking lot we were in, was a no entry without a show ticket. I went out to look, but when I wanted to go back in, I had to evade the security by squatting down and duck walking on the opposite side of a car entering the campground. I was so insanely obvious, but no one saw my duck squat, and I eventually found a ticket about an hour before the show started.

We went into the show, and there was Bobby wearing jean shorts, so short, that you would swear he accidentally put on the shorts of one of the hot girls he was with the night before, and didn't realize it!

54.
E BLOWS INTO TOWN, LITERALLY!

E flew into LA to stay with me for two weeks. He landed at 6 am and I couldn't pick him up due to work. Some random guy he met on the plane had a fat bindle of cocaine, and he and E kept trading off going to the restroom to do *sky high* lines the entire flight. I eventually picked him up and he was still high-as-shit.

We ended up at Harley Troy's house later that evening, doing blow with him, his brother, and our friend John A. These guys were young, but already hard-core bikers. Not patched MC club guys. Hard Core Independents. Troy ran the auto body repair and paint program for Chino High School. He was a classmate of mine at first, then went on to teach the program.

Troy was super cool and fun to hang with. He was only a few years older than me, but he looked like a gnarly biker straight out of 1971. He rode a clean '49 Harley and had a '63 Chevy Apache pickup. Six foot five, long hair, bandana, beard. Black T-shirt, OG bell bottom Levi's, and big black motorcycle boots was all I ever saw him wear. His brother was six foot eight, with a huge reddish beard to go with his massive frame. His brother could get a little hard-core, like when E snorted the biggest line on the mirror at their apartment that night and he snapped on him. It was scary for a minute, but it blew over as we blew a few more lines.

The next night we went to watch Greg's band President Joe rehearse and again got wasted.

The night after that we did acid at Alan's place with him, Liz, and Joey V. It was an all-week party.

55.
E GETS THE DARK STAR, I GET DIRTY DISHES.

By this time, I conceded that I had to give up my tickets to The Greek, because I could not get someone to cover my dish-dog shift at the chicken joint. E took the sparkling, shimmering, rectangles of ticket love, and he and Al drove off in the VW Bug to Berzerkely without me. They saw a rare "Dark Star" while an actual shooting star flew over The Greek Theater during the song! What? I was crushed, since I had certainly never seen a "Dark Star" before, but I got over it knowing Ventura was on the horizon for this upcoming weekend. E and Al eventually got back from up north and we planned out our trip to the legendary "Vendirta" County Fairgrounds.

56.
I DISENGAGE FROM MY DAD'S RAGE.

My dad *hated* the Grateful Dead. Pure hatred. He disliked all my other music, but he never hated any of it like this. All he saw was a drug fueled hippy rock and roll band derailing his son's chances at a good, straight, normal life. And he was right.

My dad never listened to rock and roll. Ever. He won tickets on the radio to see the Beatles in 1964 in St. Paul, Minnesota and never even picked them up to go.

At this point in life, to get to see the shows I wanted to attend, I had to make up a plan to tell my folks, because they just did not get it. Ventura was a big pre-planned escape. I told my folks the Dead were playing one night, not two, even though we had tickets to both days for months already. It was one of our last teenage missions and we had to do it right.

We left my house at 7 am on Saturday. The last thing I did, was tell my dad we would be home that night after the show, knowing full well in my head, we would not be back until late Sunday night, or maybe even Monday. We drove away in my blue Pinto wagon, and I was dreading my return in a few days. My dad could be the coolest dad ever, and most of the time he was, but he could also be a hard ass. He was getting more and more fed up with my all-encompassing Grateful Dead lifestyle.

Like the smoke from some distant-fire, I could see confrontation smoldering in the future. I was still trying to be a good son and live up to their expectations, but my own expectations for my life were quickly taking over. I had stopped going to college after a year of doing quite well. I burned out taking too many classes at once, and ended up washing dishes and killing roaches at the Golden Rooster chicken joint in Chino with Greg.

E and I put in a cassette from RPI '78, and smoked a bowl as we drove to Al's place.

I could worry about my old man later. I forgot about everything in the rear-view mirror. The highway leading to the Grateful Dead show was the only thing we could see through the dirty windshield. We were already gone.

57.
VENTURA IS THE SHIT!!!

We were super excited when we drove into the parking lot camping area. Al parked his '63 VW next to us. Tents were being set up and vendors were already selling stuff. The various food items being prepared smelled awesome. There was a mobile pizza oven hawking slices, and a guy had a huge mountain of beer he was icing up and selling.

E and I were in rock and roll paradise! We got a good camping spot next to some girls (always camp by chicks at shows!) and set up our spot. We made friends (got stoned) with our neighbors and then went exploring in the parking lot. This was one of the best and most fun things to do at a Dead show. Go see what's where. Who's got food, water, beer, booze, T-shirts, weed, acid, mushrooms, stickers, nitrous balloons (never camp by the nitrous tank/salesman), jewelry, clothes, tickets, after show parties, all night bands, band photos, ride shares to shows, pipes, bongs, papers, posters, and flyers all the way down to extra sunscreen. E and I got totally caught up in the parking lot madness. Only problem was after buying gas, buds, and Budweiser, we were broke. We lived on peanut butter and sprout sandwiches all weekend! We drank our beer, smoked our weed, and wandered around taking it all in.

The shows didn't start until 3 pm so we had time to cruise around and explore more. We took a walk out of the fairgrounds, and by that time the whole town had been taken over by Dead Heads. Every restaurant was full of Heads and every store was selling out of everything. No more beer, no more ice! This was not the first time I had seen a whole town completely flooded with all things Grateful Dead, but this was one of the most complete. "We are everywhere" never seemed more right on.

E and I were loving it! The whole town transformed into a whole different place for those few days. Everyone is there for the same happy reason. Celebrating the music we all love with the brilliant musicians who make it. But the town gets turned inside out and the locals usually do not get it, nor do they like it. Every business in town (except perhaps the laundry mat and the hair salon!) makes a shitload of money every time the Dead played, so they normally tolerated the weirdness in exchange for quick profits.

58.

FOLLOW ME E, I'VE BEEN
HERE BEFORE!

E, Al, Craig and I dosed and went into the show. This was the second time they played Ventura, and it was on fire! I was so stoked to see shows with E after two and a half years, that it made these shows all the better! He and Al had gone to The Greek a few days before, but I was sadly, not able to attend. I felt compelled to make up for lost show time.

The band hit the stage, and the dust came rolling up from the rodeo grounds as soon as they played the first notes of "China Cat." Everyone started moving around and it got grimy and sweaty out there really quick. E, Al, Craig and I wedged into Jerry's side about six Heads back, right in front of him. The band ripped through the first set. It's always fun to be that close and see what all the band members really looked like. I could see their expressions and the soul they put into the music as they played. I was now up close! It got more personal for me after that!

They closed out the first set with "The Music Never Stopped!" It was perfect. Even though I never met the band, I felt like I was getting to know more about them, now that I saw them. This show brought on a phase of me wanting to be up front and watch them play.

Being up front was tough to get and *ultra-competitive,* even at a so-called hippy show. It was not at all easy to get up to the stage. At general admission events, Heads would wait in line at the gates all night to get in first and claim their hard-earned, up-front spots. They would run full speed to the front as soon as they had their ticket ripped and got through the gates. I watched this at Ventura for the first time. Heads literally racing each other, clutching blankets and backpacks. It was like a tie dyed, dreadlocked, scarf and colored fabric 100-yard dash. We ran right along with everyone and got the aforementioned spot. We held onto our upfront spots by trading off going to the bathroom, and soon we started to get extra high on the acid we took. The acid always hits you harder when the music stops. I remember being in the porta potty while heads danced on top of them and feeling like it was shrinking down on me from the heat. Like it was going to melt over me. I was freaking, so I pissed quick and got back out into the comfort of the show. I looked back and every porta potty had someone dancing on top of it.

59.
SECURITY REQUESTS DOSE! PLEASE COMPLY. OVER.

We met this cool girl up in the front. She dosed the Jerry's side security guard (he asked for a hit) so he could be high as he worked during the show. Not a bad job. She dropped a hit in a soda cup, handed it to him like it was just a soda, and he finished the drink. He got a free dose, a front row seat under Jerry and he got paid. Truly, a job with great perks and benefits!

"Sugaree" opened the second set and by the time "Truckin'" came on later, that security guard was high as fuck! The grin under his mustache was huge!

Then they jammed yet another killer "U.S. Blues" encore to end out the afternoon. Filthy dirty fun!

We shuffled out through the dust clouds to the parking lot and straight to the ocean. E, Al , Craig and I were so dirty from the rodeo dust, we felt we needed to go swim in the ocean as the sun set. These hot girls from Chicago we had met joined us, wearing just their panties, and we all tripped on the darkening water, the small waves, and the orange setting sun.

60.
CALL OF DOOM.

We made plans to meet the girls later, and walked to a phone booth (a what?) to make a courtesy call home and tell my folks I was not dead. I also had to tell them I was not coming back that night. I told them we got parked in (remember the news footage from Woodstock mom? It's sort of like that), and there was no way we were getting the car out before the end of the weekend. Which was not necessarily a lie, we just did it on purpose!

My folks were super pissed-off. I was threatened with a whole bunch of penalties, but I didn't give a fuck. This was important to me, and I was doing it. I told my mom I would be fine, I loved her, and I quickly hung up. I was still super high, and I didn't want to start babbling and freak her out. Once that was done, we walked back to the Fairgrounds and got busy being Dead Heads!

61.
SHAKEDOWN NEVER SLEEPS!

That night was insane. We ran around everywhere! Full on hippy throw down. Live bands and bonfires, fireworks, and party-favors. Costumed jugglers and fire breathers. All sorts of things to entertain! And, as always, it would not be a Dead show parking lot without one super-duper high guy playing his massive sound system until the break of dawn. That one never fails. I've *heard* that guy at every show I've ever camped at. He is *always* there.

62.
DAY TWO VENDIRTA.

I woke up in the back of the blue Pinto wagon to see Al taking pictures of E, who was still asleep in the front seat.

The beach was still hazy, and we got up and smoked a fatty. I went on a mission and found a real shower. It was a big communal tent with dirty water up to my knees. It was gnarly. I took a quick shower anyway, and when I got out in the sun and saw how dirty I still was, I went back to the ocean and rinsed the shower off.

We walked around a bit before the show. Sometime in the afternoon, the entire Ventura chapter of the Hells Angels rode in on their Harleys in a huge double line, and parked up front in a large open spot, clearly designated just for them. We heard them long before we saw them. The sound of their straight pipes was thunderous. The Angels always arrive on the scene in a grand and spectacular fashion.

63.
FREE BALLING THE APOCALYPSE.

E wandered off and went up in the grandstands. He saw some guy who got super happy on whatever drug he took, and walked around the whole corral naked as the day he was born. E said he didn't look like the day he was born though! He was an older, much more-hairy version of his just-born self! He finished his circle of the rodeo corral, turned, then faced the grandstands and started dancing wildly along with everyone else. The crowd cheered and he seemed oblivious to everything except the music! E said he just *kept on dancing*! No one ever told him to get dressed, and he swung around freely and happily for the rest of the show.

64.

JERRY IN RED AND THE ORANGE HAZE.

I had never seen Jerry wear any other color than black at any show I had been to. To my surprise, he wore a red shirt that day and he even *moved* around a little bit. Wow! Phil kept relighting a fat joint just off stage and then tucking it back into a notch in the speaker. Palm trees behind the stage were swaying, and reddish clouds of dust would roll up from below the crowd when the Dead got cooking.

I climbed the stairs to look out at the hazy ocean during the show from the grandstands, and I all I could see was this huge, temporarily abandoned hippy city by the sea. It looked beautiful to me! I only saw a few people outside that day. Most everyone got in! There are always some people who can't get in or don't come in for various reasons. Some are hungover, some have no ticket, some are too high too soon, some are watching little kids, and some just came to party or vend in the lot.

We walked out together and two days on the beach ended far too soon! Afterwards, they cleared the camping area, so E and I had to drive back and face my dad. I decided we would wait him out and let him go to sleep, so we went to a make-shift party out on a desolate road in the cow fields of Chino, California.

My dad refused to look at me or speak to me, and E and I avoided him as much as possible before he flew home a few days later. This was the time of the fracture. The separation of parents and child. My folks knew I was doomed! I was hopelessly caught in the Grateful Dead Web, and the ultra-venomous Tour Spider was about to bite me with red, white, and blue fangs.

65.
LEGENDARY SHOWS! FIRST TAPER SECTION ESTABLISHED!

Berkeley Community Theater

Berkeley, CA

11/29-31 - 12/2-3/1984

Five shows, with Halloween being the third evening, was the show plan! Tons of energy surrounds this venue. BCT is small and sounds fantastic!

The song selection and the placement of those songs in the set list was wide and varied. "Down in the Bottom!"-"One More "Halloween" Night" replaced "One More Saturday Night," and "Ain't Superstitious" and "Weirwolves of London" were show highlights.

Each night was exceptional, and the tapers *finally* got their own private section to record from. They had TAPER stamped across the tickets they received. Far-L got in the famous group photo, with Dan Healy and his fellow tapers, that David Gans shot for the legendary book, *Playing in the Band*. The taper section forever changed how we hear Grateful Dead shows, and the recordings stepped up to new levels of quality not heard until then. It was glorious!

66.

ML GETS KICKED OUT OF CONNECTICUT, AND GEORGE FOLLOWS HIM WEST.

Someplace along the line here, ML got out of a short jail stint for youthful offenses in Connecticut. His parents were sick of his bullshit. His mom presented him with a one-way plane ticket to California, and pawned him off on his older brother Ken, who had previously moved to San Diego. Shortly after that, George had come out from Connecticut on a trip to see Dead shows and stayed. Soon, we all started bumping into each other again. Bumps being the operative word here.

67.

NEW YEAR'S EVE. TRIP NUMBER TWO.

Civic Center

San Francisco, CA

12/28-29, 31/1984

I ended up telling my folks in November, that I could get paid to help move Al's sister Laura, and her husband Jeff the next month. I planted the seed early in my parents' heads. I said they needed to move by end of December, and we were going to drive the truck for them and help with the heavy stuff. They agreed, because I needed money, and off Al and I went again.

We drove up to Santa Rosa, went to the Grateful Bagel, experienced rainy, cloudy days, ate awesome vegetarian food, and smoked a ton of weed. We had three nights of killer shows coming up, and we were relaxed and ready.

This New Year's show was also at the Civic Center in downtown San Francisco, but it was a bit more aggressive this year. I saw a guy wrapped in a blanket, run, do a weird half a front flip, and smash the glass out of a window. He hit it with his back and the whole huge sheet of glass blew out all over the front hallway. The jumper rolled right onto his feet and kept running right into the show, seemingly without a scratch. No one even tried to stop him. Everyone was shocked.

On the side of the Civic, they have emergency exits with stairways that are outside the building, with the bottom floor fenced off to keep people out. Two guys had climbed up the fire escape sides and were trying to get the doors open three stories up. These events just ended up with everyone outside getting delayed going inside. I must say though, I never saw a glass shattering break-in like that before. Ever. Crazy shit was going on.

68.
LOVE AND SYMPATHY FOR BIG STEVE WAS EVERYWHERE.

These shows were heavily saddened and overshadowed by the news of Steve Parish losing his wife, daughter, and unborn child in a tragic car accident on December 28th. A beautiful, flower adorned wreath, was set on an easel on the side of the stage, and the crowd collectively sent out our love and condolences to him for his tragic loss. Everyone's heart in the building was with him that night. Big Steve is said to have urged the band to play and not cancel the show, that he needed his stage routine to keep himself together.

The band obliged and played well, encoring with what I believe to be the best "Day Tripper" the band ever performed.

69.
NOT WHAT IT APPEARS TO BE.

Al and I walked into the San Francisco Civic show for the second night of three, ate some acid as usual, and met up with Craig and Kip. Kip was our buddy from Whiskeytown, California, and we were stoked he was with us. We had a full night of great song versions, along with a killer "One More Saturday Night!" We got moderately high and had a great show together.

Craig and Kip went in one car, and we went in Jeff's truck, back to Santa Rosa. Alan's sister and brother-in-law were total health food, natural as it gets hippies. All organic in every way. His sister made a bunch of super healthy food for us to have before the show, and we saw there was some left when Alan and I opened the shell window.

We climbed into the back of the pickup truck and gave a thumbs up, as his brother-in-law lowered the back window and latched it shut from the outside. We both just took a piss, so we were fine to be locked in the back. Alan found nuts or some sort of snack, and we started to take small bites, trying to figure out through our acid buzz if we could eat anything yet. We figured out right away that we were still too high and that even a little nibble of food was not working.

I looked in the basket of natural snacks, illuminated by the streetlights, and found a bottle of organic blackberry juice. Stoked! I really needed something to drink at that point. I looked out the back window and watched as we drove onto the freeway headed north. I opened the juice, took a drink, and immediately handed it to Al. I was parched and didn't waste a second taking a huge swig. As soon as I got the juice in my mouth, I started waving my hands around frantically. I'd tasted what I thought was juice, but I realized why my taste buds were freaking out. It wasn't organic juice like the label on the bottle said, it was reclaimed sesame oil in a reused juice bottle, and I had a mouth full in the back of a locked truck.

I panicked and looked at Al. I go for the window latch, even though we both saw it latched and locked five short minutes before. I am freaking out, and I cannot say a word without spitting sesame oil all over Al, and all over the back of the truck. I'm pulling everything out looking for a container or a towel to spit out the foul shit. This of course, makes the acid we are still very high on, get way more intense! Way, way more intense! I cannot find anything to spit the shit into. I look at Al, who now has the bottle in his hand. I wave my hands at Al in a NO gesture, and with no other choice, I swallowed it down. I shriek and choke out, "Fuck, what the fuck? Sesame oil? Oh shit." I start yelling, "Fuck! Gross, aaahhh! It's so strong, dude I might puke back here! That's the worst thing I've ever had in my mouth!"

Al started laughing insanely hard, and I automatically go overboard in my head because of the acid, thinking about what it's going to do to me. I say to Al, "Dude, am I going to shit my pants in the back of a locked truck before we get back to Santa Rosa?" All I could think, was that the oil was going to go right through me and act like a speedy laxative, and blow out my backside any minute. That thought made me get really, really freaked out, and now I was totally sure I was going to shit my pants at any second. I felt like I could smell it already. High as shit, with pants full of shit, with no way to tell the driver. Holy shit! Am I about to shit? I better clench my butthole closed the whole way home!

And that's how your brain works on acid. Everything seems way bigger and far more intense, and *it is*.

To this day I'm still not sure why I didn't just spit it back into the bottle. That popped into my head after I swallowed it. Fucking acid. Luckily, I did not shit my pants, and we made the ride back home with clean undies and my worried overactive mind doing double time. Not to mention a terrible, terrible taste of used, undiluted sesame oil, as a foul reminder to make sure you know what you are putting into your high little mouth, the next time you pick up an innocent looking bottle of blackberry juice!

70.
NEW YEAR'S MADNESS.

We had a day off on the 30th to re-coop, so we could come roaring back on New Year's Eve.

I love the Civic Center. Beautiful art deco hallways, and its long sweeping interior balcony that wraps around the whole place.

When the balloons came down at midnight and the band busted out "Sugar Magnolia," Bill Graham came riding down through the air on a giant lightning bolt. This year they added a bunch of huge beach balls, and four-foot blowup soccer balls, to the normal 5,000-balloon mix. They didn't pop like the balloons did, and they bounced around with us for the rest of the show!

71.
JERRY AND JAILTIME? NAH.

In 1985, Jerry got busted in San Francisco, parked in a NO Parking spot, while he did drugs in his car that had expired tags. He had a large amount of used and full bindles with him, cocaine and heroin, so we thought he might have to do some time in jail. Was tour going get cut off for a while? Nope. Jerry *was* a rock star, after all! He got off by doing some sort of benefit gig and Dead Tour went on.

72.
LET'S SKATE!!!

My buddies Gayle, Barrows, and Far-L bought me Magenta Rat Bones skate wheels and Bones Bearings as a 20th birthday gift! We drove down to Rip City in Santa Monica, and I bought Trackers (I was young and dumb), and an Alva Fish shape with Mondo Beck graphics. I grew up with *Skateboarder* magazine, and Alva was coming back strong, and I gravitated right back to his shit! TA is always on fire!

When I was not at work at Lindley Wholesale delivering floral supplies, we were skating Mt. Baldy Pipeline (at six after work). Then riding down the fifteen-foot-deep concrete drainage line, five miles down, to the climb out ladder below Euclid Ave. The square cement spillway was steep and had rocks, rusty barb wire, sticks, rattlesnakes, low flying owls hunting rattlesnakes, sand, gravel, and huge iron runoff gates that drained away the winter snowmelt from the heights of Mt. Baldy.

My friend Salba, the legendary pro skateboarder from that area, calls it "shooting the line." Everyone starts heading down the ditch at the same time with only a few feet between each other. It has some super steep fast parts and it's all downhill. There was only one thin skateable path through all the shit that littered the spillway floor. Brothers Steve and Mickey Alba, Todd McDonough, and a bunch of locals, would ride down the line and make the thin but skateable path, after the mountain runoff water dried up for the summer months. It was a blast, and the only time it wasn't fun was when it was your turn to drive the car back down while everyone else skated.

At night, we would head over to the original and infamous Upland Pipeline Skatepark when it cooled off. We had the Claremont College's 100-foot-long red curb, the Victorville round pool, Dolphin Pool (Salba got one of his *Thrasher Magazine* covers there!), and Simon's Pool (Simon liked the Dead and I saw him at Irvine Meadows shows).

We also did all sorts of early street mobbing missions, along with random pools and ditches up in the foothills. The banks on the Claremont Library were steep and fun as fuck! We would play a crazy version of skate tag on the college campus at night. We had a whole game and scheme set up around the science center. It was hella fun!

We had fast speed lines all the way through the campus from where you came in at Pitzer, all the way off campus, through town, and down to our house off Indian Hill Blvd. St. Bonaventure St. to be exact. It was a fantastic time, and my life wasn't always about a Grateful Dead show.

73.
KAISER WAS A MAGICAL PLACE.

Henry J. Kaiser Conv. Center
Oakland, CA
2/18-20/1985

Henry J. Kaiser Convention Center was a magical place. The building had a true, old school feel to it, and a smaller intimacy that made it perfect to see shows at. The ornate hallways around the venue, the arched walkways you went through, the basement bar with speakers, and an early video feed set up playing the show going on. You could go get a beer and not miss a thing. You got two free drink tickets when you came into the venue, and it was $1 a beer or $2 a drink after that. No one even looked twice when I used my fake ID. Wandering in and out of the various parts of the dimly lit Kaiser Convention Center will forever be a great adventure, and I was fortunate to be on it! Twenty-nine different times!

The shows had a wild feel to them, and during the drums on Chinese New Year, the dragon dancers did the best, most wonderfully choreographed routine I ever saw at a Dead show. They snaked in from the dark sides, writhing all through the crowd then wriggling out, as if by secret dragon tunnel. It was an incredible performance that was truly visually stunning!

74.
BILL G AND ME.

I liked to skate the red curbs around this little parking island, way back in the corner behind the Henry J. Kaiser Convention Center in Oakland. If I had a ticket and had made some money, I went and skated until I felt like going into the show. I had started to see a lot of shows at that point, and I was not really into being anywhere special inside anymore. Just being inside was good enough for me!

I was with some friends, and we were skating back behind the venue one day, when Bill Graham walked up and started talking to me. It was strange because he acted like he had spoken with me before. He said hello and asked how I was, which surprised me. He chatted for a bit, commented on us not getting too crazy as we skated, and then just watched us skate for a few minutes. It was very cool. Bill Graham was as much of a legend, and as much a part of the Dead legend, as the Dead themselves were to us. He was that voice that had all the best intros for the Dead. That magic, unique, always special and heart felt intro that we all loved so much. Bill's intros!

Bill certainly didn't get along with everyone, that was well known on tour, but he was always cool to me. That was the first time Bill came up and spoke with me, and it continued many times after that. Bill would see me skating in Oakland, and many other venues, as he was cruising around, checking out the crowd and the parking lots, often on a bike, moped or a little Honda 50? I would skate by him and wave. He would pull over and we would talk. I'm sure he never knew my name, I was probably just that skateboard kid to him, but that didn't matter. Bill Graham was being cool to me.

I felt very privileged, and I could tell by other people's faces that they wondered who-the-fuck I was when Bill would engage me. He allowed me to feel like I was a little deeper part of the Dead scene and I always appreciated that about him. When he died in a helicopter crash many years later, I was particularly affected by his passing. Long live the memory of the great Bill Graham!

75.
GASLESS AND DANGLING ON THE GRAPEVINE.

I got a lift with Al up to this set of concerts, but he was going to Redding with Craig. I needed to find a ride quick, since it was 12:30 at night and I hadn't even bothered to look for one until then. I wandered around the parking lot, loudly proclaiming, "I have good weed, who's going south? I need a ride!" It took all of ten minutes. Done!

I scored a ride with a crew of four, and one nice old dog, in a worn Toyota pickup with a shell on the back. When we stopped for gas, I gave the two Heads in the front a bowl to smoke since we had no window to pass it through. I must have fallen asleep because all I remember is the truck sputtering from running out of gas, and I could tell by the way I was laying there that we must be on a big hill. I realized we were on the side of the I-5 on the Grapevine. We made it to within a mile of the summit, and we were so low on gas that we ran out due to the steep incline.

The girls in the back with me had vodka and orange juice in a little cooler. One of them made us hurry up and wait drinks, as we sat there and watched it slowly get light at five in the morning on top of the Vine. We had no way of calling anyone (what's a cell phone?), and were waiting for a cop to come by to call Triple A.

No cops came and no polite motorists bothered to stop either. After an hour, someone remembered that there was an emergency phone at the very top of the Grapevine, in the big dirt turnout that has water for overheated radiators. The driver guy and I walked the mile or two uphill and finally found the *help us* phone.

We used someone else's AAA card and by the time we got back, the gas guy was almost there. He poured five gallons in and off we went, finally cresting the top of the hill and getting a beautiful daybreak view from high above a smog covered Los Angeles. You guys drove me all the way to Chino. Way, way out of the way. Thanks again!

76.
PHIL SMILES AND BIDS US GOODNIGHT!

Berkeley Community Theater

Berkeley, CA

3/9-10, 12-13/1985

BCT always has crazy set lists, and in 1985, the historic theater lived up to its own reputation once again. The first night opener was "Bertha"-"One More Saturday Night"-"Sugaree," and the second set opener was "China Cat"-"Cumberland Blues." Not combinations they play often, if ever, and as we all know, that's what we come for!

The next night we got a "Terrapin"-"Truckin"-"Smokestack Lightning" before the "Drums." The third night we got an "Iko" opener and a "Dupree's Diamond Blues," which was semi-rare for the time.

Merl Saunders and Matt Kelly sat in on several songs at various times, which was spontaneous and fun. During the last show, we bore witness to Hamza Al-Din weaving his hypnotic magic on his Tar drum, while chanting the same rhythmic, "Ollin Arageed," that he last performed with the Dead at the base of the Great Pyramid in Egypt, in August of 1978. This was one of the rare highlights you live for seeing the Grateful Dead. Having Egyptian vibes channeled through you from Hamza El-Din and his Tar, as the Dead play, and you, are there. One of those amazing moments that makes it all so worthwhile in your mind.

To top it all off, as we were walking to our car, Phil rolled down the window of his limo, smiled, waved, and said goodnight to a few of us!

77.
I'M FREE! ALMOST!

Irvine Meadows Amphitheatre
Irvine, CA
4/13-14/1985

These Irvine shows were monumental gigs for me because I knew I was moving out, and these would be the last shows that I would ever have to return home afterwards. I had some money saved and a good job delivering floral supplies at Lindley's. I was doing all-right. I gave it a shot for my folks, but normal life wasn't me. Time to bail out. Get on with my way of living. Or, at least, try to figure out my way of living.

The shows turned out to be fantastic. Both nights just ripping. I always loved Irvine for its epic sound. It was full, rich, and you could hear each instrument clearly on its own.

78.
I'M OUT!!!

I was out of my folk's house after giving college a year, and then working different jobs for another year. I had just turned twenty. I had made the Claremont connection and my job was in Ontario, which is just a town over. After work, I would usually go straight over to Far-L's off campus house on St. Bonaventure, with a twelve pack and a skateboard.

I had been hanging around the college scene and it was new and enlightening. I had been going to Dead shows with everyone and had seen lots of local shows on the sprawling campus. I knew Melissa and her whole dorm. I made tie dyes with Alex. I knew Matt Brandt, Charley Randall, Randy Baker, Mike Simpson, Steve Guilford, and Farrell Timlake.

Fact is, I had lost touch with my friends from Chino after high school ended and I did not want the Chino lifestyle. It offered me nothing. Zero!

I lived 25 miles away from the new people I had met, and work was five miles further. My job was in neighboring Ontario and most of my friends lived in Claremont, which was five miles from work. Why not me? So, I moved out of Chino for good and got a room at Far-L's best friend Mike Simpson's place. They had been dormmate's and both got kicked off campus for *allegedly* selling weed. Not seeing a downside to this, they took the *alleged* weed money, and each rented a very nice house off campus about a mile apart.

79.
E.Z. MIKE.

Mike had a spare room, so I moved in with him and Charley Randall in the little Spanish style house under the big trees on Tenth Street. Mike had a little, blue, early '70s Toyota with a license plate that read EZMIKE. That was his DJ name, and this was how I began to learn about the subculture of artists who knew how to spin and scratch records to make a party mood go up, and to make people dance! Collectively, this led to people making entirely new beats, by mixing up samples from a select group of records created by other artists they had been using for their party songs.

I only lived there six months, but in that time, Mike hand built his modified, dual turntable set up on risers. He got his first set of wireless headphones, and got super high-end speakers that had height adjustable stands, so they didn't sit on the floor. They hit you right at ear level!

He showed me how he arranged his albums he played at parties by using a colored sticker on the center disc of the record. If the sticker was a certain color, Mike knew what tempo the record had and when to add it into the mix. He would arrange his records before a party based on the colored dots, and then crate all his albums up in that order.

Mike then played them based on the color dot tempo, allowing him to control the mood of the party. As an example, blue dot was softer tempo, and red dot or orange dot was upbeat tempo. He would pack all his record crates and turntables into his tiny, tricked out car, and go DJ parties all around LA. He started doing a show on the college radio station a few years before I met him that got extremely popular. So much so, that hip hop fans from all over SoCal tuned in. It blew up and became the first big hip hop radio show of the time. I was always stoked on what Mike was doing because it was so unique then.

DJ to me at the time meant Disc Jockey. That means you sit there and flip the records when the songs end, and mention the title and the band name, and let the next song play. And repeat, forever.

Mike was pushing forward a newer form of music which very few people had the style, or the knowledge, let alone the talent to make at the time. The artists of that era experimented their way into a whole new musical genre that would explode around the world shortly thereafter.

I was completely unaware that I was witnessing the development of an artist who, along with his visionary partner John King aka King Gizmo, would create the sound on some of the best records of all time. Beastie Boys' *Paul's Boutique* and Beck's *Odelay* to name just a few. I was a kid living in the moment, and just happened to be there renting a room from a guy who was truly on his way to another musical level. It was cool to be able to see that, and not realize it until later. I still see Mike around and he remains a friend to this day!

80.
FEELING YOUTHFUL FREEDOM!

Frost Amphitheater
Stanford, CA
4/27-28/1985

Since I had moved out and was going through the spread my young wings phase. All I wanted to do was have sex with my girlfriend, drink beer, and smoke weed IN MY OWN PLACE! I was super happy and being overly free about my new lifestyle.

We were headed up to Frost to see the April shows of that year. As we loaded the tan Suburban that our friend Stevo had rented in Far-L's driveway, I was simultaneously smoking a bowl on the roof of the vehicle, as they passed bags up for me. Doing anything illegal outside of Far-L's house in plain site was *not* allowed. He was the weed and coke dealer for a large amount of college kids, and here I am breaking the number one rule. I got yelled at it in a harsh way, and I should have known better. I was just excited to be going to another Grateful Dead show. This would be my first time at The Frost Amphitheater, and I was stoked.

Stevo drove the Suburban the entire way up and we got a spot in the eucalyptus tree shaded parking area.

I dosed and smoked tough before I went in. On the way, a TV reporter standing along the path asked me why I like the Grateful Dead. I had eaten my acid an hour before, so it was working its way through my brain nicely at this point. I turned to the reporter to answer the question, and I got totally tongue tied and could not say much of anything. The camera seemed huge, and the fuzzy boom mic felt like it was falling on my head. My acid buzz was suddenly in full force, and I felt dwarfed by the ever-growing camera. I babbled a few things and turned abruptly and walked away fast. I scurried into the show and found a place to sit in the shade and focus on the scene, and not the guy reporting on the scene. I'm usually full of stuff to say, but not on that day.

The Frost is a great venue and I'll always love it. The trees that line the sides and the slight slope you dance on make it perfect. The weather was as good as it gets, and we saw two epic shows. We partied and hung out in the warm weather before the long drive back down to LA. We had a full vehicle, so we tied stuff to the roof. We clearly did not tie well, and I lost my sleeping bag and the hand painted shirt by Barry that I'm wearing in the picture of us around the Suburban. I waited for months for him to paint it (everyone wanted one) and lost it on the first trip I wore it. Thankfully, I still have one other Barry shirt in my collection, so I'll be okay.

81.

CANNABIS AND EUCALYPTUS.

The Greek Theatre

Berkeley, CA

6/14-16/1985

We were going to The Greek Theatre in Berkeley, and I had never been. I was anxious and eager, and we got off to a great start. We left super early and drove all the way to Valencia at the southern end of the Grapevine before Far-L remembered he had left all the tickets back at his house.

We had already driven 70 miles. Now it was going to be a 140-mile round trip to go retrieve them, on top of the 350 miles that lie between Valencia and San Francisco that we still needed to drive.

We turned around and went back, not saying much, rolling a lot of joints, and grabbed the forgotten gems. We ended up doing 90 miles an hour up the long flat I-5 and made it just before the show started. We parked in the last spot in a lot, in the hills above The Greek, with the beautiful smell of eucalyptus in the air. I instantly fell in love with the area and The Greek Theatre itself, and made it a point not to miss any shows there.

82.
SPEED AND WEED

George and ML drove up from San Diego in a red VW pickup they got for free from the repo yard. It had been a while since we had seen each other. They were haggard looking, tweaked out and had speed sores on their faces. This was the first time I saw noticeable long-term speed use starting to show its ugly side. They looked terrible, but they were still normal enough, just tweaky, so we smoked a joint and went to check the action.

83.
I WITNESS THE OPENING OF THE PORTAL!

20 Year Anniversary

The Greek Theatre

Berkeley, CA

The Dead were 20 years old, and I was 20 years old. Since that was the case, I told myself in January I wanted to see twenty or more shows to celebrate twenty years. I had seen eleven by the time The Greek rolled around. Then it was fourteen! I was way past the halfway point, and had a solid feeling that I was going to get to surpass twenty and keep on going. And I did! I ended up with forty.

The first thing we heard, before the band was even tuning up, was "Sergeant Pepper's Lonely Hearts Club Band" and the opening line, "It was twenty years ago today," LOUD and blasting through the system! This brought everyone to their feet and the applause was thunderous!

A fast "Dancin'" opened the show and the whole Greek elevated a few notches up on the amplitude scale.

The "Cryptical"-"Other One"- "Cryptical" performed at the third show, was better than "Dark Star" to me. Insanely rare and only done five times that year, and never again, and I saw three of five! I got lucky!

That Greek Theatre, "Cryptical"-"Other One" rivals any version in Grateful Dead history, in my opinion. This song combo on this day was and always will be my ultimate high point in my times of touring.

The crowd was far more energized than I had ever witnessed, and I absorbed that energy. I kept some in my mind! So, I would remember! This was the first real frenzy of Dead Heads I had experienced. I had seen it go off many, many times at this point, but this was different. Energy was evident in the air, and dancing feet moved like the floor was burning! The crowd is always loud, but when it comes down to a rare song being played, the crowd not only gets loud, but the sound also acquires depth and dimension. It morphs from a singular sound we individually make into a roar of unity! A vocally forceful thank you to the band for busting out a rare gem! Like the special magic trick that rarely gets performed in the magic act, the gems are always the best and most sought after. Waiting to pop up and do a special trick for us, once in a great while.

That special magic was spilling out of the background at these shows. With so many gems popping up, it was hard to keep track trying to discuss the shows afterwards. "Keep On Growing," the Derek and the Dominoes classic, marked Phil's return to the microphone, and as you may imagine, the place lost their fucking marbles! We went absolutely nuts! Jerry amazed us by dropping right into "Stagger Lee" and adding it back into the mix after a 13-year hiatus. They opened the second set with "Morning Dew," and later broke out the first "Comes a Time" since 1970. What the fuck! Holy shit!

The official twenty-year anniversary was becoming a year-long celebration of being twenty for the Dead and for myself! I was finally hitting the Golden Road. Sort of.

84.
GET TO WORK KID.

I returned to work delivering floral supplies, wishing I were on tour instead. I knew I had to be realistic. I needed to save some money for the Southwest tour. I wanted to do the whole tour using my vacation time from my job. That required *not* going with Far-L in the blue Toyota junker truck he bought from a guy I worked with named Jose.

I set up the deal and convinced Far-L to buy the truck, then helped him fix it up for the road. That truck made it to Alpine Valley and took its last roll there in Wisconsin. I felt bad. Three shows and one *half* of the country. Done deal. I had hooked him up with a tour lemon.

Yet somehow, he prevailed, and when he got back to the West Coast, he was driving a two-year old Chevy S-10 pickup. It was plain white, which is the best color to drive to be overlooked by the ever-present police. Perfect for the road.

85.
THE PHIL POSTER!

I commissioned my artist buddy Shawn Tracy to render me an ink drawing of Phil playing bass, from a photo I had taken at Frost. The result was amazing. I made 100 copies on cheap Xerox ink and paper to sell on the upcoming Southwest Tour. I sold out by the end of Red Rocks, and I used that money for gas to get back to LA.

During this time, Mike and Far-L made some sort of deal. I think EZ traded weed so Farrell would take me, and I moved from EZ Mike's, down the road to Far-L's house in July.

86.
RETURN TO SEASIDE PARK.

Ventura Fairgrounds
Ventura, CA
7/13-14/1985

The show time was 2 pm, and it was hot and sunny. For the first set, they opened with "One More Saturday Night" into "Fire on the Mountain." Perfectly bizarre song combo to get things rolling! Second set they performed the fourth "Cryptical" out of five, leaving off the ending of "Cryptical" and blending sweetly into a beautiful "Comes a Time."

Dust clouds were billowing, fueled by thousands of dancing feet, and a mellow sea breeze was blowing. Ventura was a dream and I liked revisiting that dream year after year.

This was my first trip in the new truck. We put a bed with *under* storage in the back after adding a shell, and now Far-L had a worthy tour machine that could handle anything. The new ride had already proved its worth, and she was destined to keep the road under her wheels.

87.
I'M ON A FULL FUCKING TOUR!
FINALLY!

Boreal Ridge,

Donner Summit

Truckie, CA

8/24/1985

We hit the highway, ironically, heading due north, to start the Southwestern Tour of 1985.

I met some friends via Dan Stein at this show. Jeff Evans, and Ken, and Andy. All from Oregon, the state to which I would be moving eventually, even though I didn't know it yet.

Some say Donner Summit was the worst show they ever played. I didn't quite consider it the worst show ever, but close. Mainly due to equipment problems from the heat. The band played as well as they could. The ski resort didn't bother with a sunshade over the stage and instruments and band members fried in the sun. Poor cooked amplifiers died in the heat, and Jerry got as red as one of his rare shirts.

Super fun, none the less!

Hot, dirty, and absolutely no security or fences anyplace, except directly out front. Walk up through the woods on the side of the venue and go right in. Everyone carried coolers full of beer with them, set them down and started tipping back cold ones.

Chairlifts carried you up to look around, and the insanity known as the alpine slide was open and running during the show. It's a sled with wheels and barely any brakes, that runs on a U-shaped, fiberglass track, down a steep, summer ski slope. This slide went curving blindly down the ski slope through the crowd at 30 mph, and people *did not* know it was coming. No fence, no railings, no signs! Total injury collisions! Someone would stand on the slide track, not knowing it was active, and *wham*! Head over heels into the dirt. Riders were going super-fast and flying out of the serpentine track into the crowd, taking out people sitting on blankets watching the show. It was a mess!

The show had equipment issues, Phil's bass was farting, the band seemed tired, and Sue and I had a parking lot blowout right before we started the 1,930-mile, drive to Houston, Texas. Oh, boy!

88.
AN ARGUMENT SPROUTED UP!

Sue and I decided to sell sandwiches together. Basic. Tomato, sprouts, and good bread. $2 each. She made most of the sandwiches and I sold most of them. She wanted more money because she did the work making them, even though I was a way better salesman and sold out quicker every time. Simple business. Do what you're best at. I said no, we still split it.

This caused a huge conflict. She didn't like *me* getting praise for the sandwiches *she* made, even though I told everyone *she* had made them. Sue had a super short temper and totally blew up on me. Me being me, I defended myself and stood my ground. We argued back and forth in the front seat while Far-L rolled his eyes and stayed out of it.

89.
WEST TEXAS BOUND.

I remember driving out of the Boreal Ridge ski resort parking lot thinking it was going to be a long, long, drive to Texas. And it was. Taking shifts driving, we would trade off when we did around eight hours. Far-L and Sue would be napping in the back as I drove. I would sleep when they got up.

We stopped in Vegas and slept in the parking lot of a roadside casino the first night. We all needed to stop moving and relax for a few hours after the show and the long drive through the desert. Then we moved on.

We got it into our heads, after some discussion, that we should stop and see some landmarks because we had time, and because we were driving right by many of our nation's most famous natural wonders. You cannot let those things go by if you are going to be that close. You may never get back that way again, so why not check it out now? We drove out of our way on US 89 near Flagstaff to Crater National Monument, only to find it was closed. That was a disappointment, because you could see the outside of the crater for miles as you approached it, but we never got to see what it looked like inside.

The second evening we stopped at the Petrified Forest on the edge of Arizona and New Mexico. We found a day park with a grill, made some food, and looked at the petrified forest. The small ancient trees in our site were all at ground level and resembled pieces of reddish marble, and you were not supposed to walk on them.

It was very cool to see something I had only read about. I wish we had time to go to the other camping areas of the park and see the full-size petrified trees, but we did not. We were out of there and down the road in a few hours, dipping out with the sunset.

We had been driving south for many hours and we needed a place to crash. We were in the mountains of southern New Mexico near Las Cruces, and we were getting weary. We looked at a map with the help of a disposable lighter but could not find shit.

We continued driving up and down mountain passes. Finally, we saw a campground sign, and turned down a long dirt road well after 2 am. It was pitch black, but we could see some stars through the trees we had parked under. We were exhausted. I made my bed out on the ground and passed out staring at those far away stars.

When I woke up, Far-L and Sue were smiling from the back of the truck above the black Chevrolet tailgate letters. We looked around and realized that we had somehow found the most beautiful campground we had seen so far on this tour. The pine trees were huge and thick, and reached up into the brilliant blue-sky hundreds of feet above us.

We were the only ones in the entire space. There was a natural spring right there, and we all shivered, rinsing off in the ice-cold mountain water. It felt like we morphed into the landscape that morning, like we discovered something a little different out there in the mountains. I recall driving away from that magical camping spot, wishing we could stay longer and absorb it, all the while, knowing I would never see it again.

Fact was, we had more shows to see and a lot more miles to drive, so off we went down US 25 over to US 10. Creeping along the belly of America on our way to the mighty state of Texas, and yet another date with the Dead.

We ended up doing another all-nighter with our driving buddy LSD. Far-L and I took a half a hit each while Sue slept in the back so she would be rested to drive in the morning. We got high in a mellow, fun way, and clicked off the miles. We had lots of weed, so I kept rolling joints, one after the other. We got stuck in a night-time road construction project and all the lights and the machinery were weaving and blending in a colorful, crazy, mechanical cacophony.

When the sun finally came up, we basked in the new daylight and put on our shades, just as we passed the gigantic sign that says, "Welcome to Texas."

This was a hell of a long trip, but we finally got to Austin.

We stayed at Far-L's buddy's college condo with roughly six guys living there. It was just what you would expect from a college apartment. Unwashed dishes piling up in the sink. Cases of empty beer bottles on the kitchen floor and full ones in the refrigerator. A filthy bathroom and a totally clogged shower drain.

I took the fastest shower of my life, with black water reaching up to my knees. I could not see my feet, but I got it done. The house was noisy and hotter inside, so I slept outside on the porch in the 90-degree Texas heat and humidity.

We got up early and had a grumpy conversation about why they booked Houston before Austin since Houston is further away. No one could figure it out, and we drove away from Austin wishing we did not have to knock off any more miles. It was brutal, but the roughness of the road was always softened by the knowledge in your mind that the ultimate prize was always waiting at the end of that merciless drive. One more Grateful Dead show.

90.
ROBBI SHINES THE LIGHT.

The Grateful Dead photo archivist Robbi Cohn was always on tour. She was the first photographer to lease image rights from the Dead to sell her photos in the Dead lots, and via mail order. Dead Images began in 1984. I can't remember exactly when we met, but I believe it was summer of 1985. Ventura County Fairgrounds most likely.

When I look back on it, Robbi was always the central point for me in what was to become Shakedown. One of the very first things I would do, is look for Robbi and her tables full of photo print albums of incredible images of the band.

This was my central point. I can get anyplace from here and I can find my way back, no matter how high I am, if I find Robbi's photo tables.

The images under the Coleman lanterns gave me comfort if I was too high. When I saw Robbi's set up, I knew I had wandered back to my zone the proper way! Look for the orange 240-Z and later the blue sticker covered van!

If Shakedown ever had a lighthouse to keep you off the rocks, it was most definitely Robbi's photo illuminating lanterns glowing in the chaotic lot!

91.
STOTTS AND THE BIG STEVE BIRDS.

Southern Star Amphitheater

Houston, TX

8/30/1985

We met famed Grateful Dead photographer Dave Stotts for the first time at the Houston show. He wasn't known for his amazing photos yet, but he was well on his way. Dave was living in Indiana at the time. He moved to Phoenix a short time later and we saw him far more often at shows after that. We still see shows together to this day, and his photos are now known worldwide.

Our concert ticket included entry to the theme park at Astro World, so we rode some cool rides and then went in for the gig. It was insanely hot in Houston, as always in summer, so we cooled off by pouring back lots and lots of cold beers.

Texas seems to favor a V shaped set up for a lot of their outdoor venues and Southern Star was one of many. The stage is down in the point of the V. The money seats are in front, and we were up in the back sitting on a huge, half round grass field. I liked the grass, and even though it was sweltering hot, we still had a little breeze up in the back.

The Dead wisely didn't start the show until 9 pm after the sun went down. The "Jack Straw" opener got everyone going with its "Leaving

Texas" reference, and it was on from there. Jerry had a new synthesizer thing connected to his guitar. They went into "Bird Song." He was experimenting with his new toy, and we got to hear all these crazy realistic bird sounds on all the notes he was playing. It was wild and different, and they played the song very well. To this day it is still my favorite version of "Bird Song" I have ever heard.

CORRECTION! By Big Steve Parish!

I called the Big Steve Hour on SiriusXM in January of 2021, and asked him what sort of effects pedal Jerry used to make those bird sounds during "Bird Song?" Was it a MIDI? Big Steve said I was way off. Way, way off and laughed in his big way.

"The MIDI didn't come around until 1987," he explained, and went on to say he and Bobby hit up a sporting goods store and bought a bunch of bird calls and regular whistles. It was Big Steve himself, blowing a bird whistle into a mic behind the drums, that created those amazing sounds.

That was *not* the answer I expected to hear, and I cannot imagine a better one ever! After 35 years, Big Steve cleared it all up with another wildly unique tale from Dead Tour. Thanks for that one Steve! He also mentioned Bobby bought his loved/hated, yet infamous, "Truckin'" intro whistle at the same time. You know the one. Marching band Bobby's "Truckin'" whistle!

Second set was awesome, and had a unique "Sampson and Delilah" with a little different guitar tone and thunderous *drumming* from Mickey and Billy.

After the "Drums" it was "Gimme Some Lovin'"-"Wheel"-"Other One" into perhaps the best "Morning Dew" of the entire summer. It was smoking hot in Houston that night!!!

92.
LOOK, NO PARACHUTE!

Manor Downs

Austin, TX

8/31/1985

We sat around high until dawn and drove to Austin. We backtracked 165 miles to the legendary Manor Downs Horse Racing Track. You get in early, or you wait. You have no choice. It's a single two-lane road in and out, and it's always crowded. We slowly rolled in and got a nice spot to park and camp, by some stubby, thirsty looking Texas trees.

In the other car Jeff drove, still slightly high on acid. Somehow, he went the wrong way, and took the round-about loop, adding multiple miles and time on the trip. Basically, going all the way around Austin and back. Ken woke and said, "Where the hell you going man?" They finally made it, and Jeff tossed his ball of rags in the dirt and went to sleep.

Manor Downs had large entrance gates that funneled into smaller gates to walk in. Just like a cow herding pen. People were hot and unhappy, but we all got in eventually.

Someone from event promotions had a (bad) bright idea. They hired a small plane to fly over Manor Downs in the afternoon before the show, and have a parachutist jump out. The whole crowd cheered and craned their necks upward to watch the sky diver make his descent down into the show. Then, the entire crowd watched in horror when the parachute never opened, and the jumper hit the ground outside of the stadium. No one mentioned to twenty thousand people that it was a stunt, and it was, in fact, a dummy.

People were freaking out because they thought it was very real. A lot of people who had taken acid or drank too much thought it had truly just happened. I wasn't that high, and you could tell when it got close enough that it didn't have any weight to it, and it wasn't falling like a human would. But hundreds, if not thousands of people could *not* tell. Girls were screaming and someone was yelling, "What the fuck?! What the fuck?!" over and over. Most people were assuring the others that it was a hoax, that no one really hit the ground. But several people did not get the humor intended, and it fucked up the day for them. It was unsettling and we didn't shake it off until a few songs in.

The first set was all cowboy, which set a drinking sort of tone (as did the fake skydiver splat), and guess what? The people of the great state of Texas can drink a lot of fucking beer! Ten thousand flattened tall cans on the ground. Allow me to explain the Texas way. Bring in your own empty cooler with just ice. Buy the beer from the venue in single 16 oz. cans. One or 24. It didn't matter how many. Fill your cooler, or they would give you the cardboard flat the cans came in so you could carry your ice cold 24 pack back to your spot. After the first set, flattened Lone Star cans two inches deep covered the entire dirt rodeo floor. Hooray for a boozy Texas!

Jeff and I got way up close at this show. The band had a country theme going all night, with song selections like "Half Step" into "El Paso" to open, and "Mexicali Blues" into "Big River" later in the first set.

Between the sets, the crowd walked down a whole 300-yard fence. They all started to walk up on it until it collapsed from the weight of 900 people. They flattened it, because it only had one gate to walk through between the bathrooms and the infield. Remember what I said about the cattle pen style gates? No one was breaking in. They were already inside. I guess drunk Texans do not wait to go through gates.

93.
BONG WATER BLUES.

Manor Downs has the worst bottle neck traffic ever. We stayed in the parking lot stoned and happy, while others battled the ridiculous traffic jam all night to get out. I loaded a last bong hit after I laid my sleeping bag on the ground next to the front wheel of the truck. It was 2 or 3 am. I was dust and I wanted to settle in with the dirt, like dust does. I took a hit and set the bong on the hood of the new truck. The hood had some contour to it and the bong did not sit up right. It tipped over and before I could grab it, every bit of its *all day long* bong water splashed all over my newly laid out, much needed and desired bed roll. I tried to rinse the stink off but had no luck. I was pissed and it was late, so I went to sleep in the dirt and dealt/smelt with it in the morning.

I called my dad on his 45th birthday from a phonebooth with a broken window, someplace in Texas. I'm pretty certain he wasn't even aware that I was not in California. I had stopped sharing my Dead Tour plans with my folks to keep my mom from worrying, and it seemed to be better that way.

94.
BAD COPS, GOOD SHOW.

The Zoo Amphitheater

Oklahoma City, OK

9/2/1985

The Zoo is a normal venue, but the OKC cops were not normal cops. When I asked Jeff about the show recently, he said, "Big cops on big horses with billy clubs."

The crowd was larger than expected and a lot of people came without tickets. There were far too many people for that small of a venue. Lots of break-ins had been attempted, with some success I might add. This made the equestrian cops start to boil over.

A Head threw a blanket over the barbed wire V, using the blanket to avoid the razor wire, climbed up, and got halfway over. A cop quickly rode up on his horse, and brutally knocked the guy off his feet into the razor wire V with his baton. The cop didn't even give the guy a chance to get down on his own. The guy fell into the barbed wire and immediately started bleeding from his hands and his arms. The other cops rode up and made the bloody guy climb out. Then, bleeding from a dozen deep cuts, they handcuffed and arrested him.

Once inside, it was a far different scene. Much more relaxed. They had a thick bamboo sided walkway, and you could hear the animals roaring and screeching as we walked past. We settled in and saw a 22-song show featuring five numbers *before* the "Drums," to welcome us to the Oklahoma City Zoo.

95.

I LOVE THE STARLIGHT
AND CRYPTICAL.

Starlight Amphitheatre,
Kansas City, MO
9/3/1985

This is still one of my top 10 venues to see a show at, even though, I've only seen one show there. The Starlight consists of an ultra-cool castle themed stage, where you can picture Hamlet being performed on a warm mid-summer night. Awesome grass and trees with a nice slope to the grounds, and a crisp clean sound that did not echo around. I loved it! I was peaking midway through the second set, and we got another "Cryptical Envelopment." It would be the third I had seen, out of five on Summer Tour. Little did we know, this night would be the last time The Grateful Dead *ever* performed it.

96.

BLOWING THROUGH MY BIRKS.

Red Rocks Amphitheatre
Morrison, CO
9/5-7/1985

I had never been to Red Rocks in Colorado. I was blown away by how big it was, and how you had to climb a million stairs just to get anyplace. Then it went up even higher than that. Huge cliff walls burning reddish-orange and tan in the late summer sun. I wandered all over the venue during the first show, listening to how it sounded from the bottom to the top. There is no bad sound at Red Rocks. It sounds good everywhere!

I went to the very top and was amazed by the mountain range, and the vista that's presented to you when you look off the backside. I danced on the steps outside the seats, and the rough Colorado cement ate up my new Birkenstocks. By the time we left, after three days, I was down to the cork.

We camped in Chief Hosa Campground, where the music never stops, and helped the party along until morning.

There is a long since, closed off, human size crack in the wall above the seating area in the cliff inside Red Rocks, and we saw a Head pop out of the hole during the first day show. He's 60-70 feet up with the best seat in the house. I was jealous. I wanted to climb up there. The crowd went crazy yelling and waving, but then we saw security up there taking him away while everyone booed. We sadly heard they sealed it off later that year.

The band did the "Logger Song" when they had shit breaking down, and we got to witness the first "Hey Jude"-"Dear Mr. Fantasy" mashup. It was spontaneous and powerful, and Brent took charge and crushed it.

It was late summer, and my tour was ending. I sold Phil posters in the parking lot, wishing I could go to Oakland. We hung out with Robbi Cohn, leaning on her orange 240-Z, smoking a joint. We watched the dusty Colorado sun set, drove out of the lot, and hit the highway. Jeff jumped in with Robbi and headed for Oakland, which ushers in the first story Jeff lent to this book.

Here is the point on Grateful Dead Tour wHere this book began. Dan and I getting an abrupt introduction to the Utah Highway Patrol while on LSD. Reread chapter one now, so it fits.

97.
JACKED 240Z

Jeff and Robbi drove off to the northwest, and headed to Oakland. We went southwest, and headed to "Copland." When they arrived in San Francisco, they did the usual hide everything in the car, lock it tight, and head up to the apartment they had. When they returned, Robbi's killer 240-Z was gone with all her and all Jeff's tour possessions, including Jeff's new shirts and all his Southwest Tour ticket stubs. Smartly, Robbi never left her cameras. She always kept them with her, and they were saved.

It was a brutal loss. We heard about it in Chula Vista a week later. Robbi eventually got the car back, empty and missing a door lock and ignition. By that time, she already bought a van, and the sleek and gorgeous Z was retired from tour.

98.
I STILL HAVE A JOB. REALLY?

Henry J. Kaiser Conv. Center
Oakland, CA
09/10-12/1985

Remember the cops from chapter one? I was not in a Utah jail, although I was in fact late for work by an entire week. This was after already having a paid vacation week off. I had to skip these three shows in Oakland, but somehow a miracle happened, and I didn't get fired from my job at Lindley Floral Supply.

99.
TWILIGHT ZONE SCARLET.

Devore Field

Chula Vista, CA

9/15/1985

Two days of tour driving and five days of work driving later, I was lying on a soft grass field, in perfect sunshine, in one of the southern most cities in California. Chula Vista.

A normal, smoking first set, led into a *Twilight Zone* theme opener for the second set, straight into an incredible "Scarlet"-"Fire." All afternoon we got weird sounds from Jerry and the sound board. A few, Bobby-Bobby, female, soundbites from Mickey (another fact correction by Big Steve-Thanks!), and more of Big Steve's strange background sounds floating in the air. I loved the Chula show and it turned out to be the perfect spot for the sun to set on the 1985 late Summer Tour.

100.
KEEP YOUR DAY JOB.

I missed the East Coast Tour, consisting of 13 shows. I had to keep my job, so I could keep a roof over my head, handle my bills, and of course, buy more Dead tickets.

101.
LONG BEACH IS A BREEZE.

Long Beach Arena
Long Beach, CA
11/16-17/1985

During the time I lived in California, it was always a treat to attend a show and be able to sleep at home afterwards, without a 1,300-mile drive before you get there! I had done thousands of miles during this last summer and a miniscule 45-minute drive to a show was effortless and epic!

102.
BACK TO THE BAY.

Henry J. Kaiser Conv. Center
Oakland, CA
11/20-22/1985

The last six shows of the year were billed as the New Year's Run, even though three of them were in November. The amazing second night show opened with the only modern version of "Big Boy Pete!" The band then went on to play "She Belongs to Me" and "Walking the Dog" during this gig. Sadly, it was the last performance ever, for all three songs. That also reflects another tough side of being a Dead Head. Never being able to see a favorite song played ever again, just because the band got tired of the song, or they just forgot to keep playing it.

103.
BENEATH THE BALLOONS.

Oakland Coliseum

Oakland, CA

12/30-31/1985

I drove with Far-L to the 1985 NYE gigs. The shows were fabulous, and the band broke out the first version of "The Mighty Quinn" and/or "Quinn the Eskimo." Rumor had it they had also sound checked with "All Along the Watchtower," both penned by the great Bob Dylan.

I had previously met a beautiful girl named Naomi B. on the college campus at a music event. I had only met her a few times, and I did not know she was attending the NYE show. The ten seconds to midnight countdown had begun. As if by some special magic, Naomi appeared out of the crowd with a huge smile, took my hand at precisely midnight, and pulled me into the crowd under the balloons raining down from the ceiling. It was incredible and magical. We danced together in the crowd, smiling, screaming, and hugging. I fell for her sweet personality and natural beauty immediately, and we spent the next six months together, before I pulled the ripcord on California, and bailed out for Oregon.

104.
INTO A NEW YEAR.
LET'S GO TO MORE SHOWS.

Chinese New Year Shows

Henry J. Kaiser Conv. Center

Oakland, CA

2/8-9, 11-12, 14/1986

This was a week of epic shows, which had multiple fun surprises tossed in. I missed the Neville Brothers during Mardi Gras week, but returned for the Valentine's Day show, and saw the last "Keep on Growing," that the band performed.

I saw three of five of these shows, and it wasn't easy.

Crazy scenarios are always abundant when all you want to do is see more shows. I was still clinging to my job, barely, and multiple shows were happening every month on the West Coast. I saw the February 8th and 9th weekend shows.

Then we drove back to LA Monday morning, departing at 1 am. I got dropped off at work at 8 am, straight out of a tour car, with all my coworkers seeing us in all our ragged Dead Head glory. I then hopped straight into my delivery truck and went right back out on the freeway, all week.

I got off early on Friday, since my route was shorter, and away we went on a return trip to SF for the last show of the five. That's twice up and back, from LA to SF in five days. 420 miles each way, ironically enough. Not to mention, as a delivery driver, I was putting down about 500 miles a week in my work truck. I estimated I put in about 2,200 miles of road time in that short seven-day span. And I would have done it again the very next week if I could.

105.
DON'T LOSE YOUR DAY JOB. MISS THE FIRST BOX OF RAIN. ALMOST CRY.

I had no means to go to the East Coast for Spring Tour. I returned to work as another 13-show tour went down. I was financially unable to attend without losing my ass, aka my job. I was broke so I stayed home to work. I missed shows from Hampton to Hartford. These were to be the *only* shows I missed, besides Minnesota, this *entire* year.

I pushed up through the quiet streets of Claremont, making noise on my skateboard, on my way to Rhino Records to surf through the albums. I ran into a few local Dead Heads, and they asked if I had heard that Phil broke out "Box of Rain" in Hampton. I had *not* heard. I was super bummed out I had missed it. As a Dead Head, you live and travel for moments when they break out a rare gem of a song.

I only stayed bummed for a moment though, then I was blown away and stoked. Phil sang one of his *own* songs again! Phil had been singing backup lately, and sharing "Keep on Growing" with Brent, which was amazing! Yet, for my first several years of shows, and for many years prior, he had not sung at all. It was a bright new day in Grateful Dead land! Phil had stepped up to the mic and sang lead vocal once again! One of the most collectively yearned for hopes, in many, many years of Grateful Dead shows, had been realized in full. Phil Lesh sang lead and the crowd fucking roared!

The band would do five epic versions of "Box of Rain" on this tour, twice as an encore. It then became a staple and we enjoyed it for years afterwards. Thanks Phil!

106.
EASY DRIVE. FULL HOUSE.

Irvine Meadows Amphitheatre

Irvine, CA

4/12-13/1986

The boys are back in California! New tune, "Willie and the Hand Jive," got its West Coast debut in the first set! It was tight and quirky with a quick stop ending! Cool version! "Estimated Prophet" and "Eyes of the World" clearly stood out as the diamonds of the second set.

The next evening, we got "Iko" to open, and a tight "Half Step" in the first. A killer second set saw a blistering "Miracle" into "Black Peter."

I was then able to realize a Grateful Dead dream! The band came out for the encore. Phil stepped up and I got to experience my first "Box of Rain." It was glorious! I was riding on a cloud for a week afterward.

We had a dozen friends staying over from far and wide, and we had plenty to discuss and celebrate after these amazing gigs. Collectively, we experienced the very first West Coast "Box of Rain" together. Fantastic times!

107.
BRRRRRRKELEY.

Berkeley Community Theater

Berkeley, CA

4/18-19, 21-22/1986

Berkeley is usually nice and warm, but the night-time was chilly in April. We didn't spend much time hanging out after the shows. You walk out sweaty from dancing and it's 42 degrees. You're headed to the vehicle, not hanging around.

One show featured a version of the Elvis song, "That's Alright Mama," a tune that Jerry Band normally plays. Then we experienced a lyrically passionate Brent interlude, when he stayed onstage during the "Drums." He performed "Maybe You Know" for the last time ever, as his emotions took over, and his voiced cracked with true sadness, mixed with apparent anger. It was intense and riveting.

All the band members were on point and every show was played superbly!

On a lighter and funnier note, Al went up to smoke a joint, and saw a couple fucking during a show behind the big curtains up in the very back rows of the theatre. Get it when you can!

108.
SUNNY SACTO. NO ENCORE THOUGH.

Cal Expo

Sacramento, CA

5/3-4/1986

It just so happened that the first show coincided with Kentucky Derby Day. "The Race is On" was brought out of the shadows and performed for the occasion, and we had a great show in the Sacto sunshine. Equipment fucked up on stage during the last song, and the band split without doing an encore, which sucked. They instead hit us up with a "One More Saturday Night" opener the next day, a Sunday, to make up for it.

109.
HAVE MONEY FIRST? WHY?

Being on the road costs money. Of which, I had extraordinarily little. Any extra went for more tickets to the next group of shows. I usually bought food at a grocery store, to save what little cash I had. Block of sharp cheddar and a good loaf of bread. That's a weekend, right there. It went further and I could eat whenever I felt like it.

In Sacramento, our friends Stevo, his girl Natasha, Far-L and Sue went into Denny's to have a proper breakfast. I made a sandwich and ate it in the parking lot. I then went in to sit with them and discuss the day's plan.

When I walked in, this super crusty hippy was standing up after eating his breakfast he had ordered. I went to the restroom and when I came out, the crusty hippy was standing by the cashier station asking me and others for spare change. This guy stood there for 20 minutes, spare changing the customers in the Denny's cashier line, until he had enough change to pay for his breakfast. I was blown away, as were my friends. The guy took the chance of not being able to pay and ate the food knowing that. Then he had the balls to ask everyone who could pay for their own breakfast, to pay for *his* breakfast. It was wild. I've seen Heads ask for everything from dog food to diapers, Similac to suboxone, but I've never seen anyone spare change *inside* a restaurant to pay for his own meal!

110.
NO BROTHERLY LOVE FROM FRAT BROTHERS.

Frost Amphitheater
Stanford, CA
5/10-11/1986

Back to The Frost and the wonderful smell of eucalyptus, and the horrible smell of cocaine. Far-L's younger brother Moffett was a student at Stanford, and we hit up him to use his dorm room to make a base camp and crash in between the shows. We came in from the road with a case of beer and a fat bindle of coke, and without missing a beat, continued our party we had been enjoying for the whole drive up to Palo Alto. This lasted about an hour before Moffett and his stuffy dorm mates had enough of our substance fueled antics. We were soon packing our gear back into the white Chevy, and looking for a new place to deliver our party.

111.

EGG ROLLS AND BLOODY ELBOWS.

When we got to the show, we encountered our friend Claremont Dan, the Egg Roll man. His hands and arms were both heavily bandaged and bloody. It looked like he got in a one-sided knife fight, and he was the one without the knife.

Dan did not have a ticket, so he threw a blanket over the barb wire on the fence and started to climb over. A lurking cop ran up and grabbed his legs, and Dan fell into the razor wire. It was brutal and I'm glad I didn't witness it. It was bad enough to see after the fact. But Dan's spirit persevered, and a kind Head gave him a miracle soon after, so he got in by walking right through the front gate.

The crowd had the "Let Phil Sing" chant going on in a loud and raucous way, when Phil jokes with the crowd about *making him sing*, not *letting him sing*, then breaks into a bass heavy version of "Gimme Some Lovin'!" Having Phil sing again was true magic, and everyone was heavily under his spell.

112.
GEORGE COMES BACK INTO THE REAL WORLD!

Jerry Garcia Band

California Theatre

San Diego, CA

05/23/1986

George's Repo career in San Diego had taken him to new heights of insanity and danger, while subsequently driving him to new lows of drug life. ML was in the same boat, and you can't paddle with a straw. They were going no-place. Fast. The longer George and ML snorted speed, the more conniving and dangerous the repo jobs became. They would do a little line, instantly get high, and obsess on the hardest to locate of the cars on the repo list. This meant dealing with other tweakers, gang members, ex-cons, pit bulls, baseball bats, shotguns, and booby traps. Bottom line, these are incredibly angry people. They have had some bad times. I've been there.

The first person you blame is the person taking away your shit, instead of yourself. That first target is right there in your driveway taking back *your* car at 3 am. That fact alone makes people want to kill the repo man, just for being the repo man.

I went down to San Diego to see Jerry Garcia Band and ran into George, skinny with speed sores on his gaunt face. Not the first time I had seen him this bad, but this time it seemed like it was a constant. No more time off from meth. Speed was a full-time job for a few years by then.

George and ML simultaneously got fired from the same repo company, and had moved to separate places in San Diego. ML moved to the meth dealer's hovel and started cooking that shit. George was saying he wanted out of San Diego and a break from meth. I offered to take him to the northern version of Claremont (San Diego has one also), and he said all right.

The musician, Dudley Taft (Dudley is a country western rock musician now!), had just moved out after graduating from Pitzer, and his room was empty up at our house. When George arrived, he was so depleted that he slept twenty to twenty-two hours a day for four days. He would get up to piss, get some water, and go back to sleep. I don't remember him eating anything at all during that time. Nothing. Water, cigarettes, and sleep. That was it. He would zombie shuffle out to the couch each day for a few hours, smoke 10 cigs out back and go back to bed.

As each day went by, I could see him coming back to life ever so slowly. Sometime around the fifth day he started to wake up earlier, eat and hang out. The old George started to come back and soon we were joking and laughing and talking about going on the road for the 1986 Summer Tour.

113.
QUIT YOUR DAY JOB!

I was still employed by the floral company driving my delivery truck, and I knew I wanted a job change and a state change. Tour would be the first step.

Driving my sixteen-foot box truck all over LA in shitty traffic six days a week had taken a toll on me. I had guns pointed at me three times, had gotten into two fist fights, and had one accident, as I drove to every flower shop from Victorville to Del Mar. I even got two traffic tickets for following too close in LA traffic. What the fuck? I don't understand. We are all going six miles an hour. Bumper to bumper. Ten thousand cars in huge slow lines. How can I be following any closer than anyone else? Probably a cop ticket quota thing.

So, with that said, you start to get an idea of why I wanted out of SoCal. My last two weeks at Lindley Floral Wholesale were about up, just as George came back to life.

114.
REPO GIGS AND THE ACQUIRING OF SHIT BROWN.

During my last few days on the job, George called the local repo/tow company and got hired on to do some repos to make some dough for the Summer Tour. I saw a red flag, but I dismissed because it was money for tour. I had some cash stashed, but he needed to put together a small grip before we split.

George made a deal to do two repos in exchange for a choice of a few shitty old cars, reclaimed by the towing yard. The first repo was an easy truck. We just rolled up to it. George slim-jim'd the door open with professional ease. Slap hammered out the ignition and started it with a flat blade screwdriver. Boom. Done. Halfway to a free tour car!

The second repo sounded even easier. Go get the spare keys from the ex-husband and drive it away. We did, and we soon got the not so fun choice of choosing between a big old gas guzzling behemoth or a shit-brown Pinto hatch back. The kind with the hinges on the back that knocked Alan's teeth out in a motorcycle wreck, years prior. We chose the shit brown Ford. It ran great and ate no gas at all. And it had tags that were good for two more years. That was perfect, as we had no intention of registering it, much less coughing up much needed tour money for something minor like insurance.

We removed the back seat and made a place with plywood for one person to fully stretch out into the trunk and sleep. One drives and one crashes out. It worked great. We even had a cassette player and two sort-of not bad, sort-of not good speakers. I promptly named her Shit Brown.

115.
RED FLAGS AND LITTLE WHITE LINES.

With the new ride secured, George took more repo jobs to stack his tour fund. The Greek Theatre was coming up fast and George talked me into helping him do a few more jobs. My old job was over, and these new jobs meant more money for rent. I could stay on tour longer and that sounded good to me.

Several of the cars we picked up were used, and therefore from a used car dealership. That means a lower paycheck since it's an older, used car. A brand-new car getting repo'd is always hundreds of dollars more.

George came home from the lot excited and said, "Let's go get this car! This one's easy money!" I should probably mention here, he also brought home a small bag of meth the other repo man at the tow yard had given him. That little bag started off a several day meth and repo binge that was bordering on ridiculous. Before I get into that though, here is how the big money Chevrolet dealership repo came into our little world.

George said, "This is all we have to do." Famous last words from him. "Take the paperwork from the repo/tow lot, to the Chevrolet Dealership. The guy at Chevy cuts you the keys from the keycodes they have on file for the new Camaro Z/28 that the buyer stopped paying on. Then we go pick it up." Sounded a lot easier than the last few we did. George said often-times the person will just hand you the keys, and he was hoping this repo would go that way.

George had been up and alive for a few weeks now and he was ready to do a little bump of speed, even though it was still sometime around noon. He put out two little mini lines and we each did one. I had not done speed since the last time I saw George a year and a half before. I swore the foul shit off that last time after not sleeping for three days, but that morning I joined right in again anyway. We snorted that little line of pure devil fire, jumped in Shit Brown, and off we went to Azusa, or Aurora, or Anaheim, to locate the address and the cherry red Z/28 that was late to the bank.

The address was a brand-new house in a brand-new development. I was wondering how you have all that and can't make a car payment? George brought a collared shirt for some weird, speed fueled reason in his head, and took off his Dead shirt and put on the collar. Trying for the soft approach? The dealership had already called the person, or so we were told. Should be easy.

George said he was going to go up and ask for the car, since we didn't see it anywhere. The house had a huge garage and we figured it was inside. He rang the bell in his ill-fitting collared shirt, but no one answered. He knocked several times and rang again and again. I was in Shit Brown at the curb. George looked at me and quickly pointed to the garage. He grabbed the garage door handle, pulled up, and it opened revealing the Z/28 IROC parked and waiting for him. He had the keys and wasted no time starting it up and backing it out.

Then George had to be George, and got out to shut the garage door, so they wouldn't know it was gone until they got home and looked. He always had to leave something to let you know he got your car. Often-times he would leave his business card in the parking spot your vehicle was in with a small rock on it. Some little sinister reminder that he got you.

We got two miles away and George waved me over, and asked me if I want to drive. That was pretty cool, considering *he* just did the repo. Driving the nice cars back to the lot is a perk not to be denied. I said, "Hell yeah!" and George let me drive the IROC all the way back, while he drove ugly old Shit Brown.

We took the slick red Camaro to our house first. The dealership didn't know when you get a car (no GPS, no cell phones then) until you return it. So, we decided to keep it for a while.

116.
WE REPO'D A GANGSTER'S CAR.

Then shit got crazy. George started going through the car checking out the personals. Here's what he found. Several gold and silver bars under the seat and a small handgun. A .38. He also found obvious drug dealing gear consisting of a small scale and bags. No drugs, which we considered lucky. We just repo'd a gun toting drug dealer of his fancy red Camaro in broad daylight, right out of his garage. Fuck!

After about six hours, the dealership hadn't called the house, so we figured we had the car for the weekend. George immediately said, "Let's get some cars." He called the repo yard and told them he was still tracking down the Camaro and wanted other repos to do while it surfaced. They said all right, and we used the Camaro to do repos that entire weekend.

We made okay money the first night and got a few cars. Then George decided he wanted to sell the gold and silver bars. I was against it, but he didn't care, as usual, and said, "He's a fucking drug dealer, what's he going to do, call the cops?"

He made a call and we drove the Z down to San Diego to a filthy meth cooking compound, where he traded his old buddy for money and shitty brown, still wet meth, so we could stay awake longer. This drug spot was insane. A long dirt road ran through a wooded scrub tree area to a house with tons of old cars stacked up and rotting in the sun. Several huge storage containers were placed around the house. Trash and junk were piled everywhere. Scrappy dogs ran around barking, then running away.

We went in through a door in the side and into a dark stinky house with only one or two naked bulbs lighting the whole place. George knew the meth cook well and told him we had gold and silver bars to trade. The meth cook was surprisingly young. I realized it was Capowitz, their buddy I had met a few years before in San Diego. I had pictured an older, tweaked out, toothless biker sort of person. This guy was semi ravaged from shitty drug use, but still looked all right. He was cool and into the trades. So, in exchange for four precious metal bars, we got money and a bag of wet brown meth. He asked if we wanted to sell the Camaro, but we were having a blast driving it and we wanted to make sure we got it back for the legit payout.

I was sketching out on the place by this time and was more than ready to go. The place smelled like a meth lab, and if you ever smelled one, it's not nice. It's a choking sort of chemical reaction type stink. Even the after-effects of a cook are not good to breathe. I was still high, of course, and was sure the cops were going to pull a huge sweep while we were there. They didn't, but George found out through ML that the guy did get busted a short time later. His-ex turned him and ML into the Feds. ML got out of town, but Capowitz got busted and did four years in the pen. I heard later that he died of cancer.

We split out of the crank cook spot in the red Z as quick as we could. All the while looking behind us for imaginary lurking cops. We did another little line of meth death and literally sped all the way back.

We returned the Camaro to the 24-hour tow yard late that night (with the gun still in it), and never heard another word about it. George picked up our check, and we were finally a little closer to hitting the road for tour while still high as fuck on tiny amounts of disgusting crank.

I was seriously wondering if I would ever be able to nap again. We got back to the Claremont pad, and I tried unsuccessfully to get some sleep. It wasn't happening.

Hours went by. I even laid out all my porno mags and jacked off. Actually, I couldn't even jack off. I could only jack. There was no off. The sun was up, and so was I in two different ways. I had a boner, but no orgasm was happening, and I couldn't sleep. I could almost cum, and almost fall asleep. But I couldn't accomplish either one. I tried and tried. I stopped after about an hour because my dick was getting raw. I folded up all my favorite magazines and tucked them away under my bed for future reference. I laid there, and sort of, kind of, dozed in and out. Mainly in. You know the feeling if you've been there. It's the worst!

Then it was time to get up(?) and drive to Berkeley, see The Greek Theatre shows and start the entire Summer Tour. I thought I may have fallen asleep, but when I looked at the clock only 45 minutes had gone by. I got up and took a dump and a shower. I grabbed my backpack. One pair of pants, one pair of shorts, three pairs of socks, three pairs of underwear, Dead shirts, hoody, toothbrush and paste, hairbrush, a fresh pair of Vans high tops, and my skateboard.

George and I got in Shit Brown and hit the road for the next part of the 1986 Summer Tour. We both had barely slept in the last several days. As we drove out of LA in the morning, we had a greenish, grayish, sickly color to our faces, and the same feeling in our stomachs. We drove over the Grapevine, and up across the California flats between Valencia and Sacto. It was insanely hot, and we hadn't been eating much or drinking any fluids beside beer. The most water I had was from the last brushing of my teeth.

We eventually got to the final rest stop on the I-5 before it gets green and starts to change into a cooler climate. We *both* had enough. Neither one of us could drive another foot. We pulled in and finally fell asleep in the crummy Shit Brown seats, and I felt that awesome feeling sleep brings on coming back to me. It didn't last long though.

When the afternoon sun poked through the dusty, eucalyptus trees, it was still way to fucking hot, and we had to get up and get out of there. It was miserable. The hot air was blowing in from the cow fields, and I was way beyond wanting to be there after just a short time.

I was so meth miserable and so tired from being up so long, that I swore that shit off, and I've never done it again in my life. That gets into the top twenty worst times in my existence, ever. Not because I was with George on tour. George was fun. It was mainly because I felt so bad from that despicable drug, that I can't ever forget it, and I still feel compelled to write about how shitty it really was after all these years.

117.
BACK TO REALITY. SORTA?

Someone had turned us on to the gorgeous Anthony Chabot Lake and Park, in the hills above Berkeley. The first time we went, we had to sneak into the campground at night. We would put a board over the severe tire damage spikes so we could drive in the exit.

The Park Rangers would always wake us up for no tents. Early! We didn't even have a camping spot. The Rangers would come up and make some noise, and we would all try to pretend we were asleep. Finally, they would yell at us and threaten us with tickets (of course, one sleeping bag jokester would ask, "Miracle Tickets"?), and every sleeping bag would turn into a little shaking tube of laughter. Then we would all get up and search through our little woven tour bags and dig out $6 each. They usually said pack up and leave, so we would go take a freezing shower, and beat it before the non-miracle ticket book came out.

118.

FIVE O'CLOCK IS THE NEW MIDNITE HOUR.

The Greek Theatre,

Berkeley, CA

6/20-22/1986

The first evening they opened-up with "Midnight Hour," which seemed funny standing there in the sunshine at 5 pm as Bobby asked, "Hey kids, what time is it?" Later in the second set, they did another rare version of "Comes a Time," and wrapped it all up with a "Quinn" encore to send us all out into the streets of Berkeley.

Second set on the second night opened with "Saint of Circumstance" into "Gimme Some Lovin'," a rare and weird combo. The "sure don't know what I'm going for" chorus seemed ever more meaningful, since I was going to go for it, it *was* for sure! I was back on tour!

I saw Sue walking afterwards, on acid, laughing, high as fuck, wandering around outside the venue, loving life.

Super tight shows, but the third day was all time. The "Love Light" had one of the best Bobby screamer endings ever and they even snuck in an almost unheard of, late second encore with "Box of Rain," when half the crowd had already left the venue. Another, Greek dream, left as a sweet memory.

These blasters will be the last Grateful Dead shows I see as a California resident. I didn't know it then, but I was Oregon bound. Destiny was doing its thing, and I didn't even realize it at the time.

119.
SHIT BROWN CRAPS OUT.

We left the shows and drove Shit Brown out I-80 and into the eastern California and the western Nevada mountains. The car was running great, and we were making good time. Driving 65 and listening to tunes.

We got into Utah, and it started to get hot. We stopped at a rest stop and I used an outdoor faucet to wash off some road dust, rinse off my hair, and cool down my head. I was stoked, refreshed, and we hopped in Shit Brown and off we went. About 30 minutes later I realized I left my round French Julbo sunglasses back at the rest stop. I was not stoked. I had to deal with the fact that we are too far gone to turn back, and I just lost my super killer shades, while nonstop driving in a car, in the sun filled summer.

Speaking of hot summers, as I was looking for my lost shades, I moved my seat back and heard breaking glass. Moments later the car is filled with the extra overpowering smell of undiluted sesame oil. I had broken a full bottle under the seat. It was so strong and concentrated that we couldn't get the stench out of the car no matter what we tried. It was choking! It soaked down into the carpet, and we had to live with smelling like an over flavored Asian food dish, as we drove across the entire country.

It was just about this time that we started to hear a rhythmic noise coming from the back of the car, slowly but surely getting more pronounced, the further we went along. We drove all the way across Utah and around Salt Lake City stressing about the bad sound. It got louder and louder and we got more and more nervous about the fact that we may have something seriously wrong. I know a lot about cars, and it didn't sound like something I could fix easily. Pretty soon it was so loud that we knew we had to stop. We pulled into, arguably, the smallest town in Utah. A tiny little nook known as Coalville.

Shit Brown had slowly burned out a wheel bearing. That was the creeping noise we heard for several hundred miles. Coalville happened because we didn't have a choice.

It's a small town with one main street. The few shops they had lined up on one side of the street. Random nothing. The town baseball field was right in front of us, and we pulled into the little park with a pavilion, as Shit Brown rolled her last roll. All the differential fluid had leaked out and burned up when the wheel bearing had finally had enough, and the whole rear end of the car was toast. That meant a whole new axle, brakes, and fluid, and we certainly didn't have that in the spare parts box in the trunk, or in our meager budget. The Greek tickets we each had to buy on the street at the shows ate up all our repo money, and left us with only gas and food cash.

120.
COALVILLE NIGHTS.

We ended up spending thirty-six hours in Coalville. We camped in the town park with our dead Dead car next to the baseball field. The first day we spent trying to find a mechanic in town who might have a junk Pinto with a good rear end in the parts yard. One guy clearly had one that we could see over his fence. It had front end damage, but he would barely to talk to us hippies, and would not sell us any parts from it. We found out later he was trying to force us to abandon the car and give it to him for free, so he could fix it and resell it.

We were stuck in bumfuck Utah. We ended up watching a baseball game with the rest of the town that afternoon, sitting in the stands, rooting for both teams, since we certainly had no favorites.

That night, we (George) made a huge fire in the town fire pit. It almost reached the top of the wooden pavilion it was in. We had a twelve pack of 3.2 beer that we got at the Orange Dot (Utah has an orange circle on the windows of liquor stores), and we had made our beds on top of the picnic tables. A cop pulled up, just as the fire was at its highest, and told us in no uncertain terms that we needed to tone down the fire, get the car fixed, and get out of town.

There were no parts to be had and tour certainly was not waiting for us. Early the next morning, we packed up what we could carry from Shit Brown and hid the rest under the bed area.

It had been raining hard, earlier in the morning that day. We left the car and decided to hitch hike away. We walked a mile down to the highway. Next to the road was a stream that was fully overflowing. A nearby pond had been inundated by the flood and fish had gotten out into the stream. George and I watched dozens of large fish swimming in the little canal as we waited for a thumb ride. George made a comment that you could just walk on down, take off one boot, and fish with the heel of it, like an old Yosemite Sam cartoon. We didn't end up doing that, but it was fun to laugh about, as the non-rides whizzed away past us.

121.
THUMB ASSISTED ESCAPE FROM COALVILLE.

We finally got picked up. It wasn't a far ride, but we were glad to get away from Coalville, and at least be heading back towards Dead Tour again. This was the beginning of lots of short hopper rides. We got in and out of three cars the first day, then got stuck for 14 hours at an on ramp in Wyoming. We had limited money, but after all that time on the on ramp and impending rain, we broke down and spent some cash for beer and a cheap room.

The next morning, we finally got a ride out. Some guy gave us a lift all the way to Iowa. Everyone who picked us up wanted some gas money.

With that, beer, and the motel, we were getting extremely low on funds. And, as luck would have it, we ran out of pot. The road was getting sparse. A truck driver picked us up in Iowa and drove us all the way to the Hubert Humphrey Dome in Minneapolis, Minnesota.

122.

GRANDMA BERTHA'S HOUSE AND COLD BEER!

We got all the way to the show, just as it was ending. Everyone was streaming through the doors with the wind blowing out from the inflated Dome pressure. We were bummed we missed a show, but glad we got back on track on tour. Even though we left our car behind, we didn't give a fuck.

We walked around the parking lot asking people for a ride from Minneapolis to St. Paul. Some weird dude gave us a ride. It was clearly further than I remembered. I think it pissed him off. He was creepy and was saying some weird shit. I had my knife out in the back seat because he was acting strange and semi menacing. Strange guy took us all the way to Larpenteur Blvd., pulled over and said, "Get out." We jumped out around 1 am.

It was too late to go to Bertha's, my grandma's house, which was only two blocks away. First, we tried to sleep under the 35E bridge. It was way too loud. Then we walked up to Western Hills Park and tried to sleep there. The grass was way too wet from rain that day. We ended up sleeping on the old Fox and Hounds restaurant loading dock. It was dry and had a little roof over it.

We got woken up about 8 am, by a liquor store delivery guy trying to drop off the booze. That was all right though, because I knew my grandma would be up by then, and we walked up the street to surprise her and drink some of her beer with her! She was super happy to see us. She was also worried. I assured her we were fine and that we hitch-hiked across the country all the time. No big deal. She was smart and intuitive and could clearly see I had nothing. A backpack, and a skateboard.

We spent that day and one night at my grandma's house on the corner of Jackson St. and Larpenteur Blvd. She made us awesome food and she had lots of ice-cold beer, as always. I had a sealed weed stash in a jar I had left years prior, and she slipped me $200 as we were leaving. We were rich again! My Aunt Teeny and my (then little) Cousin Kevin, drove us to the state line.

Our thumbs went out and we got a ride quickly, all the way to the show. A South Dakota Head was going our way and pulled over to pick us up. He was super cool, interested in our story so far, and he had some decent weed! We stopped for gas and got a case of beer. Beer is stronger in Wisconsin (6.5%), and we got smashed on the four-hour drive to Alpine Valley.

We got into the campground and went right into the show. I immediately fell in love with Alpine Valley. Rolling hills, trees, and a lot of green grass. Great sound in a big, steep V shaped amphitheater.

George kept drinking all day and night. After the show he wandered off (like I said, we had never been to Alpine Valley before) and got totally lost. He was gone all night trying to find us again. I was sleeping on the hood of the car we got picked up in, with some chick I had met, when he finally found his way back around daybreak. He looked like he wanted to cry. He was so happy to find us, he was almost like a lost child. Then the big lost child lay down on the grassy dirt and went to sleep in the hot sun for half the day, as we stepped over him doing stuff around the campsite.

The show was insanely good the night before and I was surprised, high as I was, that I didn't get lost as well, in the massive venue grounds.

123.

CHRIS AND WILLIE AND THE GREEN AND RED VANS.

When he finally crawled out of his dust nap, George went wandering before the show to figure out a drug and money hustle, and somehow met a guy named Chris. Chris was an acid dealer from Memphis. They apparently got along well from the start, and George somehow convinced him to front him a sheet of acid, which he sold immediately for a profit. George was a practiced and skilled hustler and showed motivation to sell drugs. Chris was clearly impressed. George introduced me to him, and we talked about Shit Brown's sad death in Utah and the subsequent hitchhike across the midwestern states. He had a 1974 VW Westfalia camper bus, and he was rolling by himself. He invited us to come along, so we got in the van and off we went on the rest of the tour.

Now we had a new friend with a great vehicle, acid to sell, and lots of good pot. Chris also had a two-foot U.S. Bong in the cupboard of the van that we kept full of smoke the entire time on the road. The bus was a green VW pop top, with a newly rebuilt 1756cc engine with a big, two-barrel carb. For good reasons (weed and drugs) the bus only had one small Skull and Roses sticker behind a black tinted back window with curtains. Lack of Dead stickers was always a safer way to travel to avoid cops back in those days. Cops got wise to Dead Tour quick, and many of them saw a Grateful Dead sticker on a car as an easy bust. The bus came equipped with expired Arkansas plates. No tags, no registration, no insurance, and no paperwork in the glove box. Illegally stealthy. Rolling dirty with acid, weed and money through the middle of America. Lucky for us, it was long before computers in cop cars tracked license plates and lapsed registrations. We went unnoticed and drove thousands and thousands and thousands of miles in that awesomely ugly greenish box on wheels.

We had a radar detector that Chris named The Dog! Every time it went off the three of us would start saying, "The dog's barking," in lousy country accents. That was a good dog, and it saved our asses a lot of times that summer.

This was also the show that I met Willie Waldman and his younger brother Fred. They were selling balloons full of killer nitrous. His brother had a connection and the red van had two huge tanks in it.

I remember Willie and Fred running around making money hand over fist. He said his neighbor sold all the (legal) nitrous in his area, or his dad did, and the kid worked there. So basically, they lifted those tanks from the hospital grade rack as the Dead Head son looked the other way, and they went on to get Hippie Rich on Shakedown at the next several shows on tour.

Chris had the green van, and Willie's red van was posted up with tanks. They would leave the red van somewhere off on its own and run one tank at a time. They would creep over to the red van, and run the nitrous line for a while, then shut it down. Then they would come back in an hour and fire it back up, just to play it cool. When the cops would show up, we would all scatter.

The next show was at Riverbend in Ohio. We took the four-hundred-mile drive in style, reclining in Chris' VW and eventually pulled in and parked with Willie, Fred, and the other Heads.

124.
SNEAK, CLIMB, JUMP. RUN, RUN, RUN.

River Bend Music Center

Cincinnati, OH

6/24/1985

Epic show! We saw "Ship of Fools" into "Smokestack Lightning" into a great "He's Gone." The boys encored with another "Quinn," and it was hot and humid dancing in the belly button of our nation.

This venue is where I witnessed one of the best sneak-ins to a show ever!

The amphitheater is shaped like a big V on a bend made by the river, hence the name River Bend. If you're sitting on the upper grass area looking at the stage, to your left is the equipment truck parking area.

A Head had climbed a tree next to the far outside of the fence. He climbed hand over hand out onto a tree limb and got over the barbed wire that topped the fence. He dropped on top of a truck and climbed down to the ground inside the fenced in area. A few of us spotted him, but no one said anything. He hid behind and under vehicles and secretly made his way to a semi-trailer that was parked right up against the fence, separating him from the upper general admission area of the show. The big grassy section on top.

Suddenly he made his move! He climbed up the front of the semi, over the hood, up the windshield, over the roof, and onto the top of the trailer, where he started running full speed. By this time the crowd had seen him, and cheers were going up as he approached his dismount.

Running full speed on the top of the semi-trailer, he jumped over the whole barbed wire V of the fence, which was almost as high as the truck, and cleared it easily. He landed on his feet, did a front somersault to absorb the impact of a fourteen-foot drop, and he was off and running at full speed without missing a step.

The only security guard even close to him was a big, heavy, slow farm fed looking guy, and he was easily out raced by the jumper. Heads immediately started to walk in front of the running security guys (they caught on quick and joined the chase), and got them slowed down enough so the jumper finally got away into the crowd.

Now, I don't condone breaking into shows, but occasionally someone does it so well you're compelled to admire it for the creativity involved. Here's to you Riverbend fence jumper. Amplitude, aggression, and stylish execution. Nice run!

The crowd pretended to hold up score cards and you received perfect tens all around!

125.
DYLAN AND THE DEAD.

Tom Petty, Bob Dylan and The Grateful Dead
Rubber Bowl
Akron, OH
7/2/1986

Parts of this tour have slipped away from my memory. I'll do my best to trace our route. We drove down to The Rubber Bowl in Akron, Ohio, and I remember a massive car tire being the first distinguishing marker you see as you approach the stadium. Turns out the gigantic tire was the actual sign for the venue. Akron is, after all, the tire producing capital of the U.S.

Dylan and the Dead were playing well, and I was glad I was back on tour and not still stuck in bum-fuck Utah. Dylan came out onstage with the Dead for the first time that night in Akron. Bob did three songs in the first set, and one song with the boys in the second set. Tom Petty and his band The Heartbreakers were opening this tour, but I ended up hearing their first few songs each night from outside the venue. They went on early, and I wasn't done hustling for party and travel cash in the parking lot yet.

126.
ALL THE HOURS I SPENT INSIDE THE COLISEUMS.

Rich Stadium
Orchard Park, NY
7/4/1986

This show was televised for the annual Farm Aid concerts. Phil and Bobby both had encouraging things to say during the broadcast.

These are football stadiums, and they are filled to the top. It was windy all afternoon with the sound being blown back behind the stage. The band played well and shredded through many rippers, despite hair in the eyes and the breeze being humid and hot. Jerry was particularly lively, rocking out from the start.

The fireworks after the show stand out as one of the highlights, besides the music on this evening. I was getting accustomed to these big shows, and fireworks seemed to fit right in with the whole grand scheme. More nitrous was in order with Willie and Fred, and the fat tanks just kept on giving up the balloons.

127.
JERRY PLAYED GREAT.
WE HAD NO CLUE.

RFK Stadium

Washington, DC

7/6/1986

When we get to RFK it was superhot and humid at around 102 degrees, which seems like a wet blanket on your head kind of humid. We were all melting away on these 100 plus degree days. We skipped Tom Petty's entire set because it was too fucking-hot. We ended up getting an old black man with a fishing rod stoned. We sat in the shade fishing with him in the river outside the venue, vaguely listening to Tom Petty, and blowing hot smoke rings in the air.

George and I said our goodbyes to the old fisherman and went in. You climb these outside, open-air walkways to get into the stadium, and it was already totally packed before Dylan went on. It continued to get more crowded before the Dead took the stage. The giant football stadium was once again filled to the very top. I walked all the way up to the furthest back part of the arena, and the stage looked like it was a mile away.

It was insane how many more people were coming to shows. Staggering would be more accurate. A trend had started, in which the Dead would be forced to play huge arenas, just to allow the legion of fans to each get a shot at being able to get in. Events with insane crowd capacity were normally unique gigs, like the US Festival, Englishtown, New Jersey, or Watkins Glen, New York. Now it was becoming the norm to have over 50,000 and upwards of 90,000 Heads at several shows during a regular Summer Tour.

It was quite a difference from a few short years before and it was a change that not all Heads took in stride.

128.
NO FUCKING WAY TO KNOW ANYTHING WAS WRONG.

We jumped in the green, bread loaf shaped van, said goodbye to Washington, DC, and headed straight to Memphis. We pulled into a parking lot, and Chris went to offload a shit ton of acid at a sketchy apartment complex. We stayed in the van to make sure it didn't get broken into. Chris's orders. Stay here and don't let the van get poached, this is a gnarly part of town. It was a low, flat, brick, apartment complex, and everybody seemed to be outside, chilling and hanging out.

Chris came back after a bit, and we left Memphis in the rearview mirror with California on our minds! We had no idea anything was amiss on tour. We had no cell phones or internet to warn us about issues or changes.

We took shifts driving so we never had to stop, and we also took some of that killer acid to stay up. The states slipped by as the clock spun around, and soon we were three quarters of the way across the country.

We had a little breakdown in New Mexico and got stuck for a few hours at seemingly, the oldest gas station in all the great Southwest. Straight out of a 1930s movie. Everything was aged and weather worn including the ancient old man who came out to help us. We had a fuel filter clog up on us and as soon as we got that fixed, we kept driving non-stop all the way to Ventura, California.

When we got there, we see cars and buses that clearly belong to Dead Heads getting onto the freeway to *leave* town. Something was very wrong, and even though we did not know what it was yet, we could clearly tell the shows were not going to happen.

The gates to enter the Seaside Park campground were shut and three fourths of the people who would normally be there at this time before a show, were not there. One sign on the fence simply said, "The Shows are Cancelled. Then we saw a "Get Well Jerry" sign, and we all got that sinking feeling in our stomachs when you find out something's wrong. Everyone who was still there was walking around with their head down. The normal festive feeling that always surrounds a Grateful Dead show was nowhere to be found.

We got out and asked some Heads what was up, and finally learned Jerry had fallen into a diabetic coma, and had been in that state for a few days already. This was a huge shock to us. We just saw 22 shows in a row (minus Minnesota) and Jerry was rocking out the whole time, on tour with Tom Petty and Bob Dylan. What happened in four short days?

No one from GDP had made an official statement yet, but it was out in the newspapers by the next day. "Rock Guitarist Recovering After Slipping into Diabetic Coma," one of the many headlines read. Apparently, Jerry had a tooth infection and an abscess that triggered a diabetic reaction which caused him to slip into a coma. It was a scary time for everyone. I recall thinking many times to myself, *is this the end of The Grateful Dead?*

Ventura, Boreal and the rest of the tour was cancelled, and we had no idea if it would ever start up again.

129.

PRELUDE TO OREGON.

The three of us drove back to Far-L's Claremont house in sad and somber moods. We had been driving for days and luckily the house was only two short hours away. I met up with Jeff Evans and Andy, who ended up being the Portland Dead Head connection. They drove down and got denied along with the rest of us.

My next life-phase was beginning. They had seriously amazing weed and I knew Jeff grew it. Chris and I noticed this, and we decided we need to grow. Chris gives us the van and some cash to find a place to grow weed indoors on the West Coast, so we can ship it to Memphis. He hops a plane back to Tennessee, and George and I venture north, up the I-5. We try Santa Barbara, Santa Cruz, Redding, Guerneville, Garberville, Weed, Ashland, and Eugene.

We stopped and saw Scott Miller, who had fled the Feds just before the meth-cook spot he was working at got busted. He had landed in Guerneville. It was great to see him, but he was still doing a ton of speed and was still caught up in that lifestyle. In retrospect, I wish we had made him get in the van and come with us. But that didn't happen.

None of those towns worked out for various reasons.

Nordy, Chino CA. Fall 1985 (Donna Nordwall)

Dan Stein, Eel River CA. Summer 1987 (Nordy)

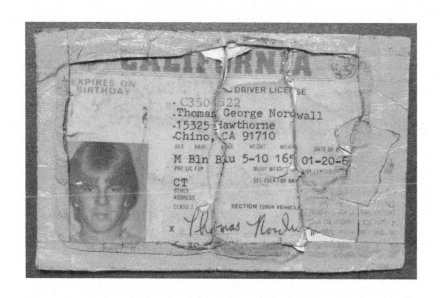

My license I handed the Utah cop while on acid.
Fall 1985 (Nordy)

UNIFORM CITATION OR INFORMATION AND NOTICE TO APPEAR	ISSUED BY:	UTAH HIGHWAY PATROL		CITATION NO.

The ticket I received in Utah while on acid. Fall 1985. (Nordy)

Young Nordy copping an attitude.
St Paul MN. Summer 1973 (Bertha Klein)

Nordy and sister Amy. I told you I knew my way around MSG!
New York City. Summer 1975 (Donna Nordwall)

Scott Miller aka ML. Bethel CT. Spring 1982
(Nordy)

Mark Rockwell with Gumby. Bethel CT. Summer 1986
(Harvey Hubble V)

George Jurdy with a dose. Monterey CA. Spring 1987
(Mark Rockwell)

Nordy and Scott Ernest aka E. Bethel CT. Spring 1982
(Heather Ross)

Kurt Ogrinc aka K. Chino Ca. 1984
(Donna Nordwall)

Nordy, Ernest and Jack in Jack's Class. Bethel CT. Winter 1981
(Unknown)

Pete Rasato. Bethel Ct. 1983
(unknown)

Jeannie Kennedy. Bethel CT. Fall 1982
(Nordy)

Heather Ross. Bethel CT. Spring 1982 (Nordy)

Greg McNeil and Audra Molachek of punk band President Joe. Chino CA. Winter 1983 (Nordy)

Nordy. NYE. Phonebooth joint directly in front of SF City Hall. SF CA.
Winter 1983 (Unknown)

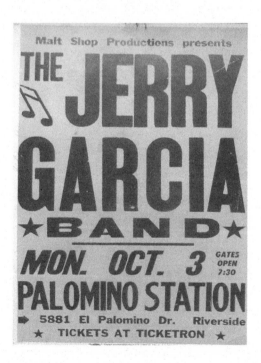

The Palomino Station gig where I met lifelong friend Alan. Fall 1983
(Nordy)

Jerry Garcia Palomino Station, Riverside CA. Fall 1983 (Alan Petrasek)

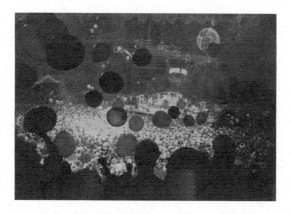

New Year's Eve. SF Civic. SF CA. Winter 1983.(Alan Petrasek)

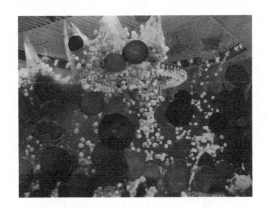

New Year's Eve. SF Civic. SF CA. Winter 1983.(Alan Petrasek)

**Vegas Marque, Aladdin Theatre, Las Vegas NV.
Spring 1984 (Alan Petrasek)**

Alan, Me, Craig Benson. Las Vegas NV. Spring 1984 (Alan Petrasek)

**Craig and Alan with Cal Expo tickets and party favors. Pomona CA.
Spring 1984 (Nordy)**

Ventura and Greek concerts parking lot handbill.
Summer 1984 (Unknown)

E, high as fuck on acid at The Greek, just after they played Darkstar!
Summer 1984 (Alan Petrasek)

The security guard who asked for a dose. 2nd set, high as fuck! Ventura CA. Summer 1884 (Alan Petrasek)

Camping chaos. Ventura CA. Summer 1984 (Alan Petrasek)

E asleep in the blue Pinto. Get out of that bed! Ventura CA. Summer 1984 (Alan Petrasek)

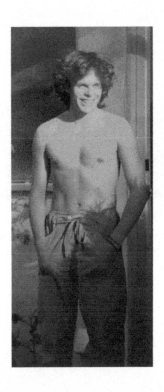

Farrell Timlake. St. Bonaventure St house. Claremont, CA. Summer 1985 (Nordy)

Natasha and Stevo up top, unknown, unknown, Nordy (short hair) and Egg Roll Man Dan. Palo Alto CA. Spring 1985 (Farrell Timlake)

Phil sings at The Frost! Spring 1985 (Nordy)

Guitarist seeks drug therapy

SAN FRANCISCO (AP) — Grateful Dead's legendary guitarist Jerry Garcia, arrested Jan. 18 for possession of narcotics, has asked for permission to enter a drug-therapy program, authorities said.

Garcia, 42, made the request Friday to a Municipal Court judge.

If accepted into the Adult Probation Department program, Garcia could avoid standing trial and his arrest record would be sealed, authorities said. To be accepted, an applicant cannot have prior drug convictions, violence involved in the charge, parole or probation violations, or felony convictions in the past five years.

Garcia was arrested last month in Golden Gate Park for possession of 1.2 grams of heroin and 1.1 grams of cocaine.

Garcia did not enter a plea during the court appearance and another hearing was scheduled for March 19.

Jerry gets busted! The Oregonian. Summer 1985 (Unknown)

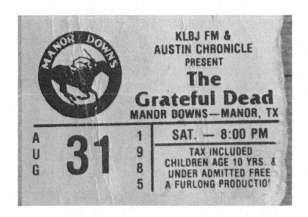

The show the fake parachutist hit the ground at! Austin Texas.
Summer 1985 (Nordy)

Famed photographer and lifelong friend Dave Stotts. Shoreline CA.
1980's (Unknown)

The Phil Poster! Originally drawn by Shawn Tracy.
I sold them on Fall Tour 1985 (Nordy)

Starlight Theatre rip-off of the 20-year poster. I love it!
Summer 1985 (Nordy)

New Year's Eve giant ticket! Oakland CA. Winter 1985 (Nordy)

Our beloved Willy saying "no vending" with a laugh! Henry J. Kaiser. Oakland CA. Winter 1986 (Mark Rockwell)

I have no idea how I got amazing Orchestra seats for two of the BCT
nights! Berkeley CA. Spring 1986 (Nordy)

Far-L's infamous tour truck. Nordy and George. Repo men
for tour money. Claremont CA. Summer 1986 (Farrell Timlake)

**Tour shirt with all the dates. Ventura was cancelled.
USA, Summer 1986 (Nordy)**

**Washington Post ad. Dylan and The Dead. RFK, Washington DC.
Summer 1986 (Unknown)**

Rock Guitarist Garcia Recovering After Slipping Into Diabetic Coma

GREENBRAE, Calif. (AP)—Jerry Garcia, lead guitarist for the Grateful Dead rock band, has been hospitalized after slipping into a diabetic coma resulting from an infection caused by an abscessed tooth, a band spokesman said. Garcia, 43, was in Marin General Hospital, about 20 miles north of San Francisco.

In a statement Saturday, Marin General Hospital said: "Jerry Garcia is improving and has stabilized. He's awake and alert and is being treated for diabetes." A spokeswoman said she did not know how long Garcia's physicians expect him to remain hospitalized.

Band spokesman Dennis McNally said Garcia lapsed into a coma but was recovering on Friday. "He's really sick, but he'll be OK," McNally said.

Concerts by the Grateful Dead scheduled for Saturday and today at the Ventura County Fairgrounds were canceled, and the promoter said they would take place July 19 and 20 at the Shoreline Amphitheater in Mountain View.

Jerry Garcia

Jerry has a tooth abscess and onset diabetes. Tour is cancelled as he goes to the hospital. Summer 1986 (Unknown)

L.A. Times ad. Cancelled Ventura Fairgrounds Gigs. Summer 1886. (Unknown)

130.
FALLING INTO PORTLAND'S ARMS.

We drove into downtown Portland and parked by the Elk fountain. It was gorgeous. Jeff Evans walked over and met us, and we ended up staying with him for a week or two while we found a house. I found the Ross Island grocery and fell in love with the Northwest. Jeff and another new friend, Craig Mosbek, became our growing guides and helped us figure out our own grow room. Things were looking damn good.

131.
REBEL SKATES.

I looked in the phone book for a skate shop and saw three shops that advertised boards. Cal Skate was one of them, and they had a *since 1976* in the ad, so I knew they would be good to go. Then I saw Mrs. A's Surfer. No surf in Portland. Pass. Then I saw the number for Rebel Skates, with a little Skull and Cross Bones wearing a top hat and I knew that was the shop I wanted. It may as well have been called Fuck You Skates. The name jumped off the page at me, and I skated my way to the address the second day I lived here.

I met Billy Reese and Bryan Zipper, the owners, and Billy took me up to Longview to skate the Kirby Gap banks. I met the rest of the extensive Rebel Skates crew after that, and we all became friends for life. You know who you are! This is the crew that first named me Tom Hippy and then shortened Nordwall to Nordy. I've been Nordy ever since. Occasionally one of the OG guys will still yell TOM HIPPY at me at a show or a skate event. We would eat slices at Escape From New York Pizza every day and talk to Garry, Greg and Phil back when Portland was a little different! I love you motherfuckers! You *all* changed my life!

132.
JEOPARDIZING JEFF'S GROW IS A NO-NO.

Luck finally ran out on us with the lack of tags on the VW van. I got pulled over for no front license plate. Not a big deal, I got a ticket. Wrong. I got pulled over right in front of Jeff's grow house.

Back then it was insanely tough to grow weed and not get caught. You did everything you could do to be stealth. It was jail time if you didn't. I bummed Jeff out by drawing attention to his grow house, and that was the last night we stayed at Jeff's place.

We searched out and rented an old five-bedroom house for $315 a month on N Holman St., off N Interstate. Portland was incredible to me from the moment I arrived, and I knew I had found my home.

133.
PORTLAND HAS KILLER MUSIC EVERY FUCKING NIGHT.

Of course, we immediately start seeing shows in Portland. I saw Steve Winwood on 6/14/86 at the Memorial Coliseum and then Bob Dylan with Tom Petty and the Heartbreakers on 7/29 at Civic Stadium. I start finding Portland bars and the local music clubs, and I start seeing shows almost every night of the week. Nine Days Wonder was *the* jam band to see in Portland and we went every time they played.

134.
FLEAS AND MOLD.
NO WEED ALLOWED!

Our house was huge and cheap. We intended to grow weed in it, but that was short lived. We got duped. As soon as we signed the lease, the land lady told us point blank they would turn us in if we tried. We had a month-to-month lease, so we moved in anyway and started to look for another place we could grow pot in. That was the plan, after all.

The place had a weird floor layout, almost as if it had been split up at some point to be used as a rooming house. It also had super bad fleas from the previous tenant's dogs when we first moved in. It was horrible. They covered your legs, jumping on them, straight from the floor. The land lady eventually got around to getting it sprayed, but not before we had been pretty much eaten to death. Brutal!

The house had oil heat for the downstairs and electric heat for the upstairs bedrooms. We, of course, did not have an extra $400 to fill the oil tank, so we made do with the upstairs heaters. That was a mistake, and soon we found the lower half of the house to be molding on the walls, from the *inside*. We moved our shitty thrift store furniture away from the walls and there was white, blue, and black mold everywhere. Needless to say, that house did not last long.

135.

THE WONDERS OF NATURE, AS SHOWN TO GEORGE, BY ME.

During the first two weeks, George and I were both happy to have a house, but we still needed to drive back to LA to get our measly possessions. We left in the afternoon and drove south. It got late so we stopped to sleep on an old logging road. If you live here for a while, you know which roads are logging roads, and you know no one will be on them, especially at night. Once the loggers cut the trees, they leave the road they made, and people start using them for dirt biking and for access to hunt and fish. They also make a great place to crash out in the van.

I got up early and walked off to find a tree to take a crap under. I saw on old four by four post that once had a sign on it, sticking out of the ground a few feet off the side of the remote road we were on. Perfect spot to lean up against and do my business. This is two miles up an abandoned dirt road, way out in the forest. No one would see it and the rain will wash it away eventually. I did what I had to do and went back to the van, toilet paper in hand, to wake up George and get back on the road.

The forest was full of birds, and I saw a huge hawk soaring up above us on the thermals. I pointed the hawk out to George, and he smiled and watched it with me. We started to drive back down the bumpy dirt road, and I stopped the van and told George in the same tone I just used to tell him about the hawk, to look over at that post.

George looked for a while and said he didn't see anything. "What were you looking at?" he asked. I said, "Look, right there. See it?" George looked again and still wasn't seeing anything. I told him to look closer, down by the bottom of the post. He finally focused on the area I was telling him to look at. He realized with a huge "Oh, fuck you man!" and a look of pure disgust on his face, that I was not showing him some wonder of nature out here in the beautiful countryside. What I was actually making him look at was the huge shit I just took underneath that old sign pole.

I had pulled a lot of pranks on George over the years, and vice versa, but this one was particularly funny because we had just been taking in nature and the awesomeness that is Oregon. It was our first month up here and it was all new and magnificent for us, and I duped him good. I was laughing my ass off, but George was pissed. I've never seen him get that upset about a prank. "Fuck you! That's so fucking gross!" he said. Which made me laugh even harder, of course. He really thought I was showing him something amazing about nature, and actually, I was. I was amazed all that could come out of me, and I felt it proper to share it visually with my good friend.

He didn't talk to me for a few hours, and still wasn't happy when we stopped at Alan's in Redding to swim in Lake Shasta, ride his motorcycles, and smoke all his weed.

136.
MEASLEY POSSESSIONS AND PULVERIZED FEMURS.

California was uneventful. We packed what we could fit in the Volks van, said thanks and goodbye for now to Far-L, and started our long drive back up the I-5. Dan Stein moved into my vacated back bedroom and promptly hung up a Dead poster. Right next to it, he hung up a huge poster of Johnny Rotten's scowling, chipped toof mug! It was perfect and was total Dan!

The day we got back, George (who drove all night) went to sleep, and I went to skate a ramp I discovered, owned by a skateboarder/roll-er-skater named Adam. I pump up the ramp, did a few kick-turns and my back wheel rolled over the lip with no coping and hung up. My back foot came off the board while my front foot stayed on. I did the splits on the way down the tranny, and I shattered my femur in nine places on a shitty vert ramp, built on an old trailer. Luckily my new lifelong friend Andy Gilbert was there to help me out. Thanks brother!

George woke up. I don't return. I disappeared and didn't come back. We did not have a phone yet and I didn't bother to tell him anything when I left. It took George thirty-six hours to find me. I had a fifteen-hour surgery. I was in the hospital for seven days and spent almost a year on crutches. And yes, I did go on tour on crutches. Fuck it!

While I was in the hospital, my new friends Bill, Sharon, and Jeff came to visit and wheeled me outside, around the corner, so I could get stoned. I could still get stoned in my room, but I had to be stealth. I got an extra pillow and kept it under my bedstand. I would take off the pillowcase and blow hits into the pillow, then put the case back on over it. By the end of my seven days stay, that pillow had straight rows of orange-tan, lip shaped marks covering every inch of it.

During my stay, three separate visitors fainted and fell on the floor. My leg was so swollen I could pour a full cup of water into the area around my kneecap and not spill any out. I guess it freaked people out enough to make them pass out!

137.
DANDELION WINE DIPSHIT.

George discovered Willamette Park and some new friends while I was laying in the hospital bed. He showed up in my hospital room with purple-red stains all over his shirt, drunk on home-made Dandelion wine. Someone in the park made a big batch and George got in on the party.

He was not just drunk, he was smashed. He could barely walk, and he was in full surly mode. He saw how much wine he had spilled on himself in the mirror in my room, and decided he needed to take a shower and rinse out his shirt.

This pissed me off! In my medicated state, I couldn't even roll over. I was helpless, and he knew it. "Fuck them. This is your room," he said when I complained. He went in and puked. He took a shower and still looked no better. I have no idea how he got into the hospital, looking the way he did, being as wasted as he was. Sneaky drunk!

I finally got home from the hospital and began learning how to deal with crutches to do anything and everything and it fucking sucked!

138.
DESERT CRUISE ON CRUTCHES.

Ranch Rock

Piute Indian Reservation

Pyramid Lake, NV

9/7/1986

A Healing for Jerry show. Andy, Ken, Chris, Jeff Evans, Stephen Brand, Pete Ferguson, George, and I took the trip. I had done the whole Southwest Tour the year before, with several of these guys, so we knew a good time was ahead. Ken had rented a huge extended van. We drove all night doing blow, eating acid, and drinking beers from the many coolers.

We stopped at dawn near a huge metal train bridge to piss. Andy jumped out of the van and started pulling his clothes off before anyone knew what he was doing. Jeff and Ken spotted him in his undies, just as he got his shoes re-tied. Andy started running up the gravel road towards the bridge, with Ken and Jeff in hot pursuit. He ran right up onto the bridge, aimed himself to dive *through* the electrical wires that spanned the side, and dove off at daybreak. Straight into the dark and unknown river on booze and drugs. Ken and Jeff couldn't catch him. Twenty-five-foot dive, blacked out in black water. No one had any idea how deep it was. Andy didn't hesitate once and went head-first straight in. I remember thinking if it isn't deep, he's dead. George said aloud, "He's dead," just as he dove. It freaked everyone out, yet it was deep enough, and he popped up, screamed something, and shook the water out of his crazy curly hair in the long rays of the morning sun.

Andy walked back like nothing had happened, even though all of us were clearly shook. He shrugged it off, so we did as well, and off we drove towards Nixon, Nevada, squinting in the new day sun.

I had a fresh broken leg, so I got the bench seat in the very back, leg stretched out flat. We stopped at the historic Log Inn for food. As we are leaving, Ken inadvertently drove through a deep pothole in the dirt lot. Long vans have a whip effect when this happens. This bump flung me *up* out of my seat, against the ceiling, and then slammed me back down between the seats all the way to the floor.

It had been only 23 days since I shattered my femur in nine places. I had metal rods put in, so I did not have a cast on. I could *not* bend my leg at all, and it was hugely swollen.

On top of all that, I was now stuck down there. They had to stop the van and physically pull me out. It hurt bad when I got stuffed between those seats, but that was only the beginning of my leg problems on this trip.

When the Nevada snowpack melts, it runs into the Truckee River and flows into Pyramid Lake. The lake itself is 900 feet deep and has been there since time began. I never got to see much of the lake or any of the cool geographic features, such as the pyramid shaped monolith that bears its namesake. On crutches in the desert, it was hop, sink in six inches, hop, sink in six inches, on and on, anyplace I tried to go. It was rough. I ended up putting flat stones under the ends of my crutches so I could stand up, see the show, and not sink in anymore. I could see the massive lake behind the stage but that was as close as I got. Hop. Sink. Hop. Sink.

Jeff and I were sitting around in the morning, when suddenly the crew ran a soundcheck on the PA with Peter Gabriel's tune "Sledgehammer" at top-top-top volume. Far, far louder than the show was later that day. It was hilarious and everyone was laughing and clapping. It only lasted a minute, but I bet you could hear it all the way up in Reno!

Kingfish played and Bobby sang, minus guitar, due to a mountain bike shoulder injury. Bobby had a bottle of beer in his sling, and he would take a swig and tuck it back while he was singing. It was a no alcohol show, since it was on an Indian Reservation, but no one enforced the rule. Mickey had a rad group. Mickey and the Daylights and Robert Hunter and his Mystery Band was on the bill. Mickey and Hunter sang a long, crazy version of "Fire on the Mountain" together during Hunter's set. It was insane. Steve Kimock with Zero, and John Cipollina with Problem Child, ripped it up as well.

Out in the desert the wind picks up dramatically in the evening. We had two rental vans parked side by side, with the sliding doors facing each other. A large plastic tarp was stretched between the vans so we could have a little camp zone. I was sitting in an open side door with my leg on a cooler because I could not bend it at the knee yet. The wind threw a good gust at us, and the tarp we had rigged between the two vans flapped super hard. I guess one of our crew had used big desert rocks to hold the tarp down to the tops of the two vans. The stereo was playing, "I'm high and all is well." Suddenly my knee exploded in pain and got wrenched backwards, hyperextending it after I had just broken it a month earlier.

A basketball sized desert rock rolled off the roof as the tarp flapped in the gusty wind, and landed directly on top of my leg, as it sat extended comfortably on an ice chest. Of all the places it could have fallen, it fell directly on my month-old broken femur, just above my right knee. It cut the top of my knee and bent it back, so it wrenched the opposite way that I had just broken it. It knocked me off my seat, onto the dusty ground.

Everyone was shocked and rushed to help me up. Luckily, only one of several rocks holding the tarps rolled off. Someone could have had their head smashed in. We changed it to a tied down system quickly after that mess. The rock injury wasn't too bad considering I was already in pain from the nine places I had broken my femur in anyway, so, like usual, we partied on!

It was such a cool place to see a show that we felt bummed leaving. We would not miss the dirt though. As we drove out of the lot, after such a great time, we hit one more pothole and up I went to the ceiling, and right back down to the floor. Wham! One more for the road!

139.
PORTLAND IS FIRE.

I saw The Band on 9/20/86 at Starry Night. I saw Stephen Stills on 9/27 at Starry Night.

Back in Portland we started to hang out with Jeff Evans, Ken, Andy, and a bunch of Reed College students. George and I found cool bars like The Pyramid Club and McMenamins Tavern and Pool, which has always had a Grateful Dead theme. We would sit on the picnic tables out front and listen to the bootlegs from George's car. We became friends with Dan Baldwin (RIP), Jimmers (RIP), Pam, Alek and Erik, who were the very generous bartenders of the time. We also met Edward Leach, Brian Decarla, Tammy LaVelle (RIP), Stu, Katy, Karen Marie, Pam, Big Todd, Minnie and Shelly. All bar regulars and all super cool people, who we would go on to see many shows with.

140.
DRIVING THAT TRAIN,
OR CHASING IT?

Then along came Clark Cazwel, like a cocaine hurricane.

George was shooting pool and winning, while simultaneously *not* winning anyone over with his east coast charm. Not the best way to make new friends. Jimmers was sitting in one of the high back booths at Tavern and Pool, when he heard *tic-tic-tic-tic-tic* from the booth behind his. He looked over the back of the booth and here is a guy cutting up a pile of cocaine on the table. Enter Clark.

Jimmers quickly switches booths, and one thing leads to another. George asks for a line, Clark obliges him, and down the rabbit hole goes George again. Clark was the coke dealer at the bar, and rented an old Victorian house off NW 23rd. This house came to be known as the House of the Rising Sun because of the nightly coke fests that went on after the bar closed. It was always an insane party that was fueled by extra pure blow, that the higher up dealer, Kelly, supplied to Clark, on a big brick basis.

During one of the all-nighters, some guy was sitting in an open second story window and drunkenly fell out backwards. We watched him disappear into the dark, seeing the bottoms of his shoes as he went out. He rolled down the small, slanted roof below him, landed in a bush, and by the time we all ran down to see if he was dead, he was already walking back up the front steps laughing. It was that kind of place.

House of the Rising Sun had lethal qualities that dragged you in. Girls loved Clark and hung out all the time, and Clark was *never* out of coke. Kelly only lived three miles away, and he *really,* truly, was never, *ever,* out of blow. Until he went to prison that is, but that's a whole different book.

NW Portland had not yet become what it is today. The old Victorians were all divided up into small rooming houses. Nothing was new. Most places needed repairs and paint, rent was pennies, and you could still find a place to fucking park. Landlords needed cash and would literally rent to anyone. That's how Clark ended up in a two-story Victorian, four houses off NW 23rd Ave., currently one of the most expensive streets in town.

141.
NOTHING TO SEE HERE.
PLEASE PAY NO ATTENTION.

Many times, there would be people partying in the upstairs bedrooms, on the main floor, and down in Clark's lair in the basement. The foot traffic coming and going buying blow was often-times scary. I would see all these people come and go, and I know the neighbors saw it as well. Then Kelly would show up in his vintage Mustang, drop off a big chunk of a brick, and refuel the selling machine.

Kelly was a wise dealer. He didn't do a lot of his stuff. He did plenty, don't get me wrong, but he didn't consume like normal coke heads do. He was all about the money. I got to know him. We became good friends and remained so to this day. One day back then, while driving around in his Jeep, I pointed out brown paper that was sticking out from under his dashboard. Kelly pulled it out and said, "Oh, I've been looking for that forever," as if it was a lost sock. The brown paper bag contained $13,000 cash.

I would crash out on his couch once in a great while, after we ran around and he'd sold to everyone. Kelly would dump all that night's cash on this big dresser top. It was a money mountain every single time.

I had seriously shied away from coke and Kelly knew I didn't want his blow. That helped our friendship grow. Kelly was athletic and an excellent skier. We started going to Mt. Hood shortly after my snowboard career took off to ride fresh powder, and enjoyed several road trips to ride big mountains in the West. Good times man!

142.
COOL TRANSITIONS!

We started to get the house set up, and Greg (my old punker buddy) and Audra, his lady (also a good friend), moved up from SoCal, and joined us in the N Holman Ave. house, then on to the SE Lincoln St. house. I'm stoked they moved up and our few years living together were epic.

143.
THE TRIUMPHANT RETURN/JERRY DIDN'T DIE.

The Stone

San Francisco, CA

10/4-5/1986

Jerry Band announced two return shows at The Stone in San Francisco. It sold out in minutes. I went anyway, with no tickets, but I did bring lots and lots of weed. I went down early and hustled for two full days in SF trying to get tickets.

My diligence, even on crutches, paid off and I ended up trading weed for both. The tickets said, "The Triumphant Return of The Jerry Garcia Band," across the top. Got one ticket on the street for herb. I waited in will call with a local Head, who I also gave a bunch of weed, for the other one. I knew him from tour, but I can't remember who he is now.

We waited all day to get in on the steep side street and it rewarded me big time. Front fucking row!

We peeked under the stage curtain repeatedly, and finally there was Jerry, who smiled and nodded at us. The curtain bottom was super heavy. Like you're not supposed to lift it up kind of heavy. We must have looked hilarious from the band's point of view, with this lead weighted curtain holding us down by our necks, and these huge stupid grins on our faces.

We pulled our heads back out, the curtain went up, and Jerry opened the show with "Get out of my Life Woman." It was as if he was singing about his illness, and using the song to show he was back, and that he's gotten the sickness out of his life. He looked so much slimmer and healthier than he had just a few short months before. His weight was a third of what it had been, and he was smiling and moving and playing to the audience. A lead weighted stage curtain of worry was quickly lifted, as we, the lucky crowd who got in, watched Jerry regain his licks and embrace his audience again.

Jeff was there having his own ticket hunting dilemma. Melissa and Jeff had been seeing a lot of shows together, and she was already inside. Jeff was out scouting. Tony the Bouncer came out and gave Tour Legend Kurt (RIP) unripped tickets, and they went back into circulation. They had some sort of deal set up, Steve Goldsmith said years later. Jeff knew Kurt, like everyone on tour did, and just happened to see him first! He got a $50 quick ticket, and in he danced for the second set of the first Jerry show.

The show we all thought we may never see again.

144.
MY CLOSEST ENCOUNTER. JERRY AND HIS MANAGER BIG STEVE PARISH.

On the second night, Jerry got out of a black car and stopped right in front of us, and said hi while we waited in the will call line. The stage entrance

171

gate is next to the ticket window, and Jerry and Big Steve had to stop and get let in.

He was shorter than I had imagined. Maybe six feet tall? I was slumped over my crutches, so it was hard to judge. He always seemed larger to me since he was always up on a stage. Of course, Big Steve looked huge!

That night, the show was once again superb! It was clear to all in attendance that Jerry was back for good!

145.
PUTTING IN THE WORK.

This was one of those sets of Jerry shows that took supreme effort to get into. Sometimes you are so busy just trying to make the next ticket and show that you never have any time to rest. When you tell people your tour stories you don't usually include how many miles you drove, how many miles you walked that day, selling stuff and searching for tickets, how you had to repair something on the car at 3 am, how many drugs you've done, how much you drank, or how many *kind* burritos you've eaten in the parking lot. So many things that go on just trying to be there, can exhaust even a young healthy person like I was. Tour ain't easy sometimes. But it is always fun as fuck!

146.
HALLOWEEN IS HELLA FUN!

Henry J. Kaiser Conv. Center
Oakland, CA
10/31/1986

Jerry Garcia Band and Kingfish played together for Halloween. It is always a treat to have a show on a holiday, and Halloween is the best one, outside of New Year's Eve.

This was Jerry's third show back. This time playing in a normal size venue where everyone could get in. Costumes were blazing throughout the Kaiser as Kingfish, with Bobby, opened and stirred up that Halloween hype.

More earsplitting cheering than I've heard in a long-time greeted Jerry, as he hit the stage and tore through a 10-song set. He opened with, "How Sweet It Is To Be Loved by You," and shut it down with a killer "Werewolves of London" to end off a howling Halloween night for all of us!

147.
PORTLAND KEEPS GETTING BETTER!

I saw Dinosaurs, Zero and the Holy Modal Rounders on 11/3/86, with an incredible vintage Gary Ewing Light Show at Pine Street Theater in

Portland. The full size, hand screened, multicolored posters, by Gary Ewing and Bruce Webber are rare collectors' items now. This is also the show I met my friend Russ at. Here's to years Russ! I saw David Crosby on 11/15/86 at The Pine Street Theater.

148.

BILL AND SHARON, MY SPEED DEMON FRIENDS!

I was five months in on my broken leg and I was feeling semi mobile, but I still could not bend my leg at the knee. That meant all the shows I was going to, I had to have a way to ride with my leg straight out and flat. It sucked!

I got a ride with our friends Bill and Sharon to the comeback shows in Oakland, in December 1986. Bill had a red-orange 1976 Datsun B210 hatchback, and if you put the back seat down, I could lay there looking up out of the hatch back glass. I had not often ridden with Bill, but I needed a ride.

Turns out Bill likes to go fast, and his car was very un-modified. Bone stock with far-from new tires. Regular street tires, not snow tires. We had several mountain-passes to go through on the way to the Bay Area, and Oregon was having a rough winter.

I remember being scared, while remembering a story Jeff told about riding with Bill and waking up to see he had the speedometer pegged. I was laying on my back looking up and out at a snowstorm, as we went through the Siskiyou Pass (4,300 ft), well above the speed limit, passing everyone. All I could see was the tops of the cars and semi-trucks we passed, since I was on my back. That alone made it far more frightening than just the speed and the snow.

I had heard rumors from our friends about Bill's need for speed and I'd shrugged it off. It was a wild ride, but I had to get to the show, so I had willingly hopped right in. Sharon seemed oblivious to Bill's lead foot and chatted away, while I did a death grip on whatever I could find to hold onto. I felt the rear end shifting around below me several times on the iced-up highway, but Bill pushed on unaware. We ice skated through it all and we got to the gigs way before everyone else in our crew from Portland.

149.
IT'S FUCKING ON AGAIN!

Oakland Coliseum

Oakland, CA

12/15-17/1986

Jerry's first Grateful Dead shows since he was sick, and the crowd was super hyped up. The first Jerry shows at The Stone were small and insanely hard to get into with a total capacity of only 700. Now we're back at The Oakland Arena/Coliseum and have 9,000 seats, and everybody got in this time.

The energy in the building was at a frenzied level! The lights went down and the crowd roared, like only a mother-fucking Grateful Dead crowd can roar. It was loud and forceful, and it was delivered to the band from us that way on purpose! We, as a crowd, felt collectively, without even speaking, that we needed to give the last bit of energy all of us had, back to the band to show our love, support, and devotion. And we sure as fuck did!

"Touch of Grey" was clearly the right choice to open with, and when Jerry sang "I Will Survive," the roof almost popped off the top of the Coliseum. The collective happiness and the energy that was created at that show made it one of the most memorable shows I have ever seen. It felt incredible to be back in the bubble we enter when we attend a Grateful Dead show. The band was so tight. Each song said, "We're back!" a bit stronger than the one before it. We knew it was on again. The biggest cheer of the night came when Jerry sang, "Won't you tell everybody you meet that the *Candy Man's* in town." It was deafening, and it felt great to lend my voice to that roar.

150.
QUICK PICK UP. LET'S ROLL!

Tour would roll on as usual, and we were all relieved and excited. Although the initial shows were in SF/Oakland and West Coast, it was clearly back on the road for all of us. This is how quick it was back on again. Jerry Band/Stone, two shows in October. Jerry Band/Kaiser for Halloween, one show in October. Grateful Dead/Oakland Arena, three shows in mid-December. Grateful Dead/Henry J. Kaiser, four more shows for NYE. Ten shows in all and each one getting better and better.

151.
MY FIRST BIG LETDOWN!
NEW YEAR'S EVE DENIAL!

Henry J. Kaiser Conv. Center

Oakland, CA

12/27-28, 30/1986

The first three nights were sparking with electric current, but by New Year's Eve my electricity had been cut off. I did not get into Henry J. Kaiser on NYE 1986. I was truly bummed out. It was the only time EVER, that I could not somehow, some way, find a ticket.

I crutched up to the far end of the road where all the incoming highway traffic was, asking for tickets way before cars even got close to the venue. I went to the BART station and hit up Heads as they got off the train. I hit all the parking lots just as people pulled in. I even offered an OZ of Oregon weed as a trade. No luck! I crutched up and down all day from 9 am until 12 midnight looking for that elusive ticket. I never found it. I was so disappointed. I had let myself down.

Lucky for us, Bill Graham was cool, and set up speakers in the park out-front, so we got to hear the show at least! Thank-you Bill!

I was really upset with myself. Some random Head was handing out free doses at midnight, and I took a full hit right away without thinking about it. "Sure, I'll have one," I said, not realizing that it won't really start to kick in until about 4 am, when everyone else is starting to come down and crash out. All I remember was wanting to change my head space after a disappointing day of failed searching.

The band played on, and the second and third sets were killer. I sort of danced around on my crutches with all the other show orphans outside, until everyone came out and I saw my friends. I was getting higher and higher and soon we all went back to the hotel to talk about the show and celebrate the onset of 1987.

Seemed like a good plan. Hotel equals safe cocoon normally, but I was getting higher by the minute, and I didn't seem to be near the peeking stage anytime in the foreseeable future. I was highest when everyone, except maybe George, had passed out.

It was getting light out, so I stuck my head under the curtain. I was laying on the floor with my broken leg at the bottom of the window. I watched the sunrise upside down, laying on my back with a hotel drape cutting off the rest of my body from my head. I didn't need my body, so I left it behind while my head merged with the sun to share the daybreak together.

152.
OBSESSION SETS IN. BIG TIME!

1987 turned out to be my biggest tour year. I saw the most shows I had ever seen in 365 days. Grateful Dead and Jerry Garcia Band shows combined. Amazing times.

On we go.

153.
MIND OVER MATTER?
NO WAY, I'M ON ACID!

Civic Auditorium

San Francisco, CA

1/28-30/1987

My Jan 28th ticket says, Most High on LSD Ever, written on the back.

I went overboard on acid on January 28, 1987, and I felt like the entire show was bad. I've been higher, but in good, fun ways. This was highest ever in a bad way. I have vivid recollections of being freaked out and that the band was just plain losing it. Each member forgetting lyrics, and every time they forgot the words it seemed to me to be getting worse.

Red liquid that looked like wine was flowing out of Jerry's mouth when he sang, and Bobby's head kept popping six inches off his neck when he threw it back. In my acid laced brain something was going wrong! I was starting to over think it, like you might sometimes do when you're *highest ever*!

They lost it, they can't play or sing anymore, what's wrong? It's over for them! It's over for me! I was really freaked out, but I wasn't quite losing my shit. *Yet.*

In the comfy hippy cocoon inside of the show I was okay. I felt like it was normal to be extra high, but when the show was over, I had to go outside into the San Francisco winter night, and I was not ready to go yet. I sat inside until most of the Heads cleared out, but I just couldn't get my brain to calm down.

I finally hobbled out and Shakedown Street was going off, although it didn't change my head space. I was way too high and seriously over thinking my situation. I hopped around on my crutches and tried to talk to my friends, but I was clearly getting higher now, than I had been all night. I freaked out and needed to crutch back to Dan's condo. The after scene outside the show was too heavy for me. Everyone was trying to sell me something I didn't want at the time. A veggie burrito, or a tie dye, or acid. I wasn't hungry, I was wearing a tie dye and I certainly didn't need any more acid, that was clear.

Dan being typical Dan, would *not* give me the key. He was messing with me and my high, telling me, "Just be mellow dude." Knowing full well he was making it worse on me and laughing about it when I turned away. But that's why I love Dan, he always pushes it to the next level!

After about 30 minutes, I had hyped up my drugged brain so much that after asking ten times and being teased ten times, I freaked out. With big eyes and a totally scared look, I angrily demanded the key. NOW! Finally, he gave it to me with an, "Okay, okay, I get it dude," and I hobbled back to the ultra-fancy high rise in Opera Plaza that Dan's mother had a time share in. The door man knew we were staying, and normally Dan was with us, but I think he saw it in my eyes. I needed to get out of the world for a minute and rearrange my already rearranged brain. I told him my leg hurt and he buzzed me right through. I got in the elevator and could not remember the floor number. I was standing there on my crutches with huge saucer acid eyes, blankly tripping on the numbers and lights when the elevator door opened, and there's the doorman again, staring at me because I hadn't pushed anything. I didn't expect that, and it freaked me out, so I just started pushing buttons to get it to close. It closed and I shrunk to the back of the elevator. Then the door started to open again, then close. I could not figure out why no one was getting on. I forgot I had just pushed several buttons in a panic. I was really tripping and staring to breath hard. The door opened and I quickly crutched off.

I somehow went through my pockets and found a matchbook with the room and floor written inside. My normal brain was saying, "Why did you get off? It was in your pocket the whole time." But my acid brain was like, "You know why. You're fucking freaking out, that's why."

I pushed the button again. Same doors opened. I crutched back onto the hellevator and somehow got to the room, but the room was swelling and shifting around, and I started to freak again. I knew I had cold beers, and Dan's stolen beaker from the science lab bong was on the patio. I instinctively chose the best thing to do when you're too fucking high. You get high on something else! You combine old and new to make a new high to change your head space! It is a well-known trick and it worked perfectly!

I sat on the balcony for an hour smoking bong hits and tossing back brown bottles of Henry's, looking at the San Francisco city lights. I was slowly letting my overactive acid head go back to the fun part of being on acid. The good side of acid! The side I prefer to stay on. But when you eat LSD, occasionally you don't get to choose the good side or the bad. It just decides for you, and you're rolling with it, like it or not.

My friends came back a few hours later. I was vaguely back to normal and that's when the heckling started. "You should have seen your face." "You looked so scared." "We were laughing so hard." "Didn't think you could move that fast on your crutches." "Want another dose? I got one for you." It went on and on. My friends! Got to love them!

I was always curious if it was just me that night being way too high or was the band just off that night. Perhaps both? I went back and listened to the show years later, and it had vocal mistakes in every single song except "Walking Blues." Bobby and Jerry pretty much equally blew it during every song. It wasn't just me being acid overboard, they really did fuck up in almost every song that night. Some songs multiple times. I'm not talking shit here. Don't get me wrong. I just thought it was me all these years. Take a listen. Just skip the acid. Or don't!

154.
RICKY WAS A RACE CAR DRIVER.

Someplace in here I get a ride to Eugene from a California show, and get dropped off at midnight on an off ramp. I had no choice but to hitchhike on the I-5 in the dark. The highway does not go through Eugene, it goes next to it. Hence, not a lot of lights.

I managed to get a quick and lucky ride, but they were only going 20 miles. I took the ride thinking it may get me to a more visible spot, since I was in darkness with no streetlights where I was anyway. That was not to be.

I got dropped off in full blackness on a highway exit out in the cow fields. I stood there on my crutches (yep still on crutches) in the total darkness for two hours, as trucks and random cars went by and did not stop. It was so dark I was not even sure they could see me until they were past me. It was getting very cold by then and I was about to crutch off the road and try to build a little fire.

As I was thinking about putting on every bit of clothing I had, a car went screaming by going about 90 mph. I was sure he had not seen me since he was going so damn fast, but he had. He locked up his brakes and came to a giant Duke Boys screeching stop, tossed it into reverse, and came barreling *backwards* down the highway to get me. That was my first inkling that this was going to be an interesting ride. The passenger window was down and as he stopped, he said, "Shit man, I almost didn't see you there." He yelled, "Hop in!" and I can tell right away this guy was high as shit on speed. I know the look and the tone of voice.

He introduces himself as Ricky. Says he is, "just out cruising around (it's 3 am by now) in my new (to him, not like new, new) Camaro." I put my crutches between the seats, barely sit down, and he floors it, doing a huge smokey burnout. I fish around on the floor for my seat belt, and he roars off down the freeway until he gets up to 90 and levels off. This seemed to be his comfort speed, I was to find out. He had a little vial he pulled out of his pocket, and he tapped a little bump out onto his hand and snorted it right up his nose. He offered it to me, with huge, round, wide-open eyes and says, "It ain't coke!" in a sort of demonic, celebratory way.

I politely declined, so he did "another one for me," as he accelerated mentally and physically into the Oregon night. He hadn't even asked how far I was going yet, no doubt due to the meth bumps he was snorting. When I said, "Portland" he said, "What the fuck?" with a shrug and told me he was cool with driving me all the way. And he did, with Ozzy blasting on his cassette player and him telling me crazy drug stories and doing 99% of the talking.

He was driving fucking fast, was doing meth bumps like it was coke, and here I am, in yet another truly scary ride. I had no choice at this point. Luckily, his car seemed to run and handle well, and I needed that ride bad. He drove me all the way to my front door on Lincoln St. in SE Portland, safe and sound. He hopped out, took a piss in my front yard, burned out in his car, and took off just as it was starting to get light.

I was exhausted, nerve wracked and all I wanted was a few bong hits and my own bed. I had hidden a huge green bud in the speaker for when I got back, but when I went to find it, I saw George had gone searching in my hiding spots and smoked it up. I was super pissed because I really needed to relax after the Crystal Meth Cannonball Run I had just experienced.

I finally found another hidden stash George had not pillaged, and I puffed up and passed out. I remember it feeling damn good to be back home in my own bed for once.

155.
PORTLAND ROCKS ON!

I saw Burning Spear at the NW Service Center on 2/13/87. I saw the Neville Brothers on 2/21 at Starry Night.

156.
BIG HEADS CAN DANCE!

Henry J. Kaiser Conv. Center
Oakland, CA
3/1-3/1987

The third night was Mardi Gras, which featured huge ornament festooned heads with hair made of shiny ribbons. They looked like giant PEZ dispensers. The head with the mustache looked quite a lot like Billy. No one ever said they were supposed to represent the band, but there were six of them! The heads marched all around the hall while little people in all white tuxedos and top hats danced on the stage. Beautiful and fantastic, it lent a full New Orleans feel to the entire night!

157.
HEROIN DON'T CARE ABOUT YOU.

When we were in Oakland at the Kaiser, we had developed a way of keeping our main stash at the hotel, a mile from the venue. We would take cabs, which were driven by local Dead Heads, back and forth to get more weed after we would sell out. I was mainly on the weed game at that time. I was up in Oregon and the herb was plentiful and super good! The cab system was good, because you never had too much of a drug charge on you at the park in front of the Kaiser, in case you got busted.

It went like this. Call and request a predetermined cab driver (we knew the proper ones) from the pay phone, hop in the cab, light a fat joint, get high while you get driven back to the hotel. Pick up more weed and stash the money, get back in the cab, smoke another joint, and do it all over again in an hour. All day long, George, Big Rick and I did the loop, as we called it.

During one of these round trips, Far-L and I went into a hotel room with Santa Cruz Paul to buy this incredible southern Oregon made hash oil. I loved this oil and could only get it on a rare occasion.

We got into the room, only to find a guy who'd drank too much whiskey and chased way too many hits of heroin the night before. He was violently ill and begging to go to the hospital. He was pleading for the ER in between the most severe dry heaving I have ever seen in my life. It was truly brutal. He was retching and heaving and as pale blue as anyone I have ever seen in a bad drug OD situation, who wasn't already dead. He apparently drank a bunch of whiskey, then (even though he was not new to heroin by a long shot) started smoking foils.

Smoking foils, or chasing the dragon, is a technique in which you heat heroin from under the aluminum foil it sits on and inhale the smoke it produces through a straw. Being that he was already whiskey smashed, he did far too many foils, and combined a whiskey hangover puke fest, with a big fat heroin overdose. That combo is normally lethal, and this guy was lucky he didn't just die right then and there. He was making the most horrible sounds and begging for the hospital.

His friends repeatedly kept telling him to, "Shut the fuck up!" They made him drink water, which only stayed down as long as it took for him to swallow it. Then he would heave and fall out of bed on the floor into his own puke and start begging for the hospital again.

His buddy was yelling at him that it's his own fucking fault and he needs to shut the fuck up and ride it out. "You drank the whiskey, and you smoked the dope and now you're overdosing and it's your own stupid ass fucking fault." His friend had absolutely no mercy for him and kept letting him know that every time he would try to say something. Then he would grab him by his ponytail and pour the gallon jug of water into his mouth, make him take a swallow, and the retching/begging cycle would start all over again.

I was in the room for about 15 minutes max, and I was shocked. I had never seen someone that ill from partying. I got my hash oil and got out of there. We got back in the cab and didn't say anything the short ride back. There were no words. The guy was on the verge of death, and we just had to witness 15 minutes of his real-life hell. It was something I will clearly never forget and at the same time it's something I try not to remember.

Word to the wise kids, don't mix your whiskey and your heroin. Ever! Or, better yet, stay the FUCK AWAY from heroin altogether! You'll be better off in the long run, because you will actually *have* a long run!

158.
IN A JERRY BAND BLUR.

I somehow missed Jerry playing on the Navy Ship. I then saw The Dinosaurs on 3/7 at The Catalyst in Santa Cruz, then Jerry Garcia Band, 3/8-10 at The Stone in San Francisco. I rode down to Los Angeles with some Heads whom I do not remember, and saw Jerry Garcia Band again 3/13-14 at the Wiltern Theater in Los Angeles. I do know I rode the Green Tortoise home and that I was *not* going on the spring East Coast Dead Tour.

159.
I WAS A FREEZING THIRD WHEEL.

UIC Pavilion
Chicago, IL
4/9-11/1987

I had missed a whole section of East Coast Tour trying to make money back home, and I was jonesing to get back on the road. I flew out to Chicago in the spring and stayed with Jeff Evans and Melissa Schoen in a hotel. They met up at the airport in St. Louis and had a nightmare flight coming in.

I third wheeled them big time during this trip. I tried to stay out of the room as much as I could, but it was still winter. March is still very cold in The Windy City, and we were all super bundled up.

I had called my good friend John Walker (John and brother Paul Walker were Tour Head friends), who was living in the Midwest at the time, and we made plans to meet up. I'm not sure how I found him but there was John in his car in the parking lot. I hopped inside to get warm and see how my friend was doing. John was just fine, and soon, I had a tray on my lap with a bunch of stinky weed on it. John was puffing up a particularly fat one as I was rolling up joints for the show.

John and I were catching up on lost time and did not notice two huge beat cops (cops who walk are called beat cops and the area they patrol is called the beat) walking through the parking lot. They came up from behind us and walked right next to my side of the car. I had all the weed displayed openly in my lap, for all to see. I saw a shadow and looked to my right out the closed window. All I saw was a cop gun belt and a huge leather jacket, slowly moving by.

Fear grabbed at me, and I felt like I saw a shark while I was swimming. I didn't have time to ditch anything, and it was too quick to even act startled, but they didn't seem to notice us. They stopped five feet away at the front passenger fender of John's car and had a conversation. Yes, we had a joint going. Yes, we had weed openly displayed. Luckily, the windows were up, since it was March in Illinois. John snubbed out the joint in his hand, and I tried to hide the weed loaded rolling tray before the cops turned around and saw us in the cloudy VW. We were sitting ducks, shitting bricks.

Somehow, they did not see us *or* smell us smoking. We lucked out! John and I saw those big ass Chicago cops arrest a lot of Heads those three days. Both of us knew jail in Chicago was not the place to be for a young hippy, and we opted to be a bit more observant while we were openly partying after that.

160.
ABOVE THE BEAST!

There was a crazy open balcony area above the drum sets on the first night only. Bill and Mickey were looking up at all of us, 15 feet above them, in this crazy 270-degree nipple shaped balcony. We went so crazy they closed it the next two nights. We got lucky to see it from that perspective and share that with the drummers, who fantastically shared with us that night. Mickey was looking up, holding different sticks and getting cheers to play different drums, and Billy was keeping a sweet rock-solid beat. It was the coolest way I was ever to see the drummers perform. From *above* The Beast. It was in the 117 or 217 sections that curves around behind the stage when they have a concert. My ticket was from Section 208, Seat F7, but all I probably used it for was to roll joints that night anyway.

Cold weather and excellent shows, and it all ended with a scary train ride back to O'Hare Airport, late at night, through some of the sketchiest parts of beautiful Chicago in 1987.

161.
GO PORTLAND MUSIC!

I saw Kingfish with Nine Days Wonder on 4/12 at Pine Street Theater in Portland. Gary Ewing did the fantastic lightshow and amazing psychedelic collector's poster.

162.

WINDS OF CHANGE?
OR STILL JUST BREEZES?

Irvine Meadows Amphitheatre

Irvine, CA

4/17-19/1987

I did not see it, but I heard about it, and others have written about it. Hundreds and hundreds of people crashed a gate down and ran into the venue, making it all the way in. That's roughly a half-mile, and all those people ran the whole way in a group. Determined, I guess. I was wandering around somewhere and did not notice any of it. Irvine was a comfortable place where I had seen 30 or more shows, and I was oblivious to any shenanigans going down.

What I *was* aware of, was the ever-increasing lot creeper. This started to get heavy in the mid-eighties. Here is the depressing definition: Someone who tours just to hang out and sponge off the scene. Never in the show. Ever. Always wanting a free beer, spare change, your weed, your food, and a free ride to the next lot, without a thank you. Always dead broke, dirty, and stinky. "Hey man, can I finish the rest of your cig, joint, beer?"

"No, beat it!"

163.
TWILIGHT ZONE'S WITH EUCALYPTUS OVERTONES.

Frost Amphitheater

Stanford, CA

5/2-3/1987

We cruised down to Frost, once again. Always a pleasure, since it is in such a beautiful setting. Second day technical problems in the first set led to the boys jamming brief versions of "Itsy-Bitsy Spider" and "Beer Barrell Polka." Then Brent busted out a quick song about scooping up field mice and bopping them on the head, which I found out later is called "Little Bunny Foo-Foo." It was funny, and he had everyone laughing and cheering.

Deep in the second, "Space" and "The Other One" had a very heavy *Twilight Zone* feel to it, as the band teased up the song before ripping into a very vocally enhanced version, which was common in '87. Bob Bralove had been tossing in strange sounds and weird vocal distortions from the soundboard for several years now, thus adding yet another level of unique quality and listenable desirability, to a Dead song.

The weather was warm, and the shows were hot. Perfect combination.

164.
CHILLY SKELETONS ON STAGE!

Laguna Seca Raceway

Monterey, CA

5/9-10/1987

I had an ongoing battle in my head between the venues in Laguna Seca and Ventura County, as to which one renders you the dirtiest after you leave the shows. Both are dry, dusty, and windy, and both leave you and your tour rig looking much like I see vehicles today returning from Burning Man. Dust would get in everything. No crack or crevice was safe. At night, the air would get moist, and the dust would loosen up a little, only to be baked back on in the morning and layered all over again during the day. We would drive all the way back to Portland and the cars would still be covered in a dirty tan party skin. VW Mike's cars and van always had the heavy filth layer after those shows! It took a serious two hour washing to make it flow away down the street drain.

Laguna Seca is wide-open, and set on rolling hills with a serpentine racetrack that runs all over the property. The stage was down in a small valley and the camping was set up all around the venue perimeter. We had a great camping spot up above Brent and Jerry's side of the stage, and when the show ended, we got to be a part of the Dead's video for "Touch of Grey." I was extremely excited to hang out and be in the audience.

I only had one problem. I was hella sunburnt, and it was freezing cold at night. High desert kind of cold. Hot all day, but nothing to retain the heat at night. 95 down to 45. You could see your breath. Watch Bobby in the final video version puffing steam as he sings!

Any video or film project, especially one with life size puppets try-ing to mimic the Dead members, is going to require a lot of set-up time and a lot of re-takes. I was correct in this assumption, and held out for as long as I could until I retreated up the hill to add a layer and warm my cold ass up. We watched them shoot and reset for hours. I hopped into my sleeping bag to warm up and wind down.

They were still shooting takes well past midnight, and the hardcore crowd you see in the video stuck it out all night. It was funny to hear the radio version of "Touch" played dozens of times, over and over, as they got each camera angle right, and that's what I fell asleep to.

165.
HOW DID I MOVE THIS FAST? PORTLAND ROCKS ON.

We clearly drove back early the next day, since I have a ticket stub for a show here in Portland that night, and then the shows kept on coming.

I saw Gregg Allman the next night on 5/11 at Starry Night, Portland. I saw Dinosaurs on 5/16 at Starry Night. I saw King Sunny Ade' on 5/20 at Starry Night. I saw Hot Tuna on 5/22 at Pine Street Theatre. In Seattle on 5/23 at The Backstage. In Eugene on 5/24 at WOW Hall, and in Corvallis on 5/25 at Greenhaven. Hot Tuna mini tour? I'll take that ride!

166.

SEASIDE PARK AND ALL
THE ACID YOU CAN EAT!

Ventura County Fairgrounds

Ventura, CA

6/12-14/1987

Vendirta County Dirt Grounds, as I've called it before, is one of the best. Loose and easy, warm and breezy. We had a three-day run, which meant we, collectively as Dead Heads, erected an entire city of our own. We had a few cars we made a compound with, and set up in our staked-out space in the recently founded beach town of Shakedown by the Sea.

These were Phil heavy shows, right out of the gate. Not singing. He was dropping bombs and plucking fat, heavy bass tones. The version of "I Need a Miracle" on the first night was thundering and his fingers were walking all up and down the neck during "Black Peter."

Day two saw the first "Masterpiece" from Bob Dylan's song catalogue, which the Dead frequently draw from.

I'm not sure what was going on with the backing vocal effects, but it made Jerry sound like he was singing on a fat hit off a Helium balloon. "Scarlet Begonias" is always a great song to see outdoors. I'm not sure why I feel that way. It just fits the outdoor mood well, I suppose. Jerry was up on the "Scarlet" vocals and the band smoothly jumped into "Fire." "Playin'" and a crispy "Terrapin" followed into some hammering "Drums" from Billy and Mickey.

The crowd was swirling and whirling. Sunny, dusty and divine! I should have saved a little vial of dirt to remember Ventura by. Toss a pinch in my eye from time to time, while I listen to one of the old shows!

167.
NAOMI YOSPE AND I MEET.

Portland Oregon 1987

I met my future lady Naomi Yospe and became good friends with her in mid-1987. We kept in touch over the years and got together in 2010. She is the best and I love her!! This is a small foreshadow.

168.
ANTICIPATING THE PORTAL.

The Greek Theatre
Berkeley, CA
6/19-21/1987

The Greek has special magic that would bubble up and over the swirling cauldron of dancers, and could be felt more intensely than other venues. This was the case once again during this Berkeley run. The "Desolation Row" was ten minutes long and performed so well. Bobby screaming out, "Is that some kind of joke?"

Second set had a fierce, distortion heavy "I Need a Miracle" that Bobby growled through, and a beautiful and soulful "Stella Blue" that Jerry sung sweetly, with extra emphasis on the line, "Dust off those rusty strings just one more time!" The dreamy guitar at the end was drawn out and clean, and they flew into "Turn on Your Love Light!"

The next day the show got going with "Hell in a Bucket," and later a gorgeous "Bird Song." Second set got rolling with a short *Twilight Zone*-esque "Space," into a Phil heavy, funky "Iko-Iko!" Jerry's vocals were dominant and crisp!

Top jewel of the day, by all accounts was the breakout of Dylan's hit, "All Along the Watchtower." I hadn't heard a peep about them playing it that day, and it blew me away. It was one of those songs that you attend so many shows for. The giant chunk of pure gold. Another fantastic, magic moment that you can only experience at The Greek. Maybe it's the beauty of the venue, maybe it's the sound of the perfect amphitheater, or perhaps it's a portal to another dimension and we got to see the Dead open it up a few times here and there. I am honestly going with the portal theory. I was there and I know this! We all left and went someplace extra-dimensional that night during "Watchtower."

Day three started early. That is rare and wonderful at The Greek. It was a beautiful Berkeley day, and we all walked inside around 2 pm. They got busy in the first set with a semi-rare "Walkin' Blues," and lit the second set on fire with a killer "Crazy Fingers" into "Saint of Circumstance." They also did a deep second set "Masterpiece," and sent everyone off to Alpine Valley with a traditional "Brokedown Palace."

Except us, that is. Willie's trusty van needed repairs. We ended up in a hotel room on Judah St., all the way down by the curved seawall in Ocean Beach. We got a room and stayed after The Greek shows. After three days of shows we all crashed. Burnt out, but not happy! The circus was leaving town without us.

169.
HEADS FIXING HEADS

We woke up the next day and pitched in for the engine repairs, so we could get to the East Coast and continue the tour. The red Dodge van had smoked an exhaust valve on the drive up from Ventura, and the heads needed resurfacing or replacement.

We were missing shows and time was burning. Dead Tour does not stop. I needed a break, so I cut out and went skating. I met Chris Cook of Alva Team infamy for the first time at Embarcadero, before he migrated to Venice.

Meanwhile, Willie was replacing the heads on the van in the parking lot of the old school motel we were staying in. The whole top end of the van's engine needed to be replaced. He traded in the worn heads for new ones and paid a bit extra to get them right away. And that was it. Willie had mechanical skills and got it all done in a few days.

170.
PATCHED BIKERS AND THE ACID QUEEN

Candy was the biggest LSD dealer I've ever known. She was *the* Acid Queen! She went big and didn't look back. She was tough as fuck. Her stories about being in jail in Mexico were brutal.

Candy went off to work (i.e., buy extremely pure drugs consisting of crystal LSD and pure cocaine) with a patched biker and proceeded to get super drunk on shots of tequila with him. She wanted/needed to impress him for business reasons. He was trying to fuck her. Unfortunately for him, he did not know she was a lesbian, and she certainly did not tell him because she wanted the best price on her drugs she could get. I always admired her style. She had it going on! Straight hard ass business hustler.

The Acid Queen was small in stature. Not what you would expect from a heavy weight in the business, and because of that, when she drank booze, she got extra fucked up, extra fast. The biker dropped her off shortly thereafter and she started to get violently sick. She was wasted. We all felt bad for her, but she got her good price, and the booze and puke were part of that deal. She could not stop dry heaving even though she had heaved everything out of herself. We kept trying to pour water into her, and after a whole day she finally smiled a little and started to come around.

That day, good food was in order. We went out and had sushi in Japan Town (my first time, thank you Candy) and everyone was feeling better! When we got back to the dirty orange carpet of our luxurious Ocean Beach roach motel, Candy broke out the chemist grade cocaine she got from the biker, and it was party time from there on out! We did this ultrapure blow, and it was magical. AND I HATE COCAINE! It had the shiniest little glass-like rock shards. It didn't burn a bit. You got extra high with no anxiety. You could do half the amount of normal and be higher! When you didn't want any more you didn't jones! You could even go to sleep without much trouble.

171.
SONGS FOR THE WIND AND SEA.

We all did another fat round of gacker lines, grabbed a twelve pack of beer, and walked down 13th to the curved ocean seawall at Ocean Beach. Willie brought his trumpet, and we watched the San Francisco Bay while he blew tunes for us for hours. Willie stood on the cement seawall and played to the water, and the lights, and to anyone who happened to be walking by. It was a chilly summer night in The Bay, and I knew in my mind I should remember this one. Willie was just too damn good on that horn and I knew we were getting a special performance by a rising star. A captive audience of three by the oceanside in California.

We stayed up that night until San Fran Paul decided to start smoking his coke. It was so pure he could not resist doing ultra clean base hits. I hate free basing and I don't care to watch someone do the Dr. Jekyll to Mr. Hyde, so I went to bed. Luckily, this shit-hole motel room was split into two.

When I woke up six hours later, Paul was on his knees on the floor, looking for rocks he had previously cooked up that he *thought* he had dropped. He was out of coke and Candy refused to sell him anymore because he was tweaking out. So now, he was doing the coke smoker freak out, looking for nonexistent drugs in a dirty orange carpet in a shitty motel room. Did I mention I HATE COCAINE!

Candy got some sleep. She felt better so she got out the crystal acid and the Everclear, and started to make some sheets she could drop there in San Francisco, before going on to Memphis. We were late to the next bunch of shows on the tour and were missing seven of the upper East Coast dates, but while the van was getting fixed, why not get rid of some acid? Even in San Francisco she could get top dollar for the purity aspect alone. These drugs came from an infamous chemist's lab down south in LA and had been made to the highest standards I have ever seen.

We got a base sheet of thick poster board paper, got some pins to hold down the serrated tab blotter paper sheets she had, put on double gloves, mixed the crystal acid (in very precise amounts so we knew how strong each hit would be) with Everclear, and sucked it up into a syringe. Then we pinned down the corners of the 100-hit blotter rectangle to the cardboard paper, and slowly, and very evenly, syringed out the liquid acid onto the tabs. If you did it nicely, evenly, and methodically, you get the same amount on each hit, so they have similar consistency. Meaning each hit is about 200 mics. Normally you'd make them a bit weaker. Like 150 mics, but these were going to her friend so she "juiced them up" to 200.

The poster board paper we had been using was covered with multiple coats of acid on the edges, where the hits had been soaked with the syringe. We cut that paper up and made some "super hits," as she called them. I did some a week later in Philadelphia and it was all time.

172.
WHITE LINES ACROSS AMERICA.

Willie got the reconditioned heads bolted on the red Dodge, put the top end of the motor back together, and it fired up right away. We ran it and he adjusted the valves. On went the valve covers and off we went. Paul stayed behind and flew out. We peeled out down the I-5 and over to I-40 with two grams of crystal LSD, which turns into roughly 20,000 hits, sealed inside a normal condiments jar in the bottom of the cooler, under the ice, food, and beer. Put it out of your mind and enjoy the company and the ride.

This was one of those "we ain't stopping fer nothing" drives, and we all knew it would be a long stretch as we left San Francisco in the rear view.

So, like the best travel buddies do, Candy took matters into her own hands. She got out the blade and cut up a bunch of fat lines of that super pure, chemist grade cocaine, and Willie put his foot down on the chrome, '70s Barefoot gas pedal, and floored the red van across America.

173.
I MISSED THE SHOW.
STILL GOT A STORY THOUGH!

I mentioned earlier that we missed seven shows due to the van motor fucking up. Funny thing is, even though I wasn't at the show, I still have a tour story to tell via Jeff. Jeff and Melissa did the whole upper East Coast Tour and saw a majority of the shows.

On Independence Day, Schaefer Stadium, as it was then called, was sold out. Tickets were scarce even in a football stadium. Someone came up with an unused ticket for a different event altogether. Jeff figured he may as well try, since the ticket looked similar, was the same color, and was intact. Apparently, older gentlemen had the job of taking tickets that day in their red suit jackets, and he thought he might get past them. Jeff went for it! He strolled up and handed the ticket taker his ticket faker! The old gent didn't even look at it.

Jeff rolled the turnstile forward and was in, but then the taker called out, "Hey you! Hey!" Jeff turned to face the bust and eminent ejection, but all the man said was, "You forgot your stub," accompanied with a smile! Jeff walked back, grabbed the stub, and danced his way on in.

Jeff retained that ticket and still has it to this day. It reads: "Boston Harbor Fest Presents: The Sixth Annual Chowder Fest!" His seats were in general admission, someplace *else* in Massachusetts, and they cost a mere $5. The only thing that was actual and correct on the ticket was the date. July 4, 1987.

174.
DEA IN DIAPERS.

Civic Center

Roanoke, VA

7/7/1987

After leaving San Francisco in the mirrors, we drove The Acid Queen and her psychedelic potions non-stop to Memphis. We did a brief stop of less than an hour to drop off our Queen and her crystals, before we rolled on to Roanoke, Virginia. Still another 700 miles.

When we finally got into Virginia, I realized we were going to be stuck and late for the show if we didn't stay ahead of traffic, as it was now midday. Willie was sleeping in the back, and I was driving eighty just to beat impending gridlock. We didn't have the bulk acid on us anymore, but we still had some acid, weed, and some of that superb cocaine of the time. I was watching all three mirrors as far back as I could see while looking forward for radar cops ahead of me. I hauled ass and we finally made it into the lot and onto Shakedown, only to get a huge shock.

Cops, cops, and more fucking cops. Not the normal kind of cops either. Drug Enforcement Agency agents. The DEA training facilities are in Roanoke, and they had every cadet in the program on full maneuvers. All the rooftops had cadets with binoculars scoping out the scenario, then radioing to the undercover cadets on the ground who they should bust next. It was a hands-on class for the rookies on how to observe, and then arrest, with a nonaggressive bunch of easy targets to practice on.

This went on for a bit, but everyone had spread the word loud and clear, and the word was DEA! Or maybe junior DEA. Honestly, they were clearly cadets in training. The undercover cadets did repeated busts in the exact same undercover clothes. You could see groups of cadets on every rooftop, so the arrest rate slowed down quickly once everyone opened their eyes and ears.

I skated around as always, and soon ran into Far-L and Sue. I still saw them and hung with them at every show, but since I lived in Oregon, and them in California, we rarely traveled together much anymore. I quizzed Far-L on the shows that I had missed and pressed him for set list details. He had all that information at hand. He had always been a taper, and I knew he had been recording all the shows that we had not been able to make it to on this tour.

Far-L, incidentally, is the guy in the flowered shirt, waving in the second row of Taper Heads, behind Healy, in the infamous Blaire Jackson photo of the very first Grateful Dead/Dan Healy "Authorized Taping Section," at the Berkeley Community Theater on 10/27/84. The photo has appeared in many publications, but was originally in the David Gans and Peter Simon book, *Playing in The Band* which came out in 1985.

Robbi Cohn still managed to hustle selling her amazing photos. Her stories about the obvious undercover cops was a good laugh for us at the next show!

We eventually left the kid cop practice session after seeing awesome gigs! We wiggled our way around DC, and jumped on I-95, which Willie had actually worked on as a cement crew member a few years prior.

We were pointing it towards Philly, and I was getting super fired up! Philadelphia is one of my favorite places to see shows, and I knew we were headed directly into the East Coast energy I love so much. The power of the crowd is intense, to say the least. I wanted some of that intensity and I was about to get it.

175.
HOW MANY HEADS FIT IN THIS PLACE?

JFK Stadium

Philadelphia, PA

7/10/1987

Driving Willie's van in Philly traffic with Fred and Chris, looking for a cheap motel, we came across some cute girls who yelled out the window of their car, and asked us if we were in town for the Grateful Dead. We said we were and started asking them about motels at a stop light. Right away the super smiley driver girl said, "Follow us and we will figure it out." We stopped at a gas station and made our intros. As soon as we met face to face, and they realized we were not scummy or creepy (or both), the three girls invited us to stay with them at their apartment. They even let us take showers!

It turned out to be a cool old Brownstone, and we had a great party with our extra generous hosts. We made food, listened to tunes, got drunk, and did some sort of drug. Maybe X? Crazy laughter ensued with the girls all night long. We ended up high as fuck on the roof of the Brownstone as the sun came up over Philadelphia.

It was super fun and truly represents how much of a good time and a bonding you can get from a shared love of music with people you never met before in your life. The Grateful Dead did that to people! They brought you together with a commonality.

We all went to the show together and had a blast, running around dancing on the floor of the huge football stadium that was known by its initials. JFK.

Brent was at his best on the keys during the "Iko" opener. The place was so packed the Dead had to revert-back to the old game of "take a giant step back," as people were getting crushed up front. They finally got everyone to move back a bit. Then, with tongues in cheeks, and all puns intended, the band went into "When Push Comes to Shove!"

Dylan came out and was on top of it this evening. This may be the best show they performed together. His vocals were strong, and he played his guitar parts well. Bob and the boys kept it tight, with Jerry doing many of the vocal accompaniments. Great versions of "Memphis Blues," and "Gotta Serve Somebody," with heavy vocal backing, and a speedy "All Along the Watchtower" that Dylan sung at his own, almost mumbling, slow pace. It made it unique, and it sounded epic! When he sang, "and the wind began to howl," he let out an "Oh yeah," as the Dead took the fuck off and jammed it out!

176.
PIT STOPS FOR CLEAN SOCKS.

We had a day off, so we stopped on the way out of town to do laundry. I dropped something on the floor and when I went to grab it, I noticed a wad of money. Willie had dropped roughly $600 under the washing machine when he was putting his clothes in it. That was a good eye score, and as a treat, Willie took us to an amazing pizza joint, if I remember right!

177.
THAT HORN SPEAKS!!!!

I had not seen or heard of Willie in 33 years. I knew in my head that he always said he played with a horn player named Green, who was a famous, older, Memphis Jazz great. For many years, I had many other interests and I had not tried to contact anyone Dead related, besides Grateful Dead friends I still see here in Portland. Willie and I traveled a lot in three years and had many adventures together, and I felt it was necessary to have him fill me in on what I had forgotten about our road trips together. I always need more than my own memories for this shit.

I started online by typing in Memphis horn players named Green. I found Hermann Green pretty quickly. I looked at all the pics of his bands that I could find. I didn't recognize Willie in anything. Then I saw a link to a Memphis music article about Green's birthday jam, and I saw a quote from his longtime, trumpet playing bandmate, Willie Waldman. I found my old friend! I reluctantly got on Facebook, and there he was.

Willie had done a lot in those 33 years, and I had been totally unaware. He is now a world-famous trumpet player, producer, and collaborator with some of the biggest names in music. Willie moved to Los Angeles and got his big break with Sublime, playing trumpet on "Date Rape." He did Snoop Dogg songs such as "Vapors," "Me and My Dogs," and "Soldier Story." He played on "California Love" by Tupac, and on tracks for Wu Tang Clan. He then went on to form Banyan with Nels Cline, Stephen Perkins, Mike Watt and Rob Wasserman. Grateful Dead related gigs with Phil *and* Bobby on New Year's 2001 also became a reality. He now produces and has The Willie Waldman Project, an improv group with a revolving cast of players including Norwood Fisher, Terry Saffold and Steve Kimock.

178.
ME AND E IN NEW JERSEY!

Giants Stadium

East Rutherford, NJ

7/12/1987

Ernest came down to the Giants Stadium show. I skated around the area he said he would park in, and low and behold, there he was. He even had cold beers waiting in the trunk of his Monte Carlo. We had not seen one another in several years and we spent the time catching up and talking all things Grateful Dead.

The show was awesome. Dylan was stepping it up with the Dead firing up his motivation! We had been seeing the Dylan-Dead Tour get better and better with each new show they played. The band went back to two sets after several shows, with only one Dead set and one Dylan set. Heads were grumbling about it, but everyone quit complaining after they resumed the normal two set format.

Ernest and I had seats in the upper heights of the stadium, and it was packed. E was looking for an opportunity to get down to the field, but we needed to get by a big, serious looking woman doing security, and she was not letting anyone pass. We waited for our window. She eventually got distracted by some shenanigans going on and we made our move.

Ernest is a big boy, but he was always quick and light on his feet, and we ran all the way down to the rail above the field. We looked over and nobody was sitting down there. Perfect. Sixteen feet to the field? "Let's do it!" E said. We climbed over, hung dangling by our arms, and let go. We free fell backwards and landed it no problem. We did it so quickly, no one even cheered or yelled at us, and we ran up Jerry's side of the stadium and seeped into the massive crowd. I don't condone sneaking into shows, but I'll take a floor spot in General Admission at an 80,000-person gig, and not feel the least bit bad about it. We *did* still pay for our tickets, after all. Not to mention surviving a drunken backwards drop, while on a drop of acid.

Bobby told everyone to take a step back "like an Egyptian" to help the squished masses up front, before they fired off the second set with a stellar "Morning Dew." The "Other One" was exceptional in its 1987 weirdness. Slow, creepy and distorted, breaking into clean, hard hammering of the beat. Phil pulverizing the background with his subtle force. "Other One" is my favorite Dead song of all time, and I saw a ton of smokers during this year.

Dylan sang with more force and more swagger than in Philly, and "Highway 61" was fucking ripping! A real groove was developing that night. Dylan laughing in between lyrics and having fun! His guitar was more heavily in the mix on this night, and he played like we always knew him to! It was amazing!

An eerie, "Ballad of a Thin Man" crept around the stadium filling our ears with its strange lyrics and weirdly transfixing melody. Sadly, "Wicked Messenger" saw its only performance at this show. It was a snaky version, twisting all around, with Dylan's vocal rasp coming out in full force.

179.
DC TANKS OUT

RFK Stadium
Washington, DC
7/13/1987

Fred had to run from the cops as they swooped up on him, and he was forced to leave a nitrous tank behind. That put a huge downer on the show, and left us with no nitrous connection after that, since the tank had serial numbers on it. No one got busted, but no tanks ever came from that source again.

I told Willie I would see him out west in a week in Eugene. I jumped in the white S-10 I knew so well, with Far-L and Sue, and some college friend of his. This kid's family was super rich, and we stopped to crash at his house. His parents' horse farm in New Jersey was straight out of a luxury homes guide. His mother was horrified to have dirty hippies at her place (she peeked at us through the curtains the next morning–never came out). The kid said we could not go inside the fancy house. He disappeared inside, so we used a bathroom in a horse barn and slept on the lawn next to a garage full of fancy cars. I do not remember seeing him again.

We left the fancy-ass horse house early the next morning and I went to the airport via commuter train. Far-L and Sue drove off towards Eugene, Oregon, towards the next show, via the long highway. Touching the eastern edge of one coast and a week later touching the western edge of the other.

180.
AND PORTLAND NEVER QUITS.

Brand new music in Portland was blowing up! The legendary PDX band Dead Moon was forming with Fred Cole on guitar, his wife Toody on bass, and my buddy from the Burnside TriMet bus, Andrew Loomis on drums. Dead Moon became one of my favorite bands of all time. It was incredible to see them so many times over the years!

I also met bass player Davey Loprinzi, aka Davey Nipples, singer Dave Merrick, and phenom drummer Brian Lehfeldt! Young, beer swilling rockers, who would go on to form another legendary Portland band, the incredible, undeniable, Sweaty Nipples!

181.
EVERYBODY (MUST GET) IS GETTING STONED!

Autzen Stadium,
Eugene, OR
7/19/1987

It is always wonderful to see shows in Eugene. It's a magic place.

I am pretty sure we got the first "Maggie's Farm" of the tour in Eugene, even though it was a bit ragged. The "Simple Twist of Fate" a bit later changed all that. It was a gorgeous version. "Rainy Day Women" had the whole place looking like Mt. St. Helens had just belched a plume of smoke into the venue. You don't play that song in Eugene, Oregon, without getting a huge smokey send up from the pot connoisseur audience in attendance. The chorus had the entire stadium smoking out and singing along in a happy haze, inside a giant, chronic, herb cloud. Welcome to Oregon!

182.
OAKTOWN IS GETTING DOWN!

Day on the Green,

Oakland Coliseum

Oakland, CA

7/24/1987

Oakland had great sound, with Phil coming in thumping all day. Second set saw a weird "Uncle John's"-"Dear Mr. Fantasy"-"Need a Miracle"-"Bertha"-"Sugar Magnolia"- "Sunshine Daydream" mash up after the "Drums" to end the Dead set. A unique combo of songs, with Brent putting the vocal pipes to good use, blasting out the lyrics during "Fantasy," and finalizing with a rare, end of show performance of "Bertha."

183.
FLY THROUGH THE NIGHT.

Dylan and the Dead came out and did what they do together, and I decided to eat a dose sometime during the Dylan set. I don't remember much except the hit didn't seem strong and I sort of forgot about it. We went back to downtown San Francisco to a random hotel. We all drank, smoked, and partied it up, and I started getting higher and higher and higher! As everyone started to retreat to their beds in the big hotel room, I just kept getting higher and higher on my late-stage acid trip.

Pretty soon I was the only one awake, high, and not even close to sleep, or even rest of any sort. I had a small light and no music. I couldn't handle it, so I did the only thing I felt comfortable doing at that point. I grabbed my board and my weed and skated off into the San Francisco night.

As soon as my wheels hit the sidewalk my entire mood changed. I was free of the hotel room that had been closing in around me. Now I was flying in the night wind down the street on my skate. I suddenly felt alive and unstoppable. A skateboard and acid can be a great combination to reset your head sometimes! I skated down to The Civic, onto the bricks of Market Street, and down to Justin Henry Plaza at the south end of the Embarcadero.

It was just before dawn. A few skaters were there even at sunrise. I figured they had been up all night, just like me. I skated for a long while on the bricks and ledges, as my acid buzz wore down along with my trucks.

The sun got high as I got less high, and I rolled back and hopped in Far-L's truck for the long, hot ride down the I-5, to the home of Mickey Rat, Disneyland, and Knott's Berry Farm! Sunny Anaheim, California.

184.
DEAD DREAMS IN LOS ANGELES.

Angel Stadium
Anaheim, CA
7/26/1987

Went to Stevo and Natasha's house in Venice, ate breakfast at the infamous Penguin, and drove to the town of children's dreams, Anaheim, California.

It has been very well publicized that Dylan launched into "Mr. Tambourine Man" to open the show, after never rehearsing it with the Dead, ever. It was an awkward version, but they pulled through and the rest of the show lit up like fireworks. Dylan was playing his guitar, as opposed to strumming it, and his voice was at its most powerful yet. The band was clean and tight and filled in all the right shit. This was perhaps the best Dylan-Dead show that they performed together. After six shows, the mojo was working better than ever.

I wish they had done another six to twelve shows. I believe it would have turned into an exceptionally smooth band project. I think this is evident by how tight this last show they did sounds. The groove was getting true definition, right when the tour was ending. It's a shame it didn't go on. Scale it back to smaller venues later that fall? Woulda, coulda, shoulda. I'm not a tour manager. I was just a hopeful fan, and I was fantastically lucky to see the shows I did see.

185.
RED BACKPACK, BLUE BACKPACK.

I took the Green Tortoise bus line back from Venice to NW Portland. The Tortoise was great! It was a reconditioned Grey Hound that was made into one big bed. You got your own space next to the other riders, and you could sit up against the sides by day, and stretch out on clean, comfortable, sheet covered padding and sleep by night.

They only stopped to pick up or drop off, and an occasional piss break on the long stretches between bus stops. The bus had speakers every five feet, with an adjustable volume knob on each. They would play one tape of each person on the bus, keeping the tapes in a long row to keep it even. You could even smoke weed on the coach and party in transit if you kept it cool. It was a fantastic way to travel, and I utilized the services of The Green Tortoise many, many times.

The driver would get on the roof and hand down the bags at your stop. He would call out, "Green backpack! Blue backpack! Red backpack!" Twice, the same driver, on different trips, handed down my aluminum Zero Haliburton suitcase (that I did indeed smuggle weed in), and with a straight face, called out, "Drug dealer's suitcase!" and then just kept on going down the line. "Orange backpack! Gold backpack!" I loved the Green Tortoise! It was like nothing other.

186.
PORTLAND FLOWS ON.

I had money to make, even though I have no idea how I did it back then, so I skipped seven shows, and probably came back and trimmed and sold some weed. I saw Duran Duran and David Bowie for the Glass Spider Tour with Greg and Audra, on 8/14 at Civic Stadium in Portland. Greg is a huge Bowie fan, and it was super cool to attend this show with him and Audra.

187.
THE HEADLIGHT ON THE NORTH BOUND TRAIN GOES OUT.

Tour legend Kurt, the man who was at *every* show, died in Colorado at Chief Hosa campground during the Red Rocks run.

Sleep in the stars!

188.

NO FROGS AND ANGELS WITH PATCHES.

With Carlos Santana

Angels Camp

Calaveras, CA

8/22-23/1987

I caught back up with tour at Angels Camp, in Calaveras County. The same place they have the famous Frog Jumping Contest, and surprisingly, we did not see any frogs anywhere. We did see Carlos Santana play with his band and perform two songs each day with the Dead. They got busy with "Good Morning Little School Girl" and "Midnight Hour" on the first day, and busted out "Iko-Iko" and "Watchtower" together on the second day. During all four songs, Jerry and Carlos tossed lead licks back and forth, getting tighter and faster with each exchange. It was blazing fast, and they both had fun feeding off each other, as we collectively went fucking-crazy out in the hot central California sunshine.

We had a whole Portland crew with us on this trip, including Naomi, Otto, Clark, Jimmers, George, Mark, Stu, VW Mike, Chris Feeney and even Memphis Willie.

189.
DANNY SARGENT AND JERRY GARCIA.

Jerry Garcia Band

French's Camp

Eel River, CA

8/29/1987

Jerry Garcia Acoustic Band was performing for the first time, along with the normal electric, JGB. The show was at the Eel River at French's Camp in NorCal. The area is amazing, with huge trees mixed in with scrub brush, and a slow, shallow river that meanders through one side of the venue. We rented little cabins in an old growth forest, not far from the show at the Singing Trees Inn and Cabins.

Dan, Mark, George, Russ Never Sleeps, Willie, Clark, and Jeff all attended. I also took Danny Sargent on the trip. Danny was a good friend, and was the top sponsored amateur skateboarder in Oregon at the time. All his sponsors (Concrete Jungle Boards, Independent Trucks and Spitfire Wheels) were based in San Francisco. He had outgrown/out skated the scene in Portland. Not being in San Francisco, where the main action in skateboarding was at the time, was keeping him from his true potential, and he knew it. We had a last curb session as a sendoff the night before, and early the next day we hit the road.

The Eel River shows are more like a little Ren Faire than a concert. They had booths inside selling or offering things, and people were making plenty of good food. Back then, good mountain bikes with suspension were a new thing. A company named Slingshot had demo bikes we could ride around inside the show. Danny and I got yellow ones and kept them for way longer than the 15 minute-each time-limit. We had them for over an hour, cruising around the concert, checking everything out. It was trippy. I was inside an outside Jerry show, riding around doing wheelies and jumps on a mountain bike, while Jerry was ripping away on stage. Epically bizarre!

We all went swimming in the Eel and washed off the NorCal dust. Clark got Russ to get in the water. Russ could not swim and notoriously avoided anything deep. Clark showed him it was shallow, so Russ reluctantly got in. Then Clark made him take a big hit off a nitrous balloon and go under the water. Russ got a bunch of weeds stuck in his hair that looked like weedy dreads, and he had big round eyes from the nitrous in his head, as he slowly surfaced. So good!

The new acoustic set was superb, and a cool country venue like French's Camp was the perfect place to combine the newer sound and bands.

Somehow, we got back to the Singing Trees Cabins and raged on.

After a long night of acid, beer, and big dark trees by our cabins, we drove down to San Francisco to see Bonnie Raitt. It was her birthday, and she was playing with Jerry Band at The Greek Theatre. As we got into downtown, Danny guided us to the back of Justin Henry Plaza, the skateboard mecca of the time, known as Embarcadero or EMB. Danny high fived us all, tossed down his board and rolled off into skateboard history.

I would see him every few months as I saw shows, and within a year he had turned pro. He got his own board model on Schmitt Stix (Barrell-Full-O-Monkeys = rare-as-fuck), and had gotten his first cover of *Thrasher Magazine* wearing his Jimi Hendrix shirt. It was very cool to have been there when he was coming up, and I am truly proud of my friend for making it all the way. Yeah, Danny!

190.
BONNIE PLUS JERRY
EQUALS MUSICAL LOVE!

Jerry Garcia Band with

Bonnie Raitt

The Greek Theatre

Berkeley, CA

8/30/1987

What a unique combination for a show! Turned out Jerry and Bonnie knew each other and enjoyed each other's music, very much. A show together would be a good pairing, and so it was set up.

August in Berkeley is normally perfect weather, and the day did not let us down. Nice and breezy, with the weed smoke blending in nicely with the ever-present smell of eucalyptus in the air. Bonnie opened and ripped it up. Jerry came out and played a killer set, and then invited Bonnie onstage, where they did two songs together. "Think" and "Knockin' on Heaven's Door." They tossed around vocal bursts and smoking guitar licks back and forth, and lit the stage up with a crazy dual musical energy. Both guitarists complement each other well, and the energy flow was rushing hard that afternoon.

191.
GO EAST YOUNG MAN!

Civic Center

Providence, RI

9/7-9/1987

Six days later I flew back to the East Coast. Somehow? I have a vague idea of what I was doing for money. I know it was a weed hustle. I may have flown with a half-pound of weed. I trimmed every three months for Bill and Sharon during this time, so that makes sense. I believe I bought a one-way plane ticket in advance for this East Coast run for cheap, and then rode trains up the coast as the tour progressed.

Ernest picked me up someplace and we drove to Providence. We got a roach motel and went to the first show. E didn't have a ticket, so he ran up and down the streets looking for them. Up to the off-ramps. All through the parking lots. He finally found one and got in just as the show started.

I found myself in the same ticketless boat the next day. I had a system that worked every single time. I said loudly and clearly, "I need a ticket, I'm from Oregon. I want to trade, and you will *love* the trade." That's all it took. If you knew anything at all about weed, you knew exactly what I was implying. In the 1980s *all* the good pot came from California and Oregon. That was it. The only real places, so, if you smoked you knew!

Quickly enough, someone would excitedly wave me over. I would show them, and let them get a smell of an eighth ounce of weed, and the ticket was mine. They would always ask if I had more to sell, and I would hook them up for the going East Coast rate of $80 an eighth ounce. More often, than not, if they had tickets for the other nights or other shows on the tour, I would do the same eighth ounce trade for $17.50 tickets. It worked out great for everyone. Then, they always smoked me out on my weed, and vice-versa, because now I had the seats next to them in the show! I made some fun tour friends that way.

On the same note, these shows were becoming huge. Even in large venues, tickets were getting harder and harder to come by. By end of the tour at The Spectrum, my weed and cash were dwindling, but we will get to that. These shows saw a marked change in the song selection and order. They did "Iko" (with Brent going off on the vocalizations), "Saint of Circumstance," and "Ship of Fools" all in a row to open the second set. The ender saw the band ripping through a sizzling "Good Lovin'," only to have Bobby scream, "Listen!" in the middle of the song, as Jerry blasted off into a Spanish sung version of "La Bamba" that had the whole place jumping up and down and climbing on the seats! Incredible and power-ful! Again, another one of the reasons Dead Heads try to see every single show they can. Gems like these make it absolutely worth it, every time.

The second night "Hell in a Bucket" into "Fire on the Mountain" was the weird and killer combination of the evening. We got another strangely enhanced "Other One" that came out of a slow "Space," Phil playing with extra intensity, fingers all over his bass. Bobby's voice was distorted and amazing. Brent's keys sounded higher and more frenetic, and *then,* Phil started dropping bombs, a few of which shook the whole fucking build-ing. I love these strange high energy versions! East Coast baby!

I got in early on the third night and I'm glad I didn't lag. I loved Brent and tonight was his night. He started tuning up and we could hear "Hey Pocky Way," but the Dead often tuned and teased, and then went the opposite way into a standard of their own. Not tonight. Brent did his sideways head shake he would do when he was on, and put every-thing into this debut right out of the gate. The version wasn't thunderous. It was groovy, and had a swing to it that set everyone up for another kick-ass show! A normal, yet fast paced first set went down after that, until Brent, once again, stepped up and blew us out of the arena by bust-ing-out another set of surprises, with "Devil with a Blue Dress On" into a short, tight "Good Golly Miss Molly," and back into "Devil with a Blue Dress On!" Four new Brent tunes in one set? What the fuck was going on? It was insane! These were only the *first* three shows of fifteen! We heard *five* new songs, not to mention several Dylan songs the Dead kept in the set lists, after tour with him ended a month before. The "Not Fade Away" chant normally drops off a bit until the band comes back, but this night the crowd got louder and sang it perfectly. The band came out and jumped right back in, finished it up, and dropped into "Mighty Quinn."

That is why tour is so compelling, if not totally addicting. Shows like these.

192.
ZIGZAGGING BETWEEN SHOWS.

Capital Center

Landover, MD

9/11-13/1987

We drove all the way down I-95, to the Cap Center. Sometimes you wonder why they stretch out the tour in the way they do. While traveling Providence to Landover, you pass NYC and Philly, then you must return to these cities, to see more shows. I know it's a booking issue for the venues, but man, some of the gaps were frustrating. Knowing you're coming right back by the next tour stop, while you pass it by 300 miles. On this tour it went, in this order, Providence, Landover, New York City and Philly. That meant two trips through Philadelphia during the tour, only to return a third time at the end of the tour to see the last three shows, back in, yes, Philadelphia.

The first night they opened with "Bertha" and Jerry sang, "I had a hard run, running from your window," then sang, "I had a run in, wonder if you cared," checked his mistake, and went right back into the "I had a run in" line in its proper spot. Nice save Jerry, although it didn't last, and he blew the lyrics twice more. It got us all laughing and cheering and in a good mood as the boys warmed up. No one ever cared, and forgetting a few lyrics was just part of the whole trip. It always left me dumbfounded though, when Jerry would forget the lyrics to a song he wrote, with twenty something words in it total, such as "Crazy Fingers," but he would never forget a Dylan line while performing many of Bob's most lyrically complex songs. Go figure.

Phil came out prior to the second set and said, "Today is Mickey's Birthday!" They then proceeded to perform "Sugar Magnolia" into "Sugaree." We got a sweet "Fantasy"-"Watchtower" to huge cheers, as Brent and Bobby once again went off vocally! A smooth and chilling "Wharf Rat" came next, and they wrapped the set with a "Sunshine Daydream." Epic night! Happy 44th Mickey!

Second night tore right into a fierce "Hell in a Bucket," with all the Bobby vocal wildness you could ever want! Then we had a "Tom Thumb's Blues" with Phil sounding clear and sharp and another funky "Hey Pocky Way" towards the end of the first set.

A weird placing for a "Cumberland Blues" was what I remember when they opened the second set with it, but it was all-right by me. "Cumberland Blues" gets the whole place up, moving and shaking every-time! A rollicking "Truckin'" came after "Space" with Bobby singing, "Living on Crack, Vitamin C and Cocaine," and they did a double encore of "Saturday Night" and "Black Muddy River."

Day three melted away from day two and we walked in to see an "Iko-Iko" opener. The fourth song, that seemed to be a mere tease, turned into the song "Fever," notably covered by both Eddie Cooley and Elvis Presley. Otis Blackwell penned the song, but it was made most famous by Peggy Lee. Bobby just broke it out of the mist. Later, after "Space," we got a wickedly distorted "Other One," with Mickey and Billy beating out the background sound, as they seemingly chased each other around the drumheads establishing the rhythm. Bobby then kicked down a heavy "Throwing Stones," and following that, Bob and Jerry did the "Lovin'"-"La Bamba"-"Good Lovin'" combo again, to everyone's total motherfuck-ing delight!

I have tended to write a bit more about this tour concerning song details, because in retrospect, I consider this my favorite tour I ever went on. It was truly incredible. Well played and as high energy as any Dead shows I ever attended.

193.
MOTEL HELL.

This East Coast Tour was staged in a variety of huge venues, so every hotel/motel in every town was way overloaded. But if you're a Dead Head, you usually have lots of friends who you don't mind sharing with. You would have six, eight, ten or twelve people in a tiny Motel Shit room with one or two small beds. We traded who got beds each night and everyone had just enough room on the floor to lie down, if you really felt you needed to sleep. All the doors to the rooms would be wide open with music blasting. The balconies and walkways would be clogged with partying Heads. Everyone in a Dead shirt with open beers and burning joints, talking about all things Grateful Dead.

As you can imagine, it usually did not sit well with any hotel management policies, even though the rooms were totally sold out ($$$). All they saw was twelve hippies in a room meant for two non-hippies and it made some of them real, real mad.

The overload of Heads meant an overload on the motel. All the towels and sheets in the whole place got used. Heads would unload and repack their entire tour bus, or rebuild part of their motor or suspension right in the parking lot. Every ice machine was constantly working or empty. Trash bins would be way overloaded and spilling out.

The entire hotel would stay up all night raging before and after the shows, and every room was totally blown out with various fluids everywhere. Spilled beers, bong water and booze. Several Heads even redecorated their rooms with tie dyes and Dead posters, colored light bulbs, even hand sewn Dead blankets made from old Dead shirts.

That really freaked out a few housekeepers, and enraged one motel owner so much, he called the State Troopers and had the whole place kicked out, and some people arrested. He walked around to every room yelling at Heads to get out. "You broke the rules and I have the right to make you leave!" No one paid much attention accept to say, "Okay, we understand," and "Sorry man," the first two times he was yelling things. Then he got a friend who was a much larger and more menacing looking, East Coast style tough guy, and shit got crazy.

The manager was red faced, screaming, "I've called the police and you are all going to jail!" Big thick neck guy kept yelling, "Get the fuck out or go to jail! You stole from this motel! That's theft of services charges!" and various other things. When you hear the manager talking to the cops on his phone, with the cord stretched all the way out the door of the office (no cellphones then kids) so he can give descriptions of people to the cops, you know it's time to leave. Like, right now!

We knew at that point we were about to meet the Rhode Island State Troopers face to face, and that did not sound appealing to us at all. We had weed, acid, and some mushrooms. Get out now! Me and a Tour Head, whose name I've long forgotten, grabbed our stuff super quick, as did the rest of our overcrowded theft of services roommates, and we split. I ended up leaving a bag with killer tour shirts and other small things behind, as we literally ran to the car. We pulled away as multiple cop cars rolled in, and swooped up all the Heads that did not heed the motel manager's angry police threats. We heard at the next show that a lot of people got searched and went to jail.

That motel (and many more) also created a "banned from renting a room here" list, for everyone who previously rented a room from them during Grateful Dead shows. This was to become a regular thing in coming years. Bans on Dead Heads, not bans on the Grateful Dead, but on us, the fans. The future of tour was starting to show its ugly side. Soon it was to become no rentals, no camping, no parking, no vending.

No soup for you!

194.
BACK WITH THE HOMETOWN HEADS.

I rode the train, or perhaps a series of trains, up to Connecticut. I think? I'm pretty sure? I believe I rode from Landover, Maryland to South Norwalk, Connecticut, transferred, and got off at the old ass train station in Bethel. The same one that we used to go into to warm up and smoke weed, in wintertime. Always empty. Still the same. Nothing had changed. It was just a pick-up and drop off station with no ticket sales. You bought them on the train from a conductor in those days.

Ernest picked me up and off we went on yet another adventure on this tour!

195.
NEW YORK CITY WAS RAW DOG IN 1987.

Madison Square Garden
Manhattan, New York City
9/15-16, 18-20/1987

It all started with Ernest calling in sick to work *all* week long. I stayed with E and our old school chum, Glenn H, at the Danbury, Connecticut apartment they occupied at the time. We would get up hungover each day, drive 15 miles to Brewster, New York to the train station, get Peking

Garden Chinese food, beer, and booze. We would load all this stuff on the train and take the ride into New York City.

Our stop was about midway through the train route, so it was already full of Heads when we got on. Raging on the train with 300 Dead Heads, riding through 1980s bombed out and burned down New York City. Smoking weed, drinking beer, doing shots, and making the conductors super, super angry. The train conductors would walk by and smell weed, give us a stern train guy warning, and as soon as they would leave the car, everyone would laugh and light up again right away.

This went on again and again. The train would brake coming into a station, and countless empty beer bottles and cans would roll out from under the seats and across the floors, adding more raucous laughter to the ride. On the way back it was worse! Always a total shit-show! "Hi, we're HIGH!" You would have people climbing up to sleep or trip out up in the baggage racks, big giant eyeballs everywhere. Small puddles of friends taking up the seats and talking about the magic they all experienced that night. And always accompanied by the beer bottle and can cavalcade under the seats at each new stop. All this and more, all the way to the end of the line. Conductors beware!

196.
IN THE CITY!

The 1987 Madison Square Garden shows were the first time the band had booked a five-night run, and it was sold out quick-as-shit. We arrived downtown about an hour or two ahead of each show, depending on how much we lagged or didn't.

Every morning was different. Perform the routine, and it gets to be a routine, no doubt about that. Ride the train and hit the show. I would do nose wheelies and manuals on my skateboard in the long, ultra-smooth, foot polished hallways of Grand Central Station. Each day I would try to out-do my distance record from the day before.

Our weed got tossed under the newspaper boxes by a cocky dick of a NY beat cop. I write about this later in the book when I return to the Garden for Dead and Co. shows in 2019. Someone had a room across the street at The Pennsylvania, aka The Penta.

We popped in and out, smoking and carrying on in the old school lobby that has been synonymous with NYC Dead shows for years. We went inside the Garden proper, and it brought back my old childhood memories of seeing Ringling Bros. and Barnum & Bailey Circus there a few times as a boy. The Red, Orange, Yellow, Green and Blue rings that designate the floor levels were all the same. I even knew how to get to the bathrooms without even thinking about it. Childhood memory remote control. These gigs all blended in my brain, so I'll let you listen to the shows and hear the order they played the sets in. You're on your own this time!

197.
PHILLY HAS THE FUCKING SICKEST ENERGY!

Spectrum

Philadelphia, PA

9/22-24/1987

Who was I with? How did I get there? How did I get back to Connecticut and then the NY airport? I don't fucking know! What I do know is, I got super close-up seats for all three shows. I don't know who I got these tickets from. I believe I bought them all on the street. If someone remembers hooking me up with these epic seats, just remind me. I'll add the revision here!

I walked in and still didn't realize how good my tickets were. I got ushered all the way to Section 102, Row 10, Seat 13. That's tenth row center. I was so hyped! The crowd and the roar we generated in the Spectrum is the power highlight experience of my entire Dead Tour life. Tremendous energy in that place.

We got another "Hey Pocky Way" to open, which no one complained about. Shortly after that they played a pretty "Ramble on Rose" then gave us a little *Addams Family* soundtrack teaser before slipping into a nice "Cassidy."

Second set had Phil plucking his bass strings and thumping out a rad "Gimme Some Lovin'," sung that night by the legendary Spencer Davis, who's song it originally is. That was a special treat, and the version was very well played! Spencer's guitar tone standing out clearly amongst the Dead's distinct sound! It is loud and powerful up front in Philly and my killer seats were letting me know it! "Samson and Delilah" had a thunder to it brought on my Mickey and Billy beating it up in the background. Out of "Space," Jerry started noodling on "Handsome Cabin Boy," an old folk number which turned into a five-minute jam that was slow and deliberate in its pace. It was very hypnotic, and the crowd was eerily silent until the slow segue into an amazing "Wheel." A fast "Truckin'" came after that, with Phil dropping a few fat ones on us as he played quick, banging the bottom end out.

I still have no idea where I stayed or with who. I'll find out someday!

Second night I managed to get a lower-level seat in Section K, which was right up off to Jerry's left. Stage height. Perfect!

The band had some sort of major feed-back/overload during the first half of "Stranger" that threatened to deafen everyone in the whole Spectrum. They got it fixed just before we had to wipe little drops of blood from our eardrums. The band made fun of the fuck up, as they laughed and sang, "You know it's gonna get stranger," and "Long-long, crazy-crazy night."

They were super tight right from the start, despite the equipment fuck up, and ripped. A stellar "Franklin's Tower" jumped in the mix next, and deep in the first set they tossed out a "Big Railroad Blues" into "Music Never Stopped." Philadelphia was on fire and the Dead were holding the matches!

I must have gone to piss and look around the show during the set break. I was in the very background floor area of the Spectrum, where they always had the amazing SEVA Blindness Foundation booth. I was talking to someone about the craziness that was going on outside earlier in the day. Thousands of people showed up that did not have tickets but were still determined to get in anyway.

At the back of the Spectrum, they have roughly ten sets of double doors for people to leave after the show is over. Suddenly, we heard loud pounding on all the doors. The guy who I was with said, "We need to move now." We walked about 15 feet away as the pounding grew louder. Then doors started to pop open. Apparently, if one person pulls on *each* outside door handle while someone else kicks the center of the double doors, sometimes the door will pop open. This happened, and hundreds of Heads rushed in, and opened every single door that wasn't already open. This took about ten seconds and then it got fucking crazy.

So many people rushed in, that the SEVA booth and everyone around it, including us, got pushed up against the wall opposite the open doors. Security was freaking out and being extra rough with all the intruders. I saw cops through the open doors outside on horses, swinging billy clubs, walking the horses sideways through the crowd to move people back. The inside security was grabbing Heads by the dreads and putting chicks in chokeholds. The few people who got caught, got the worst of the security's anger as they were dragged off to be arrested.

Insanity. And it was all over in about two minutes. Security got the doors shut and the back of the Spectrum looked like a hippy thrift store got hit by a tornado. I saw several single shoes, and pieces of ripped clothing everywhere. Someone had tripped or got trampled and hurt their ankle. Other people got punched or had chunks of hair pulled out by security. There was blood on faces and blood on the ground.

Security came charging up to us as we were pulling the SEVA booth away from the wall, and demanded we show our ticket stubs, which we already had in our hands. Medical staff attended to the hurt, and I went back to my seat to smoke a bowl and try to get back to the good vibe of the Dead show in progress. The weed worked and on I went, although still a bit shook up!

Second set contained a great "Playin'"-"Uncle John's"-"Playin'" jam, and the final "Good Lovin'"-"La Bamba" mash up ever to be played.

Second night show, in a great seat, feeling up close and personal. It was so worth it to do this entire tour! One more night to go!

198.
JUNKY PIECE OF SHIT!

During this trip our house was broken into by a junky piece of shit, whom we knew. He hit three of our houses, all in one day. Wiping out *all* our first pressing, vintage album collections. Over 1,000 records between the three houses and six people he stole from. He was a weed grower, who had been doing very well. He had a great car with a great stereo. He was generous at shows.

I rode home with him that spring from California, and he had two Strawberry Cycle Works bikes on his rack. A gun metal blue one for him and a pinkish-red one for his girlfriend of the time.

I was blown away. These were the most beautiful road bicycles I had ever seen. Hand built by Andy Newland here in Portland, kitted out with a Campagnolo C-Record groupset. They were clearly not just bikes, but true works of art. I fell in love with the style and beauty and wanted one right away. Then he told me each one cost $2,400. Whoa. Shot down hope.

I figured I would never be able to buy one, but I randomly said, "If you ever want to sell one, give me a ring. Maybe I could make payments?" Lo and behold, he called a few months later and said he wanted to sell the blue bike. I inquired why and he said he broke up with his girl and was getting rid of shit.

He came over and I made the first payment. I noticed his car was looking beat up. The new rims were gone, as was the rooftop bike rack, and when I looked inside, also gone was his killer stereo. I asked and he said his car got stolen, which explained everything and made normal sense to me. I thought nothing of it, even though he did not look so good at the time. I should have known. That day I assumed I was just making a payment and getting a test ride, but he let me keep the bike. I now know, he just needed a fix.

I was in shock. I owned a Strawberry. Frame 186. I cleaned and polished it, like it deserved. I now had a Ferrari of the bicycle world. Still do! The first week I rode it I got envious compliments from over a dozen local bike riders on the road. That solidified how special this bike really was.

Back to the burglary. Our two non-Dead Head roommates, Greg and Audra, had day jobs, and George was partying at Clark's for a few days. When they got home, everything was gone. I made a call home from a Philly phonebooth and heard about it. Hundreds of records, my camera, stereos, repossession and normal tools, small jewelry, and stashed cash. The only thing that was not stolen, sitting right there leaning on the wall in the dining room, was the shiny gem of a bike known as a Strawberry. That's how I knew it was him, even before I hung up the phone from Philadelphia.

199.
BACK IN THE SPECTRUM.

On the third night, I got 14th row floor in Section 101, directly in front of Phil! It was an all-time way to end a tour. Epic seats every single night! Jerry sounded a little rough during "Touch of Grey," and clearly fourteen shows is a lot for any voice. They jumped off into an unusually early "High Time" in the third song slot, then did a "Me and My Uncle" with a long "Mexicali Blues" teaser, but then shifted into "Big River" and an unexpected "Big Boss Man" just after that. Perhaps in response to all the police presence at these tour ender gigs? Who knows? It's also what we referred to as a Country Dead first set.

Second set brought the heat with a smoking "Hell in a Bucket"-"Fire on the Mountain" before "Drums." "Space" had all *The Twilight Zone* tones in full effect. It was so TWZ, that I almost expected Rod Serling to come out and sing backup on "The Other One" with Bobby! The band jammed throughout the song, once again with maximum distortion. Air raid horns and weird vocals were coming through the PA. Jerry had that nice razor's edge sound to his licks, and Phil was running a fret board marathon race. Brent's keys sounded like electric raindrops, and Mickey and Bill were separate, roaring thunder, distinctly feeding off each other. Insane!

They ended the fourteen-show run with a beautiful "Knockin' on Heaven's Door" and we all said goodnight to the Fall Tour of 1987.

200.
GOING HOME OR TRYING.

I had to fly home. I was somehow broke (What? How?) and had to borrow the money for my flight from E, and I believe I may still owe him for that flight.

We were drinking beer at the airport while E was relearning how to skate. E is a big-boy, and he broke my Alva/Dave Duncan skateboard trying to ollie. I got a new one at Rebel Skates when I got back, and five days later, I'm on my way to Shoreline in Palo Alto.

201.
GONE ARE THE DAYS,
AND SO ARE OUR RECORDS.

When I returned to Portland, we assembled our burglarized friends. We then went to the used records stores and started pulling *our* albums out of the bins. We questioned the clerk and he looked up the junky's name in his purchase book. Fucking idiot. Steals all our records and then signs his own name at the record shop when he sells them. That's a desperate addict.

We went back to our place. I called him and said I had a bike payment for him and told him to swing by. He didn't have a car by this time. His cab showed up and he came inside, only to find six of us who he had ripped off, waiting for him.

Mark locked the front door and made sure he could not leave. I went out the back way and handed the cab driver a $20. He asked, "What about the guy?" I said, "He's not coming back out." The cabbie just nodded, like this happens often, shifted into drive and took off.

202.
PALO ALTO PERPLEXITY.

Shoreline Amphitheatre
Mountain View, CA
10/2-4/1987

I have vague memories of this set of shows. I know it was a quick drive down and back, with no stopping in between. See the shows and get back home. We had been robbed and it was time to move to a new house. One note, more Dylan songs are staying in the band repertoire, namely "Maggie's Farm."

203.
YOU CAN'T HAVE IT!

During this time, Jerry performed eighteen shows on Broadway at the Lunt-Fontanne Theatre, that I sadly, did not get to attend. Tour legend Big Rick had been living in Portland. He attended all the shows and returned with the classic poster, T-shirt, and the unique Jerry Playbill that was handed out. He brought them back for me since I couldn't go. Thank you, Big Rick, wherever you are. I still have all three, although the shirt is a bit snug these days!

204.
HYPED UP AT HENRY J!

REX Benefit Shows
Henry J. Kaiser Conv. Center
Oakland, CA
11/6-8/1987

The REX shows are benefits for the REX Foundation, named after Rex Jackson. He was a band crew member, who sadly passed in a car crash. His personal spirit and outlook on life formed the idea for the foundation that gives grants to a wide range of people for multiple charitable reasons.

The boys hit the stage and Jerry's tuning up did not sound at all like "Big Boss Man," but that's what we got! Fat and funk filled with everybody singing along. Bobby growling behind Jerry's slow vocal delivery! Brent getting breathy with the organ, and Mickey and Bill smacking down the familiar "Big Boss Man" drumbeat. This is my single favorite version of this song I ever saw them perform. "He's Gone" was equally sweet, just before "Drums," and later-on, the "Morning Dew" built into a frenzy, with the group cruising at full speed into the ending.

Jerry's voice was so emotional that I also believe this is one of the best versions I have ever seen. A lot of bands have covered this song over the years, but no one does it like the Dead, and often even the Dead do not do it *this* good! This one was a pearl, a gem, a nugget of gold, a rare opal. I'm not even going to say anymore. Just put this show on. Relive it for yourself! Okay, fuck it, one more thing. The "Watchtower" is off the hook, bananas, nuts! Okay, I'm done.

Second night we got treated extremely well! First set saw a rad "Dupree's" and a "Box of Rain," after a lengthy "We want Phil!" chant with Bobby doing some weird jamming in between. "Uncle John's," "Playin'" and "Terrapin" took up 30 minutes of the second set, and the band teased up "Miracle" for a full two minutes before breaking into the actual version after the "Drums." Once again, the band left the stage while we all sang "Not Fade Away," then came back out to finish and dove directly into "Knockin' on Heaven's Door."

Night three they gave us five songs before the "Drums," with a wild transition from the "Crazy Fingers" jam into "Truckin'." "Space" bled into a long "Spanish Jam" and after all that, Phil gave a us a bass pounding when they did "Tom Thumb's Blues" into "Touch of Grey" to close out the 1987 REX Benefit shows.

205.
SKATE TO RELATE.

Long Beach Coliseum

Long Beach, CA

11/13-14/15

I always had a blast skateboarding in the parking lots of Dead shows. In Long Beach the weather was great. I encountered a guy skating around and we had a session. We ollied off the five stair and slapped a bunch of red curbs. He turned out to be Mike Ternasky, who went on to be a skateboard legend, and videographer/team creator, who put together H-Street and Plan B. I still have his Magnussen Skateboards business card and the red shirt he gave me. He tragically passed away in a car accident several years later. Rip In Peace! It was nice to meet you!

The mid-first set "Friend of the Devil" had awesome keyboards going on. Brent and Phil had a thunder fest with the drummers on "Far from Me," as he belted out a seriously soulful version. A slinky version of "Estimated" came around before the "Drums," with Bobby emphasizing the lyrics with extra gusto. The fantasy mania of "Estimated" always seemed more in tune with Southern California, so this version with its extra vocal emphasis was appropriate for this set of shows. LA, the sun, the beach, the ocean, and Bobby screaming like a manic messiah. This was such a unique version, that it stands out in my mind to this day.

"The Wheel" was more like a training wheel coming in at exactly four minutes (I checked!). Mickey was banging on something that sounded like a metal garbage can lid, and the normal jam at the end gave way to a tasty "Gimme Some Lovin'." Phil walked us into it slowly, as the band built it up around him with a very Spencer Davis group flare. Heavy '60s keyboards

235

with long drawn-out drum fills. Brent finished up by singing, "Give me some hot good lovin'," as they dropped down into a mellow "Wharf Rat" and we all got up and flew away on this stellar version.

Night number two, they hit us with "Shakedown Street" to get the place shaking, followed up a few songs later with a melodic and rolling "Althea." Second set started with the newly popular "Maggie's Farm"-"Cumberland Blues" combo, and wound it up with a "Love Light," with Bobby on top note and Phil making seismic sensors go off! We got out the door a bit later, after singing about an Eskimo, and everybody wanting to dose!

Third day we heard an "Iko-Iko" with someone backing up the vocals, and I have no idea who it was to this day. "Walking Blues" came cruising along next, and we dipped out to the bad part of town with a "West LA Fadeaway," deep down in the first set.

"Scarlet Begonias" got reunited with its best friend "Fire on the Mountain" for the first time in a long while, if I remember right. The "He's Gone" melded into a band of "Wailing Souls" for the last two full minutes, as the boys sang like apparitions from a different world. Mickey got up and started banging on something strange and the drums crept in as the "He's Gone" drifted out. A chilling "Morning Dew," with Bill and Mick playing subtle marching band beats came a little while later, with Jerry bending the guitar notes to maximum effect. They sped through an "Around and Around" and tossed out another fantastic "Watchtower." The regulation tour year was officially over, and we got a nice slow "Muddy River" to float us all to the Jerry shows, or wherever we may have been going.

These were the last Grateful Dead shows before New Year's Eve and we were moving to the Oakland Coliseum for this set of gigs. New Year's Eve finally outgrew our beloved Kaiser, and the band was forced to step up the venue size. By the looks of things then, it was obvious this was the trend to come. Bigger and bigger and bigger.

206.
ACOUSTIC WEST COAST MADNESS!

Jerry Garcia Band, Acoustic

Warfield Theatre

San Francisco, CA

11/27-29/1987

When Jerry Garcia Band decided to do the acoustic NY run on the West Coast, they only performed one show a day. I was hoping they would copy the East Coast model and do three shows a day. Matinee, early and late shows. Clearly, New York has a different scene and does not work like the West Coast, so we got what we got! Epic shows, just not as many as a young ravenous Dead Head like myself wanted!

Jerry picked a great group of talent to perform with him, including John Kahn, David Nelson, David Kemper, Sandy Rothman, and Kenny Kosek.

A tight and wonderful band that laid it out every night for us! The song selection for the acoustic sets covered a wide range of music from, "Swing Low, Sweet Chariot" to "Deep Elem Blues," all the way to the Dead's own "Ripple." Amazing sound and the shows were beautifully played. All those back-to-back-chicken shack, shows made everyone extra tight!

207.
WHAT YOU NEED MAN?

Jerry Garcia Band
Wiltern Theatre
Los Angeles, CA
12/3-6/1987

We took it slow after this first set of gigs, since we had four days off, and casually drove down to LA. Far-L had recently moved to the ultra-gnarly part of Venice when he rented a house on Brooks Ave, across the street from Howard Mermelstein, another Lifer Dead Head, on the worst street by far, in the entire area. Gang bangers (real-serious motherfuckers), and crack for sale 24-7. Cars all night long on the street. Gunshots in the alley happened a few times a week. Busts went down all the time.

I was running weed down south quite often back in the late '80s, so I stayed there a lot. The first few days I was there, the cops stopped me three or four times to run my ID and check me out, as I was skating down Brooks Ave towards Venice Beach. When they realized I wasn't buying drugs, they would warn me to not take shortcuts through these streets. "Go around and you'll be safe." Then I would tell them I was living on Brooks Ave, and they would shake their heads, look at me like I was insane, and drive off. The cops got used to me and stopped stopping me, but the crack dealers were not as cool, at first.

I was skating down Brooks, right in front of the New Bethel Church (the church CR Stecyk got the idea for the famous Dogtown Skateboards cross logo from), when a rough banger/dealer started running along-side of me. He had crazy eyes and a hard, mad look on his face. He yelled, "What you need?" I said, "Nothing."

Before I could say anything else, he runs faster and closer, right up next to me. I am still pushing *fast*. I want my forward momentum in case he wants to jack me for my skate, so I could keep running. Let him have it and not get stabbed over it. He screams, "Then what the fuck you are doing here man?" all the while keeping pace with me, hauling ass down the sidewalk.

Far-L had warned me and said, "If you get fucked with, tell them you live here and say the address." I blurted out, "I live here, 319, the house on the alley." His reaction was instantaneous. He looked away from me and slowed his pace back down to a walk, as casual as could be, and turned and headed back up the block to his lucrative little crack corner, deep in the dark part of the lovely beach town of Venice, California.

After that, no one rushed up on me or even acknowledged me as I skated by. I was totally fine with that and certainly not missing the attention!

208.
WILTERN WONDERLAND!

The Wiltern in Los Angeles, is a majestic old theater, with red velvet seats and plush décor from floor to gilded ceiling. The gorgeous, green marble exterior gives a unique and distinct look to the art deco building, built with the entrance on the corner, and the theater itself set in a semi-diamond shape. Every single detail about this venue is well cared for and elegantly preserved. From the marque to the entrance ceilings, to the ornate architectural adornments in the main hall, it is an amazing place on every level. Oh, and it sounds fucking fantastic as well!

In the Performing Arts mini magazine that they hand out, with Jerry on the cover, came a flyer that said don't crowd the aisles and don't stand on the seats. We all obliged, and speakers were set up in the huge marble lobbies so everyone could stretch out and dance, while keeping the historic theater in respectful shape.

My first night, I was blessed with an Orchestra Row M, Seat 116, on the aisle. I could pop out and dance, then dip back into my seat when the usher came around! Acoustic sets are epic when you can see them playing!

The second night my luck dropped, and my ticket was for the very last section and the very last row. Mezzanine Row O, Seat 109. I spent most of my time dancing in the upstairs lobby, since I had last aisle anyway.

My luck turned and on the next night and I was Orchestra Row X, Seat 8, which is 24 rows back in the center. The acoustics up close were so perfect. The audio engineering in that space is superb.

On the fourth night I was sent packing back up the top again, with a seat in the second to last row in the hall. Mezzanine Row N, Seat 105. I ping-ponged back and forth and had a blast no matter what section I was in. But man, it sure is nice to be that close in such an amazing space. The band mixed up the order of the songs from the previous shows and played soft and sweet, then hard and twangy, and sent us all out into the warm California winter night, knowing we caught a little music history in musically historic venue.

The Wiltern is right across from J-KWON Dentistry and Korea Radio. This is a legendary LA skateboard spot, with transitions up the pillars at the base of the building, and long slick marble benches to do tricks on. I was stoked and kept insisting we head to the shows early, only so I could go over and skate before we went inside.

I had met Alva pros, John Thomas, Jef Hartsel and Chris Cook (Team THC) at a skateboard demo in Eugene, Oregon the year prior, when they locked the keys inside their rental car. I had driven George's Volvo down and the repo tools were in the trunk, as usual. I got their keys out in under a minute, got a bunch of Alva stickers and made new friends. I hooked up with them in '87 and we skated a shit load in Venice over the next few years.

Meeting new people in the skateboard scene was propelling me in a slightly different direction and I did not even realize it. A crack was forming between myself and Dead Tour, and a skateboard was wedging its way into the gap and widening it by the day.

209.
OUT GROWING HENRY J.

Oakland Coliseum

Oakland, CA

12/27-28, 30-31/1987

The Oakland Coliseum had a different vibe to it than the Kaiser. It was huge, built for sports, and didn't sound nearly as good acoustically. A gigantic asphalt parking lot replaced the nice green park out front, and the venue was built on a rise, so you had to walk uphill and upstairs, just to get in.

I went across the pedestrian bridge to the BART station to look for tickets. I found one and I also found some excellent red curbs to skate in the parking garage below the loading platform.

First night was a decent show with good energy all around. The standout for the night to me was "Dear Mr. Fantasy"-"Stella Blue." The second night, the 12-minute "Row Jimmy" late in the first set was perfect, with Jerry playing sharp and crisp. "Truckin'"-"Smokestack"-"Black Peter" filled up most of the set after the "Drums" and we slowly walked out after another frequently played, but always loved, "Black Muddy River."

We had the next day off, and I have zero fucking clue what I did. I probably took BART over to Tommy Guerrero's apartment on 9th, and woke Danny Sargent up from his bed on the kitchen floor. I think some skater eventually moved out, and Sarge got an upgrade to a walk-in closet and a door that shut. I told you, he was going to be a pro skateboarder soon and stepping up starts with small steps! From kitchen floor to walk in closet with a door! In our broke-ass world back then, that *was* stepping up!

During this time, I had started a pattern of wanting to skate whatever I could find to skate in all the cities I was going to, instead of hanging out in the parking lot or on Shakedown.

We had driven down in George's light blue Volvo with the weed from our last crop at the Lincoln St. house. Two or three pounds that we brought into the motel behind the Coliseum.

We had it well sealed up and left it in the room. That part was cool, but our stash that we had in our pockets must have been heavily creeping into everyone else's nostril's, except our own. We walked down the hall and somehow met the OG Oakland Rapper, Ca$h Money. We all walked in the elevator and Ca$h starts laughing and telling us how much we smell like green bud! "Y'all crazy hippy motherfuckers stink like the chronic!"

The third night was on! Things were heating up. First set epic jam belonged to "Cassidy," equaled two songs later with a 13-minute foray into "Let it Grow!" The band was clearly stretching out fully before the break! Second set saw "Scarlet" once again estranged from its mate "Fire," only to be usurped by "Sampson" and his lady "Delilah." A resonating "Morning Dew" popped in late in the second set and we got "Baby Blue" as an encore, eliminating three of the 1987 "Big Four" encore songs. "Muddy River," "Mighty Quinn" and "Baby Blue," which pretty much put a lock on "Heaven's Door" being the send-off song for the year 1987, or the lead in song to 1988, if you wish.

210.
THE BIG FINAL DAY!

New Year's Eve Day is always the highest energy, even though you know you won't be getting to sleep until the next afternoon. The parking lot sparks up early, Heads start tripping in from everyplace, and the air is different than the other days. The electricity is generating itself via us and going out on the wind to everyone who is headed towards the show. You start getting excited and anxious when you get to the parking lot, and it only goes up and up from there. We all understand that this show will be over the top and be far more extravagant than any other show of the year. If you're holding that oversize Silver Dancing Skeleton ticket (your skeleton key to the show?), then you are in! You happily wait for hours before the Dead come on.

While the band tuned up at length, the crowd was screaming and yelling and carrying-on. Then they lit it off with "Bertha," and the last night of the year was off with a hard run!

The night contained any number of crazy sidebar things going on before, during and after the show. Al Franken and Tom Davis were performing comedy skits and did a tongue in cheek Jerry cooking class, of all things. Jerry's pigs in a blanket recipe.

"Cold Rain and Snow" was another first set standout. The break came and we all rolled up joints and got ready for 12 fucking-midnight.

Bill Graham, doing his usual Father Time, came in with his unusual NYE entourage, this year on a giant (actually, mini) Golden Gate Bridge which was celebrating the fifty-year mark. The Bridge was on a huge float, and everyone who was aboard got to dance under the baby Golden Gate while Bill waved from the top span!

Ken Kesey had an eclectic and very loud stream of words coming from his mind out to us, via the PA, going off in his Kesey way! It brought the energy up, and Ken was always encouraged to hijack the mic on this special night! I guess it was radio *and* satellite broadcast to the world, but I didn't get much of that part, since I was in the middle of it all.

The music medley that builds up the pre-midnight hype contained cuts from the Beatles, The Rascals and Pink Floyd. The 10-second countdown started, 5,000 balloons did the drop onto our high heads and the band tore into a fast "Hell in a Bucket" to get 1988 feeling right! "Uncle John's Band" and a long, drawn-out "Terrapin" followed. Spastic "Drums" and an outer worlds "Space" flipped into a fierce "Other One," perhaps the only one I heard all year without all the crazy vocal fuzz, added at so many other shows. Then we received a tight, thumping and extended

"Not Fade Away," a little bit of Buddy Holly, as a second set closer, and we sang the band off the stage.

More radio and TV hijinks happened during this the break. Tom Davis talks with John Barlow, and it's hilarious.

The boys came back onstage with the Neville Brothers for the New Year's Eve *only*, magical third set! It's somewhere around 1:30 in the morning and just when it seemed to slow down, it got going again, real fucking quick.

A small breather, and they blew right back into it amidst the squeaking party horns, and the acid fueled chorus of, "We Want Phil!" Phil did *not* oblige, and they rolled into a rollicking "Man Smart," followed by its musical fraternal twin "Iko-Iko." Then Aaron Neville took over the vocals for "The Banana Boat" song, which also uses a similar beat! Picture a dozen people onstage all jamming like mad with big smiles and laughs all around! The whole place was screaming, *"DAY-O!"* and dancing all over the building.

Suddenly they slipped into the fifties hit "Do You Wanna Dance?" which raised the energy bar by another few feet! It was a new fucking year man!

The band brought it all together with everyone harmonizing, and closed out the three-hour show with a beautiful "Heaven's Door" that was slow and soulful.

As we walked out into the middle of the night, I am sure I was reflecting on all the fun I had that evening, not knowing that this would be my last New Year's Eve celebration with the boys, ever. It would be fourteen years before I saw another New Year's Dead show, and by then Brent and Jerry had been gone for many years, and things were not the same as they had been in Deadland.

211.

CLOUDS ON THE HORIZON, OR SUNSHINE?

New Year's Eve is past, and I find I'm getting over it. Getting over what? Tour, lifestyle, travel? I didn't know. I was looking for other things in life. I need the things I do to be important to me and skateboarding was fast becoming the most important thing I did.

Grateful Dead Tour was changing. Far quicker than anything in Grateful Dead land ever normally changed. The world had decided the Dead were okay. Not great, just okay, yet worth going to their party to check out.

Everyone and their brother had gotten into the Dead and a lot of them got into it for the wrong reasons. Crappy bootleg Dead shirt hawkers wearing a tie dye, only to sell stuff to the real Dead Heads came first. Then came people following the tour just to have something to do besides be homeless and on the street. People who saw easy drugs and friendly people high on those drugs to prey on. Individuals running from the law who saw a traveling scene to hide behind. Organized drug dealers with *salesmen* in the parking lot, there only to pull a profit. Thousands of people in the parking lot just for the party, who could not care less about the Dead and their music. People coming in to buy cheap drugs to resell back in their own hood. Thieves targeting the parking lot and breaking into Tour Heads' vehicles while they were inside watching the show. Fences being trampled down. Mass break ins. Hundreds of people bum rushing gates all at once.

It used to be a random person would sneak in once in a while, and it was fun to see it happening and even help him get away, if possible, but those were singular incidents. When 900 people with no tickets smash down a 500-foot-long fence or force every door on the back of the Spectrum open to let 500 people rush in, it becomes a whole different ball game. When that point is reached, it's fucked. When there's torn clothing, chunks of hair that security grabbed onto and pulled out, single shoes, injured people on the ground and blood on the floor, then something's wrong.

I saw it first-hand, and it started to turn me off to touring. Interesting, because I am a very jaded person and I really had seen it all, but this aspect of tour was starting to bug me, and I slowly began to want to see less of that bummer aspect.

212.
TURNING POINTS?

I was twenty-two years old, about to be twenty-three.

I saw only twenty-two Dead shows in my 23rd year of life. My tour ended for me halfway through the year with the shows in Eugene at the end of August.

213.
1988 IS UPON US!

Henry J. Kaiser Conv. Center
Oakland, CA
2/13-14, 16-17/1988

This would be the start of the Dead's year and the first four of nine shows at Kaiser, split between February and March. First night, we all started the "Let Phil Sing" chant, deep in the second set. Phil did oblige this time and we saw a wicked "Gimme Some Lovin'" with a drawn out 6-minute jam before the "Drums." It sounded like they may be dropping into one more song before the "Drums," but the boys just stayed onstage and plinked it up for a while. "Space" before "Drums" as a new set twist for 1988? Maybe? I'm good with that!

Mickey's string machine sounded like a plane crashing, as "Space" crept in like smoke from a smoldering ember. That ember burst into a flame and the boys burned through five more tunes with a scorcher of a "Good Lovin'" right in the thick of the fire.

Second night of four was Valentine's Day, and they got going with a rolling "Touch of Grey," followed by a "Stranger"-"Franklin's"-"Walking Blues" triple pile up. Off to a rad start that night! Phil was well-pronounced in the mix and was letting his fingers dance on his strings the entire show!

Even though it was February 14th, they only played one song about love, except "Push Comes to Shove," which is about love, sort of. Isn't it? I was waiting for a "Don't Need Love" from Brent, but we didn't get that either. We did see a ripping "Love Light" to close out the show and send us out into the night.

We still had a day off ahead and two more shows to go after that. We may have stayed at a kid's camp during these shows. I'm a bit vague on this set of gigs. Someone had a connection or worked at a youth camp that was closed for the winter. We got the invite and went up and settled in. We made big meals together in a large kitchen and had a late bonfire each night after the shows. It was cold, but it was super cool to go from the city to the woods and back each day!

Third night was a crazy drum fest of an evening. One of the best "Bird Song" versions I ever witnessed found itself in the unusual spot of closing out the first set, while telling us all to, "Fly through the night!"

Crazy quick "Drums" with Batucaje setting the beat with Mickey and Billy opened-up the second set, and ushered into the hall the spectacular Mardi Gras Parade. This happens every year, and the costumes and pageantry are enormous. Literally. People on stilts, huge heads with little human feet. New Orleans themed costumes filled the floor and joined the parade.

Straight out of that came "Iko-Iko" to stir up the Louisiana themed musical gumbo just right! "The Eyes of The World" was very jazz oriented, with Brent running all over his keyboards in his fast hands style! Bells and chimes brought the second drum set of the night into the fold, and mixed up the semi-normal song order by doing "Wheel"-"Watchtower"-"Fantasy"-"Not Fade," instead of "Fantasy"-"Watchtower"-"Wheel"-"Not Fade." Sizzler versions all, and we did *not* get sent home with a slow one, which seemed appropriate after such a high energy night.

They waved that flag, ran through a jumping "U.S. Blues," and soon enough the security crew were shuffling us out into the night with good old Willy telling us to "Be sure and come on back tomorrow now!"

214.
FOREVER WILLY!

The next night, there was Willy in his famous Top Hat, as always, saying, "No vending" in his normal tongue in cheek way. Talking with the voice we all knew and loved, through his Dead sticker festooned bullhorn, as we all shuffled in for a fourth night and the Chinese New Year party.

We all woke up quick by drug or adrenaline or both, and as soon as Brent hit the keys and broke into "Hey Pocky Way," we were all wide awake and rolling with it! The "Desolation Row" was half shouted, half whispered by Bobby, who was letting his passion run within that version! The "Estimated Prophet" in the second set went on for almost fourteen minutes, with Jerry and Brent harmonizing the chorus and backing Bobby's manic savior rant about California. The "Worry 'bout me, no" section was echoing all over the theater, as Bobby screamed like he was shouting it out to the entire universe.

Jerry's "Black Peter" had a ton of soul in its delivery, and they sent us packing after the fourth night with a customary "Black Muddy River" to sing along with, as we checked off another set of shows at Henry's place.

215.
NO BAMMIES FOR YOU!

The Bay Area Music Awards
Civic Auditorium
San Francisco, CA
3/12/1987

The Dead won almost every award at The Bammie's that year, and played a killer set with all the Bay area heavyweight musicians jamming along. I did not attend, and in retrospect, I wish I had. Some tickets are pretty much impossible to get though.

216.
BACK TO HANKS PLACE.

Henry J. Kaiser Conv. Center
Oakland, CA
3/16-18/1988

A few of us used to call the theater Henry's Place, as a joke, instead of just plain old Kaiser. Like, "We're going to Henry's Place next week, are you ready?" It was a fun way to joke around while we anticipated the next round of gigs. Incidentally, the next shows were right back at the same spot. Henry's Place, and that was more than fine with us. I don't think these shows were REX Benefits. I believe they scheduled them to gear up for the spring East Coast Tour.

Jerry out-sung Bobby by a song in the first set. Jerry six, Bobby five, with a "Stagger Lee" and a "Walkin' Blues" highlighting the mix. A wobbly, "Scarlet" got straight quick and led into a long, slow burning, "Fire on the Mountain," which seemed to swim by.

You say you want to hear Phil sing? Yeah? Listen to the "Gimme Some Lovin'" from this night. There's some, "Let Phil Sing" for you! Fucking-A right!!! Jerry weighed in with a tight "Morning Dew" at the end of the second set, and we walked out the door after a rocking "Touch of Grey."

We were all stoked that more and more Dylan songs kept popping up from the former tour, and second night we got the first "Memphis Blues" without Bob Dylan. Everyone had dressed themselves in green for the St. Patty's Day tradition, but we did not get the expected "Bertha" that night! We did get Hamza El-Din playing with Mickey and Billy, chanting, rhythmically clapping, drumming, and taking us to places unknown, as he always does with the boys.

I believe a leprechaun Dead Head may have traded the band a pot of gold for this show because it was truly magically delightful! The deep second set "Fantasy"-"Hey Jude" was a benchmark performance, with the normally brief "Hey Jude" stretching to nearly a full song at just under three minutes. Brent and Bobby screaming back and forth as Jerry shredded his strings. A mellow "Black Muddy River" sent us packing out in the Oakland night, with two out of three shows under our belts, and hopes of more song surprises and epic versions the following evening.

Not a lot of surprises the third night, but a lot of very well played songs that had Dead finesse applied to them at this show.

217.
THE PISS ROOSTER.

When you go on JerryGarcia.com and you add in all the shows you have seen in your life, it gives you a pie chart of the top five Dead songs you've seen the most. Mine happened to be "Little Red Rooster," and honestly, if you asked me to guess prior to the pie chart, "Red Rooster" is exactly the song I would have picked.

If I look at it in a real and humorous sense, it ends up being the song I saw the least, because I was always in the pisser. It was played so often that it was widely known that when it came on, it was *the* time to take a piss, and the bathroom lines reflected that clearly. "Me and My Uncle" was another extra common song and ran a close second to the "Piss Rooster!"

Back to the show from the bathroom. "Bird Song" and a jammed-up "Music Never Stopped" got us going just before Bobby said, "We'll be back in a little," and ran offstage as the house lights came up.

Second set was rad, and I hate to sound like a broken fucking Dead record, but once again we got an insane "Other One," with more of the distortion that was starting to define the way the song was being played at the time. A strange change in one of the band's oldest and earliest originals, and it was morphing into something more, once again, after 23 years of being played.

Okay, is it me, or does "Brokedown Palace" always seem to be the encore when a monumental drive is ahead of everyone to get the next show? It seems that way. Tour was going on to Atlanta, Georgia, and The Omni Theater, and I was not. This would be the first time in several years I had not gone back east for at least a few shows on a tour. Skateboarding was warping my mind and pulling me in a different direction, and I was rolling with it.

218.
SILVER SUITCASE AND GREEN BUDS.

Every few months, for roughly three years, I would fly into LAX from Portland with several pounds of high-grade Oregon grown weed. It was inside my aluminum Zero Haliburton suitcase that just screamed weed smuggler when you saw my hippy ass carrying it. I would fly under a fake name (no ID required then), such as Mr. Green. I thought I was funny.

I would skate through the airport to the baggage carousel and wait off to the side until most of the bags had been picked up to be sure I wasn't being watched. When I was pretty sure it wasn't hot, I would grab my shiny, silver, airtight suitcase from the rotating carousel, and Far-L would be waiting at the curb in the white Chevy tour truck.

Other times I took the Green Tortoise bus line down and back, or I drove Mark's borrowed car. It was always the same thing though. Bring the weed down, bring the money back, and ultimately spend most of your profit while you're there living it up.

219.
JH X HR.

I ran a bunch of pounds down to Venice in my roommate Mark's borrowed Celica. I was skating with many of the Venice locals at the time. Jef Hartsel, whom I had become friends with back in 1986, told me that JT, his roommate and Alva Skateboards teammate, was hurt and couldn't go see HR of Bad Brains with him that night. He asked me if I wanted to go with him and I jumped at the chance. I knew it was going to be cool since I had seen Bad Brains several times, but I really didn't expect what happened when we got to the gig.

We walk up to the front door, security immediately recognizes Jef, and lets us cut the entire line and walk right in. From there Jef walks straight back to the backstage area and HR's security man gives him a handshake and a hug! I was thinking, okay, if it's like this already, what's going to happen when we go 20 feet further into HR's dressing room? Well, it went like this.

We walk in, and HR yells a Jah Rasta praise when he sees Jef, and the vibe went through the roof. HR in person, in this era, was dynamic and totally full of energy. It was insane! Jef said Nordy grew weed up in Oregon and we brought you some! HR lit up even brighter than he had already been, and I gave him his own fat ass joint to smoke. His stage manager said two minutes, just as he lit that joint of *my* weed! HR took hit after hit, non-stop blowing the smoke out his nose and literally smoking the entire fatty with his hands over his eyes, concentrating and getting his vibe going.

The band was already playing as HR opened his eyes, smiled wickedly at us, and ran up onto the stage. His security guy walked Jef and I up to the front row, made a spot for us right in front of HR, smiled and walked off.

What the fuck just happened? All of that went down in ten short minutes. Now I'm in the front row in front of HR with Hartsel. HR is high on my homegrown marijuana, and he is singing, "Who's got the herb," and pointing to Jef and I during the song!

It was intense, moving and so memorable. Thanks, Jef!

Sorry you couldn't attend JT. I appreciated your ticket very much!

220.
VW MIKES VAN TRAUMA!

VW Mike, Feeney and I are at shows in Southern California. Somehow, and I don't remember why, we end up going back towards Oregon through Bakersfield. We burned out the third cylinder in the van and Mike had to fix it on the spot. We stayed in a motel for a day, then drove on.

We got into southern Oregon at daybreak and hit a deer that bolted out onto the highway. We almost missed it, but it darted in front of us as we tried to slow down. It passed away instantly thankfully, but it dented the hell out of the front and one door of the van, and it shit down the entire side of the vehicle. Two hunting oriented southern Oregon gentleman put it in their truck and helped us clean up the roadway.

Great shows, but hard times for Mike's VW Van and that poor misguided deer. I have a photo of Chris, Mike and I from two days prior and the van looks perfect!

221.
IRVINE MEADOWS AND PETER MAX.

Irvine Meadows Amphitheatre

Irvine, CA

4/22-24/1988

I mentioned more than a few times now that tour was changing. It was on for everyone! I knew the Dead had reached the far limits of who they could draw to one of their shows, when I saw Venice skateboard legend (one of the most unique and creative skateboarders EVER, in my opinion) Tim Jackson walking around the lot at Irvine Meadows. I was driving in and didn't get to speak with him, but I did see him a few days later in Venice. He said he had a blast and got all kinds of fun stuff to bring back to the homies!

I also hung out with Simon, the Claremont pool owner/skater. Simon had a camper with a house style sliding glass door on the back. It even had a little porch. It was a stylish way to ride! A small world made even smaller by a Grateful Dead show.

I brought a lot of herb down to Irvine and I sold it all in $40 sacks. I would only bring an ounce at a time with me as I walked around, in case I got busted. I would sell all eight bags, usually at each group of cars I went to. George was doing the same thing, only he would walk the opposite way.

I would look for a group of friends all partying together and approach them with weed. All it took was one whiff of this herb. It stunk like a skunk. Once one guy bought a bag, all his or her friends had to have one too. And on it went, until we sold out. $320 an ounce back then. It was good quick money.

You could not do this in every city, or you would definitely get busted. Irvine was easy. From experience we knew which venues were semi safe and we exploited these places in favor of far sketchier, cop filled places like Chicago, New York, and especially Roanoke, Virginia, where, as I mentioned earlier, the DEA training headquarters are located.

First night we got a "Louie-Louie," which was awesome and the premiere version on the West Coast. Unfortunately for me, they did no more versions of "Ballad of a Thin Man." They were reserved for the East Coast Tour only, as was the only version of "Stir It Up" and a never done prior, "Scarlet"-"Fire" to open the show!

Friends who went were telling me the highlights. I was feeling the pains of missing big things, and it stung. Watching a ripping "Gimme Some Lovin'" in the second set was easing the pain a bit though!

This set of Irvine shows is the venue Far-L and I bought the famous Peter Max, Grateful Dead, 1987 Spring Tour poster at. It's insanely vibrant and is one of my favorite pieces in my collection. I recently took a minute to look them up online, and they fetch over $800 for one now! If you have one, you're stoked! Years ago, I saw the hand painted original in the Peter Max Gallery in Las Vegas, and it was going for somewhere in the $14,000 neighborhood.

Next night we got a semi-rare "To Lay Me Down" in the first set, and a "Crazy Fingers" breaking up the usual "Playin'"-"Uncle John's Band" combo in the second.

The third night was warm and sunny, but we got rained on twice before the "Drums," with Phil and "Box of Rain" to open and Bobby with "Looks Like Rain," just before the boys started beating on the skins. At the end of the night we heard the ultimate acid homage. "Quinn the Eskimo," which was written about famous sheets of LSD in the 1960s with an Eskimo face printed on them, and dubbed "The Mighty Quinn" for obvious reasons. Hence the lyric, "When Quinn the Eskimo gets here, everybody's gonna wanna dose!"

222.
GOOD TIMES ROLLIN!

Frost Amphitheater
Stanford, CA
4/30 - 5/1/1988

The first day may be my favorite show of the year. We got treated to the very first "Let the Good Times Roll," and a "Row Jimmy" that sounded like someone was playing chimes or bells. New sounds and sound elements were abundant these days. "Hey Pocky Way" developed a slick groove and had blossomed into a ripper, followed a few songs later with a 13-minute "Let It Grow" that went on forever!

The second set was ripping harder than the first, with yet another stellar "Watchtower," and an ultra-rare, "China Cat"-"Know You Rider"-"One More Saturday Night" triple encore. The only time "China"-"Rider" was ever an encore, and also the only time it was ever connected to "One More Saturday Night." When they broke into "China Cat" as an encore, everyone looked at each other and said, "What?"

Then they dropped into "Saturday Night" as a third encore and "What?" quickly changed to, "Wow!"

I wasn't sure what to think. Will this be a new trend, or a typical Dead move? Leaving us lucky ones who were there with the one off, one time, one show, triple combo? Turned out to be the latter, and the boys only did it that way one time, on a warm sunny evening in Palo Alto, California!

I don't have a big recollection of Frost, day two. The show was killer as I listen back, but I don't remember a lot about this one.

223.
THE BIG CHANGE AND WHY!

In the month of June, in the summer of 1988, I learned to snowboard on the Palmer Glacier on Mt. Hood in Oregon. It is the only place to ski and snowboard year-round in the US. You might recognize it as the mountain on the Hamm's Beer 24 pack box.

Life changed dramatically for me after that. I was skateboarding with the shop crew at Rebel Skates every day. My friend Eldon Hargraves, who worked there, kept telling me I needed to try snowboarding. Eldon was a sponsored pro for Barfoot Snowboards and was hooked up. He had a free lift ticket, all the gear, and a board for me to ride. Him and I were the same size, feet and all, and his extra gear fit me perfectly. I couldn't say no.

I finally went up to the glacier with Eldon, young snowboard phenom and future superstar Mike Estes, and Christian Dude-Bob Kopp in June. I could not believe how much snow existed there in the summertime, and I fell in love with the mountain and the mountain lifestyle immediately! I worked at the Rebel Skates Camp, the very first Snowboard Freestyle camp on Mt. Hood, and met many incredible new people such as Kris Jamieson, Jubal Reynolds and Nathan Duby.

My life of skateboarding allowed me to excel at snowboarding, and within a year, I had sponsors and was getting free boards and equipment to represent companies. A new interest, that ultimately led to a whole new lifestyle.

224.

TWO CAR SEATS, THREE PEOPLE!

The Greek Theatre

Berkeley, CA

7/15-17/1988

George and I wanted to go to the shows at The Greek Theatre, but we didn't have a car. His Volvo had been stolen. When it was recovered it needed a whole new ignition, so we decided to hitch hike instead. He left an hour or two before I did and the last thing he said was, "Unless you get a ride in a car with two seats or on the back of a motorcycle, and I'm on the side of the road, you *better* pick me up."

Mark drove him to the I-5 south, and off he went with his thumb up. Mark did the same for me a while later.

I thumbed a short time and got picked up by a guy in a small sports car with just *two* seats. My bag, which had two pounds of weed sealed in it, barely fit into the space behind the seats. I kept my skateboard between my knees up front, and down the road we went.

Somewhere past Eugene, while I was rolling a joint, the driver said, "Is that him?" I looked up to see George, thumb high, on the side of the highway. I went by holding up two fingers on one hand and a palm up, "What can I do?" with the other hand. He saw me when the driver decided to beep at him. I could see him mouth, "Mother fucker," as he flipped us off and we left him behind in that tiny two-seat car.

I eventually got dropped off on the side of the freeway and along came George, in a normal car. He told the driver that we're on the road together, then very graciously (lucky for me) asked, "Can you pick him up?" He did and off we went to The Greek Theatre in a car with a normal number of seats.

225.

WE RETURN TO THE PORTAL TO TRAVEL THROUGH, YET AGAIN!

The Greek gets busy with all the energy going on and the boogie-down factor is at its absolute peak.

This is the year of the soccer field shows. UC Berkley has soft, rubber coated, soccer practice fields just off to the side of The Greek. They were allowing overflow fans with no tickets to dance on them. Speakers were set up, but it had a hollow feel to it when you walked in. As cool of a gesture (probably by Bill Graham) as it was, I'm glad I only spent a few songs out there before locating and buying my miracle that day.

The shows were the usual top-notch performances expected at The Greek, and it came off that way once again! Highlights being "Dire Wolf," that crept back into the mix for the first time since April in Hartford, and of course, the "Love Light" encore with Phil dominating the beat on the first night.

These were REX Benefits, live KPFA radio broadcasts and a support drive for the radio station. They had all sorts of cool things happening on-air around the Dead sets, and those radio recordings came out crisp and clean. "Thank you for your support," was the quote of the day!

I believe we may have snuck into Chabot Lake campgrounds again, but I'm a bit fuzzy on those details.

The first set "Loser" and the second set "Terrapin" were the shining examples on the second night.

The third day we got a few newer songs. "Foolish Heart" to open with, a "Victim or the Crime," and then a "Believe It or Not" in the second set. This third night also featured the last "Blackbird," and by all accounts it was *not* considered one of the best versions they did. We had hooked up with Clark for a ride home and thus began another saga.

226.
GEORGE VS. CLARK'S VAN.

Clark had purchased a gorgeous, well maintained, 1967 Volkswagen Van with the 21-window package. A rare touring edition that featured all the slim windows in the edges of the roof between the main windows and the retractable top. Orange and white. It was a true classic and Clark took good care of it. George treated it like it was just another repo he was dropping off for a quick paycheck.

It was night, after some gig, and George backed Clark's VW off an embankment and stood it on its back door and engine cover at the bottom of a 14-foot ditch. Somehow it stood straight up, headlights pointing to the sky, and did not tip over to one side or the other.

Heidi, our old friend, was guiding him back into a good spot, and did not bother to say, "Stop!" when the spot ended at a drop off point. Amazingly, the body was still straight after that. No kinks. Unbelievable! Cliche as it sounds, they just don't make them like that anymore.

Okay, back on tour, sort of. We were driving back from The Greek shows, the day George blew up Clark's VW Van motor. The tiny light on the bottom of the VW speedometer had to have been red for at least the last half hour. Par for the course, George said he saw it but didn't think it was a problem.

The van motor seized up and we rolled to a stop on the side of I-5 right in the middle of Redding, California. It was 112 degrees that day.

Clark was asleep at the time, and he woke up furious, to the sound of his motor imploding under the bed he was laying on. Every time George touched one of Clark's vehicles something bad happened. We all knew to watch for the RED low oil light. It is a fucking-VW after all. Watching the oil light is MANDATORY! Now, we're stuck and it's insanely hot out.

Three out of five of us had traffic warrants in California, so we all ran 100 yards back down the freeway and hid under a small bridge, so we would not *all* go to jail if a cop pulled up. We were also hiding the drugs we each had on us.

No cop came, and we all ran out from under the bridge and got into the truck with the tow driver when he showed up. He was surprised, and said, "What the fuck?" when we all jumped in, but he rolled with it and didn't say shit. He had a crew cab, and thankfully got us out of that murderous, burning sun.

We ducked into a motel room for the night and early the next morning we split up. Clark, Jimmers and Kent waited a few days while the van got a new motor. Clark was still ultra-mad, so George and I decided it would be best to leave him to stew, and hitch-hiked out of Redding.

227.
HITCHHIKING IN AN OVEN.

We started out early to beat the heat, but it was already 104 degrees by 8 am. We were standing there burning up on the on ramp and no one was picking us up. The tar on the road got so hot that I could feel it on the soles of my feet through my Vans. We had to stand in the dirt, which was not much cooler, just to stand there at all.

After about an hour, the sprinklers for the bushes came on by the side of the Interstate. Of course, we had not brought water and we really needed a drink, and we literally ran up to the sprinklers to cool off. When we tried to get a drink and rinse off to cool down, we found out that the water lays on top of the ground in black hoses and it gets insanely hot. Way, way too hot to even think about drinking.

We jumped back from the lava water and walked back to the hitching spot. We were so defeated by that time. We turned and walked back to the 7-Eleven in Redding to buy water and try to see what we could do about a different way of getting home.

George reached into his secret pocket, did his magic act, and produced the "vague and elusive Gold Card" and got us a rental car from a payphone. Then we hitch-hiked two hours to go four miles to the tiny little Redding Airport, where they only had one car. One fucking little red Chevy Metro, or some shit box of the time. Of course, it had no AC, and the passenger window only went halfway down.

It was so typical of our travels so far this year. But we didn't care. Take what you can get and go. It's 115 degrees out by now, so we went. But not for long.

That little car did not like the mountains one bit. By the time we got to Grants Pass, the car was going between 30 and 40 mph, and that was tops.

George and I were over it. We hit the same rental car agency at the airport in Grants Pass. George put on his best dirty Dead shirt and went off on them about no selection and shoddy rental cars, while flashing the Gold. Moments later, and just like that, we had a super cushy Buick with all the options, fat ass seats and ice-cold AC. They even gave us an extra day before we had to return it in Portland. The bad turned out to be pretty-damn good in the end on that adventure.

228.
RACETRACKS AND BAD CAMPERS.

Laguna Seca Raceway
Monterey, CA
7/29-31/1988

I loved Laguna Seca Raceway. It was wide open, hilly, and perfect for concerts. Easy to get in, easy to park, easy peasy!

We had hundreds of acres to camp on, but I read that some fools camped on the adjacent Military Base property. That was the sole reason the Dead never played there again. Because of a few dipshits who refused to read and heed the no trespassing signs. Thanks a lot, fuckheads. This was a quality place to see a show.

Shut down and banned again. It was becoming a common theme. When the Dead cat got out of the bag, everyone started going to the shows and all the shitty little rats scurried in and began disrupting the good thing we had going on. Tour was sailing into rough waters and the waves were starting to splash on the deck. Anyway, back to the show.

First day, the "Blow Away" they performed showed the song really taking shape and becoming one of Brent's strongest numbers! Which brings up an example of strange coincidences happening with all things Grateful Dead.

As I was writing this and listening to Laguna Seca, 1988, first day, set two, I took a break. I was putting away a memorabilia box that I do *not* put any Dead related stuff in. As I was shutting the lid, I saw an old Dead cassette tape label in the box, so I took it out. I read it and I was shocked. It was Laguna Seca, 1988, first day, set two. Exactly what I was listening to and writing about at that exact time. What the fuck? Ghosts in the machine baby!

The second set saw a semi-rare "China Cat" broken apart from "Rider," with a "Crazy Fingers" wedged in between them, which then blended nicely into a super, "Playin' in the Band." Two more days of bliss left to go!

More sun on day two. David Lindley and El Rayo-X performed all three days, and I was super excited to see him. I had lived in Claremont, where David is from, and I had seen him several times with Naomi B, in several different venues. Hearing David play through the Grateful Dead sound system was a special treat that we all got to share those three days.

229.

THE TACO DOME RINGING IN YOUR EARS.

Tacoma Dome

Tacoma, WA

8/26/1988

The Taco-ma Dome is the worst sounding venue on the planet, yet the show kicked ass and the Dead played great. The sound just rings around inside of the hollow half shell and ends up hurting your ears after a few hours.

Carlos Santana opened the show and seemingly never got off stage. He played a long and extended set! No one cared that Carlos played late though, it was still Carlos fucking Santana!

Carlos and the Dead did not perform together as everyone had hoped, which was a bummer!

It must sound fine on stage to the band members though, because every group I ever saw there played damn good! My ears hated me for it, but they don't get to choose what they hear. They *are* just ears, after all.

The Dead got onstage later than normal, sometime after 10 pm, and played until after midnight. It felt like some of the older shows I had seen that started at 8 pm, and the band would come on at 9:30. It's fun to get out of a show in the middle of the night. We trip while the world sleeps!

I saw Zero with Nine Days Wonder on 8/27 at Pine Street Theatre, between these Dead shows, with Willie Waldman. We didn't know it at the time, but Willie would go on to play with Steve Kimock countless times in the future.

265

230.

LAST STATION ON THE LINE!

Autzen Stadium

Eugene, OR

8/28/1988

My last official (in my mind, at least) show on Grateful Dead Tour. I was with Willie Waldman, so I know we had fun!

We made it a point to go in early and not lag around Shakedown, because the incredible Jimmy Cliff was on the bill that day, and I have always loved him and his music. He played well and it was a perfect blend. Eugene is a reggae town and Jimmy Cliff playing outside in the sun was a special delight! I was hoping for a multi-band jam, but sadly, that never happened.

The Dead were, expectedly, playing just as tight as they had the rest of the year. My favorite from that day consisted of *the* "Truckin'" with "Terrapin Station" just after. Strange and cool combination for those two songs.

I don't remember thinking this was it for me on Grateful Dead Tour. It wasn't planned in any way or even conceived at that point. It just happened like a show ends. Last song. Walk away.

231.
GET A JOB? DO I REMEMBER HOW TO WORK?

Fall came around and I got a half-ass job and focused my life on different avenues.

My Tour Head days were slipping away. I didn't see any other Dead shows in 1988 after the Autzen Stadium gig. It certainly wasn't bad though! I got a job loading ass onto a chair lift at Mt. Hood SkiBowl, with Ray Krebs, and we rode deep powder all winter.

On the downside I went to a NYE show in Portland that wasn't the Dead and I felt like I had done myself wrong. Like I had cheated myself! That was one of the few times I ever really questioned leaving Dead Tour.

Green Tour VW Van and the first Portland house. Summer 1986 (Nordy)

Jerry gets well and returns to play the hardest shows to get into ever besides NYE. Stone, San Francisco CA. Fall 1986 (Nordy)

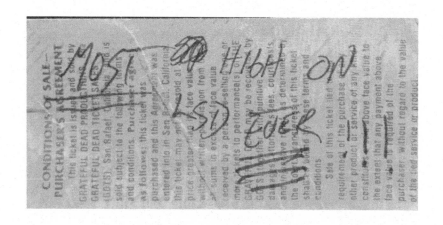

The back of my January, Chinese New Year show stub. Most high on acid ever! Winter 1987 (Nordy)

Naomi Yospe and Clark Cazwel. Laguna Seca CA. Spring 1987 (Mark Rockwell)

**Laguna Seca sound towers and crowd. Monterey CA. Spring 1987
(Mark Rockwell)**

**VW-Mike in his dirty Laguna dust bug. Portland OR. Spring 1987
(Nordy)**

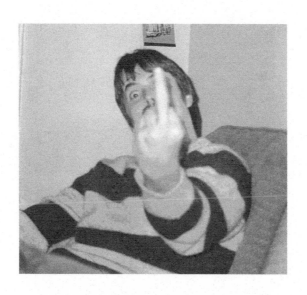

Big Rick loved to have fun but hated pictures.
Portland OR. Spring 1987 (Nordy)

Greek Theatre crowd and art. Berkeley CA. Summer 1987
(Mark Rockwell)

Oregonian ad. Dylan and The Dead. Only NW appearance. Eugene OR.
Summer 1987 (Unknown)

The amazing Willie Waldman and I having a blast! Eel River CA.
Summer 1987 (Mark Rockwell)

Unknown, Clint Wagner, Willie Waldman and myself in a hotel room with a lot of drugs. San Francisco Ca. Summer 87. (Unknown)

Mark and George laughing and having a good time! Eel River CA. Summer 1987 (Clark Cazwel)

New Year's Eve tickets! One stub was a ground score after the show.
I felt bad for whomever lost it. Oakland CA. Winter 1987 (Nordy)

Chris Feeney, myself and VW Mike. Mike's beautiful van took several
severe beatings on this trip. Chino CA. Spring 1988 (Donna Nordwall)

Frost crowds and more epic art. Spring 1988.(Mark Rockwell)

**Oregonian ad. The last show I see is Eugene. I drop off Tour
and take a break. Summer 1988. (Unknown)**

Skateboard and snowboard skills take me in a new direction.
Me with my very first sponsored snowboard from Mike Estes
and Barfoot. Portland OR. Winter 1988. (Ray Krebs)

I got a job! I even remembered how to work after years of Dead Tour.
SkiBowl, Mt. Hood OR. Winter 1988 (ski lift pass)

Pic 64. Me and lifelong friend Ray Krebs pretending to work the Multorpor chairlift. SkiBowl, Government Camp OR. Winter 1988 (Tim Lannon/RIP)

232.
1989....THE LOST YEAR.

I didn't see any Dead shows at all in '89. Not a single fucking one. I was officially off tour. Quite a change from seeing tons of shows a year to none. I sort of felt like I had to sober up from Dead Tour.

I had been traveling and hustling and dealing for years and it started to wear on me. I had gotten so deep that I had started to tour by myself. I didn't care who went with me or who didn't. I was just going. I would travel to the venue and hook up with anyone I could, in whatever place they played.

I had connections in multiple cities, so I could meet anywhere, but I was getting distanced, by my own actions, from my real-original Tour Head friends. It was a situation quite like how I had drifted off and distanced myself from my family years before, when I went off blind. No regrets, but I felt like if I kept going, I would never come back from Grateful Dead Tour.

I am not a musician in a successful band. I am just a fan following them for the memories. After many years, that aspect alone, was not enough to keep me going, and I truly felt it, so I left tour. I just stopped. I stayed home and started to focus my life back in Portland. I quit the Dead, Cold Jerky Turkey.

233.
WHY DID I LEAVE TOUR?

As I look back or listen back to shows in 1989 that I did not get to see, I tend to regret not staying on tour for another two years. Some of the songs that the boys broke out were insane. The 1989 East Coast Fall Tour was crazy good. I wish I had been there, but it wasn't to be. When I look back, I do have a few Grateful Dead Tour regrets... "Dark Star," "Attics of My Life," "Death Don't Have No Mercy," "Unbroken Chain." Breakouts, that I did not witness.

I also wish I had seen more Brent during those last two years he was alive. I believe he was just starting to come into his own and had he not passed, he would have, in my opinion, become more like Pigpen. The blues man. This is evident when you watch the "Blow Away" from Philly in '89. He stops playing entirely, and just belts out the words with such emotion it can bring you to tears. Long live Brent's memory.

234.
ME AND DOUBLE A.

Autzen Stadium

Eugene, OR

6/23-24/1990

I was living in a whole new world by 1990. I had some contact with old friends like Joe Monda, my great lifelong buddy who moved from Connecticut to Portland, but mainly I was surrounded by snowboarding. I was working for Bob Gille and the USSTC snowboard camp on Mt. Hood. I had snowboard sponsors and a good coaching job.

The late great photographer Sonny Miller introduced me to the skateboard legend, Aaron "Double A" Astorga, when he was an up-and-coming young ripper. We did clothing pics for *International Snowboard Magazine* for Sonny, and we became fast friends. I convinced him to come with me to the Eugene shows.

I had keys to Mark K's apartment, and we posted up there between the gigs. We did the usual stuff. Ran around in the parking lot, went skating all over Eugene and hit my friend's crib and the Star Wars stereo.

I ran some weed down to Mark, the sales rep for a backpack company. He lived in Eugene and had a cool apartment he often let me stay at. Mark owned a 1979 Bang and Olufsen Beomaster 2400-2, home stereo. The one *made by aliens*! The thing was straight from outer space! It looked like it landed itself in his living room. Finger sensitive everything, so you didn't have to open it up. Touch it in a certain spot on the smoked glass top, and it lights up under your fingers and turns on. Touch your finger, and the volume goes up. Orange and green lights below a black glass top.

Mark kept it under a cover on a special table, specifically for the stereo. It was so fun to be high as fuck, late night, after a show. We would unveil the Star Wars stereo and make it come to life with our "magic" hands.

The second day, Double A had to catch a train south. He lived in San Diego. We had hidden his board under a van and when we came out of the show, we couldn't remember which van it was in this sea of VW's that all looked the same. Double had to abandon his board and run a mile to the train, which as I understood, he made with one minute to spare, before it departed.

I finally backtracked enough to remember where his board was and retrieved it. I kept that deck and rode it at the first Burnside Project sessions later in the year.

235.
THE LEAN TIMES. TWO YEARS NO NORTHWEST SHOWS.

Autzen Stadium
Eugene, OR
8/21-22/1993

We had two years of no Northwest shows and it sucked! Finally, we were back! During the show I found my way down to the field for most of the second set. I sat by some people who offered me a spot on their blanket. I rolled joints and gave them a fat one. Nice folks. Remind me if I knew you!

We laughed and hung out for the rest of the show, and I slowly walked out with the massive crowd down the long wide walkways, out to the dirt and the parking lot. I heard the beer venders' "Cold beer here!" call and reached for my fanny pack I always carried then.

It was not on my waist. "Holy shit! Noooooo! I'm fucked!" I had left it on the blanket I was sharing with the Heads I met. Everything I had was in that little pack.

I turned and ran back to the gate. The guard did not want to let me in. I told him I would come back to him to prove I came back out, and he finally let me pass.

Then I tried to run upstream. Everyone was coming down the long, wide walkways from up above me. I had to scoot next to the handrail and could still barely walk back up against the huge crowd. I would scurry by, and people would yell, "Look out he lost something!" or "Oh shit, forgot something?" or "Swimming upstream?" It was a struggle.

I was breathing hard as I finally got to the top, only to go down to the field. In Eugene you walk up to get in, then down to your seat. I sprinted down the stairs, ran onto the field like an athlete, and the Heads I met were still waiting for me, keeping my little bag safe. I was so out of breath it was hard to say thanks. Thank you so much, even though I don't remember who you were. I gave them more of my weed and gave big hugs all around.

What they did not know, and the reason I was so freaked out, was because I had $700 in that bag that Mark had just given me for a quarter pound of herb. That was a decent amount at the time and I'm glad my dumb ass didn't lose it. Not to mention Mark's apartment keys, my own keys, and my ID.

After that, I marched straight back and said thank you to the guard who let me back in, and walked directly to the beer guy and bought myself two cans, just because I got lucky!

236.
MINI TOUR IN BETWEEN SNOWBOARD CAMP SESSIONS!

Memorial Stadium

Seattle, WA

6/13-14/1994

Autzen Stadium

Eugene, OR

6/17-19/1994

Mt. Hood had rain days, so I took off to go to Seattle. The Eugene shows happened in between sessions at snowboard camp. It worked out perfect! I got to see five shows! That was a stretch for me after so many years. A veritable mini tour!

Snowboard camp had hundreds of campers all summer and it was a lot of work! I don't recall much of these shows, apart from remembering they played so many songs I had never heard live before.

First night, Seattle was only "Corinna." Normal set of songs. Second night had "Eternity," "Lazy River Road," "Samba in the Rain," "That Would be Something," "Way to Go Home," and "Liberty." Six songs I had never heard live before. I realized I needed to pay more attention.

Eugene was the same with "Easy Answers" and "If the Shoe Fits." They also did gems like, "The Last Time" by The Beatles and "I Fought the Law," which were epic!

"I Fought the Law" has been covered by many bands such as The Ramones and most notably The Clash! It was originally penned and performed by Sonny Curtis of Buddy Holly's band The Crickets. It was recorded shortly after Holly's tragic passing. It has been widely believed that this song would have been Buddy Holly's next huge hit.

237.
SKIERS AND SKATERS EATING ACID!

Portland Meadows Horse Track

Portland, OR

5/28-29/1995

Paul Reyes was my hard-core skier friend. We rode Mt. Hood everyday together for years and years.

Paul has always been in the weed business and always had the means to do what he wanted. A Dead show was certainly not going to be an exception and Paul likes to go big.

He rented a 30-foot boxbed truck and grabbed his generator. Pauly filled it with furniture, a home stereo, lights, carpets, several bongs, a nitrous tank, and a couple of kegs of beer. Then he started the generator and lit it all up like a Christmas tree on Shakedown Street in the summertime.

I believe at some point, the cops may have shut him down and made him close his makeshift living room on Shakedown, but it was on fire while it lasted that night!

Mapes, Kable Roc, Josh Blaze and Danny Weikel, my skate homies, were at this show also, even though I didn't see them. All four came away with crazy stories about being given free acid at these gigs, which I recorded and put online. Funny stuff to listen to! The tales from all four are fantastic!

238.
WORKING FOR A DIFFERENT FAT MAN.

At this point in my life, I was the Head Coach at Windell's Snowboard Camp on Mt. Hood. Summer snowboard camp was extremely busy with hundreds of campers each session.

In this realm, I only had a few snowboard friends who liked the Dead. Dave Dowd, Brant Kaake, Aaron Gille, Mike Jankowski, Max Parker, Happy, Chandler Vinar, Garrick Shue, Dustin Varga, Steve Ferdinand, James Fisher, Randall Standridge, Sanford Biskar, Andrew Hopp, Tom "Wally" Inouye, Doug Loper, Brent Kaufman and Ethan Ball. Most had no idea I had ever even heard of the Grateful Dead. I didn't talk about it. All my shirts were in storage and music had gone to CD, so my cassettes were put away also.

Dave Dowd started seeing shows in Boulder in 1980. Brant Kaake is from Berkeley, and had seen many shows. Aaron Gille was the young guy Brant and I influenced from Mt. Hood and Mike Jankowski had toured often during college in Arizona. Max Parker was a young Tour Head from Mt. Hood, Happy ran away to Dead Tour at fifteen and we met when he was seventeen. Chandler was the RatSkeller bartender and my homie from Minnesota. Garrick was a ripping skier from Mt. Hood, Ethan was a 15-year-old snowboard couch kid, Andrew Hopp was a bartender and Wally Inouye is a pro skateboarding legend and chef. Steve Ferdinand and Randall Standridge were up and coming cooks from Mt. Hood, Sanford Biskar was a professional squatter and Dustin Varga and James Fisher were my snowboard teammates while riding a few different companies' goods.

Brent Kaufman was a fantastic grower and Doug Loper was a skateboarding transplant from Ventura Ca. It was a small field of players, and The Grateful Dead were not often the topic of conversation.

239.
DEATH DON'T HAVE NO MERCY.

On August 9, 1995, I had the day off and I was sleeping in. One of my favorite coaches, Lance Pitman, woke me up with a knock on my door. He said, "Hey man, I hate to tell you this, but I heard Jerry died of a heart attack in rehab." I was stunned. Lance slowly shut the door and let me take in what he just told me. Jerry was dead. Jerry is dead. Jerry. Dead. That was it. That was all.

I drove down to Portland. I did *not* go join any of the mourning Heads around town. I just did my thing at home, listening to tapes and telling myself that I had it good to be able to ever see Jerry play at all, and that I should be thankful for that. But that cold fact, lying in the pit of my stomach, made me feel like shit because it was so final. There was no going back once or twice a year for my little Dead fixes I needed so much. The Dead-End sign was firmly hammered into the end of the Golden Road and tour dissolved like crystal LSD in Everclear.

240.

FINDING FERD!

I did not see anything Dead related for years after that, and honestly, I didn't care.

To return, I needed time to get my head back around it. Enter my snowboard friend Steven Ferdinand. We had been friends for many years and Ferd, as he is called, was one of my only friends of the time that also liked the Dead and had been on Grateful Dead Tour before. He did his shows from '89 until he went to San Quentin for driving the money for a few hundred pounds of weed in '92.

His father Frank, and his buddies from work, took Ferd to his first Dead show at RFK in July 1989. His dad worked for Caterpillar, and they had a skybox for sports games. After the show, Ferd was ultra-hyped on the Dead and the entire scene, and he kept telling Frank so on the way home.

Ferd moved out of his childhood home and went on Dead Tour shortly after that. He was hooked and hit the road. Ferd said Frank told him years later that he knew taking him to that show would get him to go follow the band and move out of his house. Old Frank was right, and Ferd flew the coop in true young Tour Head style. After 18 years, Frank and Virginia wanted some peace and quiet, and that wily old fox knew how to get it.

Ferd got out of San Quentin after earning his cigarette rolling degree, and moved to Mt. Hood, Oregon.

Garrick was a long dreaded Dead Head, an artist, and a bad-ass skier with a mean iron cross that we called Hippy. Ferd had grown up with him in Pennsylvania. Hippy and I were good friends by the time Ferd moved to Government Camp, and he fit in with our crazy crew right away.

241.
CHEF DEAD HEAD.

The Other Ones

New Year's Eve

Oakland Coliseum

Oakland, CA

12/31/2002

Ferd had left Mt. Hood after many years and become a highly successful chef. In 2002 he was at Florio in San Francisco, and he called to say he had an extra ticket for New Year's Eve. This was New Year's Eve Day, I might add.

I had minimal money since it was Christmas and I had just paid my mortgage and bills. I checked all the flights and somehow found a round trip for $39. I had never seen a cheap deal like that, so I jumped on it and didn't ask why. I flew off to San Francisco, happy and eager to see a show again. It had been seven long years since Jerry died.

Randall "Scandal" and Ferd picked me up on a perfect winter day in the bay. Sunny and warm. Ferd and Scandal lived on the corner of Broderick and Haight where we got our show shit together while Ferd changed for work at Florio. Although he got us the tickets, he still had to work until 11:30. That was the trade-off. Florio gave us the tickets to see the show, via the network of Bay Area rock stars who love good restaurants, while Chef Ferd had to work and miss the opening set. He made it in just after 12. Not for the New Year's Eve celebration, but he was in, and that was all that mattered.

242.
LET'S GO SCANDAL!

I had not seen any Dead action for a long time. I knew the Oakland Coliseum well and I started to get that anxious awesome feeling. The kind where you feel the energy in the air before you even get there. I knew this was going to be good. It already had the vibe going. That's a great first indication.

Scandal and I dropped Ferd off at work and drove his car over to Oakland. We grabbed our back-pack full of Blue Ribbons and skated through the gates into the parking lot. Shakedown Street slowly built up around us the further we rolled, until we were right in the center of all the action.

It was true Heads again! The late '80s and early '90s suckerfish bottom feeders were all gone. You ever see a whale shark with all those little fish stuck to it? That was tour back then. Yet, it seemed to me they had all let go. Only die-hard Dead Heads remained, and I was glad to see that. Once the Dead's never-ending party ended in '95, all the accumulated vermin had nothing to feed on, so naturally, they swam away like the little suckers they were, to suck off something else!

243.
IT'S FUCKING ON!

This show brought me back! I needed this. I just had not realized how much I needed it. Scandal and I walked in, and every old feeling of love for the scene came right back to me.

The band got busy quick! Jimmy Herring was on guitar, which made me know it was going to be a hot night. I think Jimmy played Jerry's parts in all the right ways. They performed varying and difficult, rare tunes, and all were handled perfectly.

I didn't know what to expect from the show. I had not been paying attention at all to the Other Ones Tour, up to that point. They did a three-minute *jam* to open, and blew us all away by dropping into a long and blistering "St. Stephen," with Phil singing a good portion of the lyrics in a clear, strong voice. They dove directly into "The Eleven" and the *portal* began to open. Without Jerry!

In my mind at the time, I wasn't sure it was possible. I hadn't been in the scene for a long, long time. Clearly, I was wrong. The *portal* opened wide once more, and we all flowed through it on the incredible sound of the music. I had never seen them do a fantasy set and this night they did three of them. Essentially, three second sets, with the best combination of songs possible. All your favorite tunes, right there for you. As a final additional bonus, they played "Baby Blue," then segued into an 11-minute version of "Stella Blue" with no lyrics whatsoever. It was beautiful.

244.

SPANKED BY THE TANK.

The Gorge Amphitheater

George, WA

9/21/2003

I recall a bit of the sets they played, but I remember the parking lot more vividly. Far-L and I drove his Audi convertible in the sun and parked on the soft, green grass, right next to some girls from Portland.

We set up camp and everything was looking good until we heard it. The jet engine hiss that a nitrous tank makes when it's filling a balloon. Then we heard it again. And again. And again. Noooooo! I fucked up. And I always check. I thought we had a good spot. Never, ever, ever camp by the nitrous salesman! That is one of my top rules and I blew it. I do not love the sound of nitrous in the morning. Guess I'm stuck now. I got over it soon enough by sharing a few balloons with the neighbor girls and I rolled with it. At *least* he had killer nitrous!

We walked into the show with our new friends, down the cattle chutes that make up the walkway into the show. We settled in as the sun set over the incredible and majestic Columbia River Gorge. Once again, I'll say that this venue is one of the absolute best ever. Gorgeous is an understatement, with no pun intended. I've had great seats way down in the pit, but I always prefer to be up in the GA section so I can bask in the "wonders of nature," and listen to the best music in the world, all rolled into one fat joint known as The Gorge!

I remember they opened with "Truckin'," performed "Cryptical" without "The Other One," and did a "Sampson and Delilah" encore.

Another blow me away fantasy set, which was no longer a fantasy. This was normal for this incarnation of the Dead, and I was thankful I was able to see at least a few gigs, occasionally.

When we arrived back at the campsite, empty red balloons covered the green grass for 100 yards either way. The nitrous vendor was in full sales mode and the tank was screaming. "Ice cold nitrous, get your cold ones here!" was his chant and mantra all night long. I like nitrous, but I also like to sleep a bit, and you get little to none camping near the nitrous man. I found earplugs in my tent, which helped drown out the shrieks from the tank, and slipped into a happy little nappy.

Perhaps an hour later, I found myself being smashed in my tent. Some Head sucking on a nitrous balloon wobbled out and fell onto my tent with me inside. I was startled awake and confused. I realized it was a person outside my tent, so I started pushing him off me. I thought it might be Far-L playing a joke, but soon enough realized it was a random person. I shoved him off me and heard a "Ssoorrrryyy," in a slurred tone.

By the time I unzipped my tent he had scurried off into the lot. I was a little annoyed. Then I wondered what he must have thought when he came out of the nitrous fog and realized he was laying on someone's tent, with them stuck inside, yelling, and trying to push him off. I wish I could have seen his face. I am sure his realization expression would have been awesome to see. From "Huuuuuhh?" to, "Oooooh, shit," and I started laughing as I passed back out.

In the morning, the giant tank had finally screeched its last and the nitrous man was newly wealthy. He was also asleep, so I took a bag and cleaned up all the dead red balloons around our area and dropped them back in his campsite. Nitrous is hella fun to do, but it makes a big fucking mess.

245.
THIS TOWN IS CALLED SCAPPOOSE?

Columbia Meadows

St Helens, OR

7/2/2004

This was a treat. A Dead show that was only 30 miles away. Hell yeah! Columbia Meadows was a great place to see shows. Another horse track and event center that was surrounded by low hills covered in tall old trees. I had fifth row tickets off to Phil's side, and I was totally stoked to be up close again after years and years. It felt good to get that close-up stage blast from the amps. Loud, loud, loud, and clear!

246.
RATDOG IN THE NORTHWEST!

Roseland Theatre
Portland, OR
2/16/2007
Moore Theatre
Seattle, WA
2/17/2007

I skated downtown and saw the first night in Portland by myself. My friend worked the door and I got on the guest list. I had never seen Ratdog. I remember liking the vibe and digging the way they performed the songs! I've seen hundreds of shows at Roseland, so I felt right at home!

I drove up and attended the second show with Far-L, his lady Laurie, Howard Marmelstein, and Alan and Daphna Stein.

The Moore is a beautiful old school venue, with tall, stacked floors and steep views down to the stage. Its marble accents and slanted walkways up to the seated area are regal and elegant, in a Seattle sort of worn and wonderful way! I had seen nothing since 2004, and these two shows had an amazing and reinvigorating effect on me.

247.
RASATO REUNION!

Gorge Amphitheater

George, WA

5/16/2009

Pete Rasato, our childhood friend, flew into Portland from Denver, and ML flew up from Mexico. We scrounged George up from wherever he was, and took the scenic drive along the mighty Columbia in a van Pete rented. Seeing a show with my old friends was awesome and we ran around Shakedown until we all got tired.

I woke up early like I always do and sat in my lawn chair with the intent of waking and baking. I had a brand new ZONG, which is a Z-shaped glass bong that can lay on its side without spilling. I had a few grams of weed in my small container, and I had just taken a hit when the Yellow Shirt security kooks rolled up on me and demanded my bong and my weed. I was stunned! Weed was legal in Oregon then, but not in Washington, quite yet. The Yellow Shirt in charge said, give it to us or we will radio the cops and they can handle it. I was pissed. They took my brand new $90 bong and smashed it in the garbage can, and luckily only took my small weed container. I know they kept my weed though. Fuckers.

Then, I watched them do it to a few more unsuspecting Heads. I was not stoked, and since I was riled up already, I took it upon myself to walk just ahead of the Yellow Shirt crew, and warn everyone who was smoking or doing balloons that the Yellow Shirts were coming. I stayed *just* ahead of them for an hour warning people, and they didn't confiscate anything or bust anyone during the time I was there.

248.
THE ONGOING SAGA OF GEORGE AND WARRINGTON.

I went back to the camp site, and old friend and photographer, Dave Warrington walked by and saw me. He said hello for a minute and kept going.

George eventually woke up and went to the porta potty. On his way back he found a fat sack of buds laying in the long grass. George was stoked! He had free weed, although we all did agree that if someone came looking for it, it would be handed over.

Before we even had a chance to sample the new herb, along came Warrington looking in the grass, for the grass he lost. George and David had been friends for 25 years at this point, and often-times were at-odds with each other, normally over something to do with cocaine. Of course, I thought it was funny as hell, and totally ironic, that the two guys most likely to bicker in the entire parking lot, are the loser and the finder of the weed.

Dave found out George had the weed and demanded it back. George says, "How do you know it's *your* weed, it doesn't have *your name* on it," knowing full well it's David's lost sack. Goading him. This leads to them arguing back and forth, with George finally relenting, but still demanding a finders-fee of a few big buds. If I remember right, Warrington still did not give him any, and stomped off to sell some photos. A true parking lot dramedy, especially if you know those two characters!!

249.
TRIPLE BILL!

The show itself was awesome and a lengthy affair. Three bands total that day. The Doobie Brothers in the first slot, followed by the Allman Brothers, and to round out this epic threesome, the Dead closed out the night. Warren Haynes played in the Allmans and the Dead that day, back-to-back. We walked back to the campgrounds and raged away until we all passed out.

The next day, Pete took off just before we drove away, and returned with the show burned onto a CD. He had pre-ordered soundboard copies of the gigs! I was blown away. I did not know that they had adopted this at shows, and I was stoked and impressed. Bring it directly to the fans for $10. That's a cool deal!

250.
CHILLY WEATHER, HOT SHOW.

Further
Memorial Coliseum
Portland, OR
3/8/2010

March can be cold. Farrell and Sue were in the middle of a divorce, and it just so happened that all our old tour friends were at the show. The camps were clearly divided, and the normally friendly air was chilly, but that's the reality of life.

Personally, I was glad to see everyone, and be in the mix with Dan and Jeff again, if just for a show. Naomi and I went together for the first time. She had a loge seat, and I had a GA floor, and they wouldn't let me up, or her down. Warrington thankfully stubbed her down, and we danced for the rest of the gig.

251.
JERRY'S STATUE IN THE WOODS.

Further. Edgefield Manor

Troutdale, OR

9/28/2012

Ah, yes, glorious, and beautiful. The Historic Edgefield Manor. A turn of the century poor farm, converted into an art filled hotel, with sprawling grounds and huge old trees. You follow a path through the woods, by a bronze Jerry statue standing next to a tiny bar, built in an old shed. You get a beer, walk along a bit more, and you end up in the meadow in front of the low stage with old trees grown all around it. Another spot in my top-ten venues I've attended. Maybe even top-five, if I really get to thinking about it?

Naomi and I brought our friend from work, Tom "Jersey Devil" Dowd with us. It was his first show! Maiden voyage! His uncle, Pete Dowd, who is a life-long Dead Head, was working, so he kept texting Naomi every song, asking what songs they were playing! We had a blast and Pete got the play-by-play setlist back at the work. Far-L and his wife Laurie came down, and I ran into Ben, Charlie, and Jeff Evans from the Pyramid Lake trip. Great times at a great place.

252.
SHOWS HERE AND THERE.

The years click by, and I attended more shows at Edgefield, at The Crystal Ballroom and at Cuthbert in Eugene with Rasato, George and ML. I would attend Phil shows and go to DSO gigs, but I wasn't full-on into it. I was absorbing a bit of the old feeling I had on tour back in my day, but it wasn't the full on feeling I used to have. Moments of that deep down stoke kept me going to shows, but it certainly was not an "I'm going back on tour" feeling. I assumed that passion, that flame, that stoke, was long gone. Then came another multi-year span with no Dead. Some DSO and some Phil, but not much.

Quick Cuthbert/Eugene story. I didn't have a ticket, so I decided to hang out in the park and listen. It's right there. You can hear the band loud and clear. Every bench in the park was filled with sitting Heads.

I saw one spot to sit down and smoke a bowl. I sat next to a random guy. Random guy says, "What's up Nordy?" and hands me a bottle of silver tequila! It was my old Burnside skateboard friend Nathan "Natro" Bemiller, listening from outside as well! He thought I saw him and sat down, but I hadn't. I just sat in the only available bench spot, and there was my buddy Natro! So, I spent the show with him and the tequila!

During a bowl smoking session, a cop on a bike rolled up on us, and made me throw my glass pipe as far as I could out into the dark field by the woods. I always wondered how many pipes got tossed into that field that night?

We said our goodbyes and drove back to Portland. I got home and guess what? I had Natro's new pipe in my pocket. Sorry bro! I owe you a glass piece!

253.
DON'T TELL ME ABOUT JOHN, I SAW JERRY!

I had a few friends who were newer Heads who had been seeing Dead and Company since the inception in 2015. My dancer friend Taylor was a young, new school Dead and Company Head.

She had been telling me how good John Mayer was and I kept saying to her, "Yeah, I saw Jerry." She would give me shit and claim I was missing out, and I would counter with, "No, you missed out. I saw Jerry." Then she started to go on about how good Otiel, the bass player was. Red flags flew up! Stop, right there! That was the last straw for me. Phil is my favorite, forever and always!

I stopped talking to her about the *new* Dead. I dismissed her shit talking. She wasn't even born when Jerry left us. She didn't know what it was *really* like. I did. In *my* mind, that was. This went on for a few years and I never bothered to take her advice and listen to them.

In hindsight, I was blowing it. I hung around outside the Memorial Coliseum for the whole show in 2016. I didn't get a ticket and didn't go in. I skated around the whole place and couldn't find Shakedown. I really thought that tour had died and that was all that was left. A boring parking lot and a bunch of tired Heads. It looked to me like the candle that fired the scene was burning out. Turns out I was so wrong, and Taylor, you were so right!

After the Portland show got out, I saw my friend Guffy and his ex-wife. I said, "Hey," and he told me later that his ex-wife asked who the homeless guy he said hello too was!

254.

YOU LIKE THE DEAD? BUT YOU PLAY SLAYER AND MOTORHEAD AT WORK?

Life offered me options and I took them. I worked in the television show/ commercial production business painting sets and loved it. Most people I worked with had no idea I had even heard of the Dead, let alone, that I'm a freak who ran around the country following them for years.

I was working for Chandler Vinar and Jeff Johnson at Department of Art (DOA) when they brought in artist and custom painter Ellen Lipinski. Chan looked across the table and said, "Nordy, Ellen is a Dead Head also." I was stoked! Hell yeah!

Ellen and I would play shows while we painted the set pieces. It was nice to have someone to chat with about all things Dead again.

Ellen played Dead and Co. for the first time for me. She was also the first credible Head to say that Mayer and Otiel were fantastic and that I really needed to see the band in the new configuration. I already knew Chimenti ripped, and I trusted her word. If Ellen says that they rip, then they fucking rip! She was 1000% correct as well, I finally came to realize!

255.
HOW I RELAPSED ON THE DEAD AFTER 30 YEARS CLEAN.

Dead and Company.

Autzen Stadium

Eugene, OR

6/30/2018

The Eugene Oregon Dead and Company show in 2018 was a week away and Naomi and I had barely taken notice. Far-L had sent a text and said he would see me there, which clearly meant, I had better be there!

Naomi and I finally got our tickets, and we needed a room, but the whole town was booked up by then. Naomi wanted to dose and not drive home after the show, and I agreed with not wanting to drive. We ended up getting the last and most expensive room at The 5th. Big bucks, but we wanted to go, so we went.

We had a long walk through Prefontaine Park to the backside of Autzen Stadium. We saw more and more and more Heads on the walk, and the old feeling started to drift back up from the best parts of my memory. Dead Tour!

Then we got onto Shakedown and the "Love Light" automatically switched back on. I saw old friends Mike Dalton and his wife Kathy and Binger the ripper pro skateboarder. There was Hat Vibes Max Parker selling his hand painted hats, and Dave Warrington hawking his famous dancing hippies in Veneta photo print. As we walked inside, the feeling of Dead Tour increased ten-fold. I got the first inkling this may be something special.

Then we went in! It was the type of summer day that makes Oregon famous for summer days! We found some seats in the grandstands and I felt that weird, *did I take acid?* feeling you sometimes get when everyone else took acid and you're receiving the tripping vibe. That feeling usually signals a good show is about to go down.

My feelings were correct, and I was instantly thrust into a relapse moment, like an old alcoholic who decides to have just one more ice-cold beer. I was back in my long, pushed to the back of my mind comfort zone, and I knew I wanted more before the show even started.

I had not listened to Dead and Company extensively. Only a bit. I heard some walking through the lot that day, and the songs Ellen played at DOA, but that's about all.

I was blown away by a 13-minute "Deal" to open, that was out of this world! I could not fucking believe it.

Far-L came up from the floor and gave me a loaded pipe, and Naomi a half a hit of acid during "Me and My Uncle."

The third song was "Here Comes Sunshine," one of my favorite Dead tunes ever! The version they played as the sun set, was the song that tossed me fully back in the mix and brought me back to my love for Dead life!

This was not Jerry. This was not Brent. This was not Phil. It was three originals and three new guys, and it was fucking-amazing, so I took a hit of green and went down under the sea again. This time with a, *for life* plan in mind!

The set kept getting better! It was so good it makes it difficult to describe. I had vaguely heard they had done partial versions of older shows. On this night they performed "Dark Star"-"El Paso," just like they did just down the road in Veneta, Oregon in 1972, and this version was pure magic! They ripped an 18-minute "Saint Stephen" into "William Tell Overture," and on into "The Eleven." All that, opening the second set!

I knew right then that tour had become an option again if I could hear and see more shows like this one. This was not a one-night wonder or a fluke. They were God Damn good! I wanted back in the circle of the Dead. I was getting *sung back home*, and I was absolutely, fine with that.

256.
LOST? OF COURSE, WE ARE!

Out in the always familiar Autzen Stadium parking lot after the show, I felt all the old vibes. Lots of new ones also, all good for the most part. Naomi and I walked around the parking lot, and peeked in on Hat Vibes Max, only to see his sleeping feet through the glass of his camper shell.

We had several beers, and tried to find our way out of the giant, hundred-acre field that surrounds the stadium. Having been there before I knew that the train tracks run through the center of town. Our shmancy hotel was two blocks off the tracks, so we stumbled into the dark, across a bridge or two, and headed across several grass fields. We saw the train tracks ahead, but we had a fence in the way. Naomi was ultra-dressed up as always, and there was no way her flowing outfit and sexy sandals were going over that tall-ass fence.

We were now alone, out of the Dead Zone and we suddenly realized it. We followed the tracks towards our room, and it got darker and sketchier the further we went. We walked for over a mile until the fence turned right, past a big section of permanent urban campers. I had an image in my head that we were going to be following the endless fence until dawn, or we were going to get robbed by junkies, but we finally found a hole and we escaped through it. First show back and I'm already lost and on an adventure in the dark of night, just like old times! It felt good. Can I have another hit please? One is never enough.

257.

OLD HEADS AND A NEW ONE!

A year slipped past and my love for the new band was continuing to grow. Two shows at The Gorge were scheduled and I was ready to go. My friend Owlyn Madrone was 21 at the time, and had recently moved from Minnesota. He is a born and bred skateboarder who was raised by parents who met at a Rainbow Gathering. He's an old soul and a very earth centric guy.

His dad owns the Blood Bowl skate spot in Minneapolis, and that was our connection. My cousin/brother Kevin skates there. He has known Owlyn since his childhood, and told Owlyn to skateboard with me when he moved here a few years ago to pursue a tattoo career. Kevin said I could show him around.

I would see modern rock bands, like our friend Sunny's band, BlackWater HolyLight with him, but this was his first Dead related show of any kind.

Owlyn said he for sure wanted to go.

Fresh from New York City, Ferd had already said he did not want to camp, so I said Owlyn could ride with me. Then Ferd said he wanted to camp after all, so the three of us went, Ferd following in his car we named Black Subbath.

The drive from Portland up the Columbia River Gorge to George, Washington and The Gorge Amphitheatre is truly stunning. One of my top five venues I have ever seen a show at. Have I mentioned that yet?

The view over the stage into the Columbia River Gorge is spectacular. When the music is playing and the sun is setting, it becomes wonderful and magical with all the colors in the sky. No acid required, but it always helps!

It took forever to get into the campground (which is grassy and awesome) and it was $120 a carload, not the $20 a carload I remember from the 2000s Dead Tours. We got our tents set up real quick like. The walk is more than a mile, so we had to get going.

Ferd had some of our friend TC's homemade weed caramels in his pocket. TC makes them strong! Steve offered some to Owlyn and me. I declined because I know how gnarly strong TC makes them.

I am *not* an edibles guy. If I eat weed infused food, I get so high I can't function. At all! I have a million things going on in my head, but I cannot get a fucking word out of my paralyzed mouth. But that's just me.

Ferd, on the other hand, can eat several weed caramels and do a fistful of mushrooms at the same time and be just-fine.

So, we have this hella long walk, and a longer wait to get past the metal detectors, and the online cell phone tickets check using the venue's shitty internet, just to get in. Ferd gives Owlyn two caramels and eats two himself. Later, Owlyn said he heard Ferd say the candies were seven mgs per. Turns out Ferd actually said 70 mgs per.

With that knowledge in mind, Owlyn thought he was okay and ate both. A half hour later (huge lines), and Owlyn isn't his normal talkative self. He's sort of in and out. I could tell the weed candy was working. Owlyn thankfully helped me get our online tickets on my phone before I had a meltdown, and in we finally went.

We promptly lost Owlyn for the first of many times over the weekend. I had to piss, and was walking with Ferd and Owlyn to the bathroom through 30,000 people, and suddenly he wasn't with us anymore. Imagine that? It took the first three Dead and Company songs to get in past security, so we went to smoke a joint and listen, and figured we would find him later.

A few times during the show I called, and he wasn't making a ton of sense. I'd ask, "Where are you?" He would say, "On the grass on my back," and when I asked him to give me a landmark, he said something like, "Building with black roof and a red banner." I called him once more and he said, "Eating a wrap," so I went to the wrap booth and still couldn't find him. No problem though, we knew he was having fun and he sort of knew his way back. There are a million things to do after the show in parking lot land, so we just did our own thing, knowing he would pop up later.

I lost Ferd when he went to sit in his lower-level seat. I chilled and listened. After a truly insane show, I walked the dusty dirt mile, herded in with everyone, happy from the show, slowly shuffling back to the crazy campground scene that was waiting.

When I got back to our campsite no one was there. I figured they were out walking around Shakedown, so I grabbed some beers and went walking myself. It was insanity, as always, when they allow overnight camping. 30,000 people having an all-night party. Perhaps the biggest party you'll ever attend.

I ended up wandering Shakedown talking to a few people I know. Hat Vibes Maxwell as always, and then this guy who was in the car line next to us to get in. He had seen the last four shows in California and was giving us some juicy set details, as we waited endlessly to get into the campground. As we walked around together later that night, I realized he was high as-fuck on acid and discreetly trying to sell some paper. I was cool with that, long as I stay detached from his transactions.

We had a super funny conversation as he was telling me about his adventures, since we had last seen each other in the car line about ten hours earlier. I had a hard time keeping up with what he was trying to say because he was on LSD speak, and after about 30 minutes, I turned around and he was gone. It just happens like that in Dead Land. Even at 2 am, Shakedown is hella crowded and seemingly just getting started.

258.

NEW YORK CITY IS 3000 MILES AWAY FERD! GET OVER IT!

I shuffled back to camp, burnt out. Owlyn was in a weed caramel coma in his tent and Ferd was already asleep in Black Subbath. He slept in the driver seat for some weird reason. This caused several abrupt awakenings during the night on *my* part.

Ferd had just moved back after doing several years in the restaurant business in New York City. He was still used to locking and alarming everything, and he did just that, and went to sleep. I hopped in my tent, got comfy, and slipped into dreamland, only to be awakened by Ferd's car alarm going off and all his lights blinking and blazing, filling up my tent with red flashes and car horns at 3 am.

I got out of my tent and Ferd was *still* asleep. I had to knock on the window to wake him up. His alarm was going off! How do you sleep through that? I was to find out later, Ferd is the sleep king! He turned off the alarm and dropped back to sleep before I could even turn away from his window.

I settled back in and dozed off again. An hour later my tent is filled with brilliant bright red light once more, only this time it wasn't flashing. Ferd had moved in his sleep and pushed on his brake pedal, setting off his brake lights. My tent was behind his car, and all four of his bright ass brake lights woke me up once again.

I love my friends, but I just wanted some sleep. I wrapped a shirt around my eyes and finally went to bed for good. That is until Ferd woke up cold and started his car to warm up, choking me out of my tent with his exhaust pipe that was barely three feet away from my screen window! It was okay though, because he was rolling joints in his car.

Ferd and I started to shuffle around and prepare breakfast as Owlyn emerged from his tent with sleepy, wide eyes. We all just started laughing together without saying anything! The energy was upon us, and we didn't need words to express ourselves for a moment!

Owlyn got up and walked around, squinting in the morning Gorge sunlight, then popped back into his tent. Suddenly he came flying back out saying he just sprayed his liquid acid on his hands and rubbed it in! He's holding his hands up looking at Ferd and I, and we were momentarily paralyzed. You did what? NO!?

He had a measured spray bottle with micro dose hits. An easy way to ingest it, and to balance how much you're taking. He also had his hand sanitizer in the exact same, small blue, generic spray bottle. This was ten thirty in the morning, and we suddenly feared an impending acid meltdown crisis. Owlyn had went in still sleepy and grabbed the wrong bottle and sanitized away, much to his dismay.

We took the blue Dawn, and half our water for the weekend to help him rewash his hands thirty times! It was super funny, but not until after we made sure he was all rinsed off and wasn't headed to Saturn for the day! He ultimately ended up only getting a small dose, which started his day off for his big trip later that evening.

We were all a bit amped up at that point, so we smoked a fat joint or four, and yeah, we gave Owlyn his own to avoid residuals. We then made egg, sausage, and vegetable frittatas and had a gourmet breakfast overlooking The Gorge. Ferd is a world-famous chef. Perhaps I hadn't mentioned that yet. If you ever meet him, he'll tell you so.

259.
OH BROTHER!

My skateboard homie Taylor Bradley, was hanging out with Joel Kelly, the trippy fine artist, and his buddy Snake, using Macho Man and Hulk Hogan voices to describe how the show sounded to them on acid. Picture a whole evening of, "Ohhh man" and "Yesss brother," as they adopted the gravel tone wrestler voices. Pure comedy all night as the band played epic sets well into the chilly evening.

Dave Tobin, my Portland skateboard homie and lifelong OG Dead Head, camped right along the walkway to my camp site, so I saw him on every walk to show or Shakedown! I see him at gigs all the time. We need a portable Dead Lot mini ramp Tobin!

260.

OWLYN'S UNEDITED DEAD & CO. ORIENTATION. FIRST SHOW AND IT'S A GO!

I could not find a way to properly edit Owlyn's interview, so here it is, as is! It's better this way!

O. We were really ready, ya know? I remember waiting in line and hiding my fucking weed in my sock.

N. For the search.

O. I remember I sprayed, I gave myself a hit and a half.

N. Nice. Out of your squirt bottle?

O. Yes! That's thirty sprays!

N. Damn! There you go!! You know what would have been funny? If you fucked up and sprayed your hand sanitizer in your mouth!

Laughter!

N. So, like thirty sprays of your bottle, your micro dose bottle?

O. I think I counted it out to be a hit and a half? And I might have even taken another hit during the night too? I remember rolling in with you guys, high as fuck. Then they broke into "Deal." I was like, holy shit! What is this? Oh my god, and I got swept! Good god! I lost you two right away. Gone. And then I just got pulled by my, the whole whooooshhhh, to this grass section, like middle of the way probably. I think it was just

309

mostly that second set that really just fucking. You know we had missed half the first set by the time we got in.

N. Yeah dude, we missed like four songs each night trying to get through that bullshit.

O. So, um, that second set was just amazing, and I remember being just absolutely, from the heart captivated by what this was, and I just like, felt so deeply, just like this place of home, like yeah! This!

N. That's so rad!

O. Like how have I not been here? It was that moment that every-thing changed. I remember dancing, then standing completely still and not moving a muscle. Just so focused!

N. Rad!

O. And after that just being soooo high! You know, The Gorge and the people and so many joints were being passed!

N. That view from where you're standing up on the grass over the stage, down into the gorge when the sun is setting, is as good as it gets man! That is one of my top five venues that I've ever seen any shows at. Out of the roughly thousand shows I've seen out of every band ever, that place is all time!

O. That was my first and only time going to the Gorge!

N. Well they'll do more and next time they do you can come out and visit. We can all drive up together again.

N. Tell me a little bit more about your adventures in the night after the show got out. I know you saw the sunrise.

O. That's when shit really went off, cause like, at this point, I feel like because of when I took the acid and when I was peaking and everything, I felt like it was the longest peaking of my life! From the second set through the night, you know! I remember leaving the show and just being so high and so many people.

N. Oh, I know! You go through the snake. It's only like 12 feet wide, for like a mile.

O. I remember it being so tight, and then noticing this couple of people that were just as high as me and we just fucking locked in. We locked into each other, and we just went. They had been there, and they knew how to do it. Suddenly, I'm following this lady named Alley Cat and her clown dressed friend. They are just bobbing through, skipping and I'm just like, follow them! We went through this mass of people, and I just kept following them and we didn't even go to Shakedown yet. We went through this hut right by this prime camp spot.

N. Oh, you went through the expensive camping spots. You can see the venue from there.

O. Yeah and they were carrying balloons now. We stopped at a camp spot, and we were preparing to go to Shakedown, decompressing after the show. Someone asked me, "What was your favorite songs?" and I was like I couldn't have an answer because it was only one song to me.

Laughter.

O. How do I differentiate one song from any of that? The whole show was one song to me at the early point. That's all I could answer!

Laughter.

O. So, after the usual, where's my bong, oh here it is, we smoked a bunch of weed. Still, I felt like I hit another highway with my trip that I needed to take, so we all finally got up, walked over, and entered Shakedown, and my mind was kind of just blown. I loved it in the day-time, that was my first experience. I showed up at night and it just blew my mind. Just that one long section that was all lit up!

N. Yep, yep!

O. I mean, it was alive you know?

N. Fuck yeah!

O. I walk in and just am like, wide eyed and trying to process, you know? All of a sudden, I got pulled into this person and was talking to this young man probably about my age. We had this conversation and all of a sudden Alley Cat and my crew were gone. Disappeared. Just gone!

Laughter.

O. And I was so bummed! I was so bummed. I was like, I just met all these cool ass people and now they're gone, like, damn, fuck. So, I sort of went through the night trying to find them.

N. Yeah, I've done that.

O. I think I just ended up walking Shakedown the rest of the night. I remember looking for them, walking and looking and I couldn't find them. I walked back into where I thought we came from, and it was just tents. I'm like nope, walked back.

N. You're like nope, wrong way.

Laughter.

O. So, then I was like, okay. I'm on my own. I just started wandering. I remember the highlights, you know. Just the wild characters that were clearly knowing how insanely high I was. I felt like everybody could see me and what was happening.

N. People on tour are exceptionally intuitive at Dead Shows.

O. Yeah, for sure.

N. They know what you're on!

O. And they knew it was my first time.

N. Yeah, even if you didn't tell them they just knew! In a good way, ya know?

O. Yeah, yeah!

N. In a very good way!

O. Yeah, I was glad, and I didn't try to hide that in any way.

O. I remember I was walking back and forth, and things were different on Shakedown again. Slowly, as the night went on, people would shut off their lights, people would close down. So, every time I hit one part and end up turning around there would be different people doing different things. I swear all the tents were different every time. I felt like I was walking in a straight circle! But I was actually just pacing basically.

N. Yeah, yeah.

O. And, it was the biggest mind fuck, because I'm so high that every once in a while, I'm like fuck, where are my friends?

Laughter.

N. You're like, I need those guys back!

O. Yeah, I mean I was holding it down. That was where I had my first fucking hit of nitrous!

N. Like, the first one ever? Your first ever?

O. Ever.

N. Wow.

O. I never felt drawn to it.

N. Ice cold fatty!

O. I know!!! I kept hearing that and kind of was catching on to what was going on. Nitrous fucking jockeys walking around, fucking blue and shit. Shaking and blue. It kind of showed me the dark side of it a bit.

N. Okay, on my YouTube channel, look up the one that says Nitrous or Notrous? I wrote a whole big thing about, an extensive thing. It's the whole thing about how crazy it's got. Ferd and I went on, we saw like sixteen shows in a row and the nitrous scene all the way across the East Coast was insane! Go ahead and check that out when you get a chance. I think you'll be entertained by that story. Nitrous is fun, but it can be the evil of the show sometimes.

O. And that pertains to the first night when I thought people were reaching for me from the shadows. That's where I really started to feel that dark energy that's swirled around with that insane positive energy vibe.

N. They exist together unfortunately.

O. Yeah, and that's what I come to really feel that's such a huge part of it. You hear the rumor, maybe you've heard it, correct me if you know, about Jerry writing "Dark Star" as, you know, the thing that *was* the Grateful Dead, ya know. Like it was the "Dark Star." It kept expanding and growing. I also heard that "He's Gone" is written about how he has to die before it can stop. Have you heard that?

N. "He's Gone", was, it's more like, the beginning to "The Other One," "Cryptical Envelopment," is, I think what you're thinking, because "He's Gone" was written about, actually about Mickey's dad who ripped the band off for a couple hundred thousand dollars. He was the manager. That was why Mickey wasn't in the Dead for a bunch of years. He just bowed out after his dad fucked the whole band over.

O. What year was that?

N. That was like, Mickey was out from '72-'74. Then he came back in '75. But I think

His dad did that shit in '69.

O. That's like Keith Godchaux days huh?

N. Yep, yep! If you listen to "Cryptical Envelopment," which is the original beginning to the "Other One," that they dropped off it, I think that is what is part of that he was referring to. It has the line; "*You know he had to die.*" I can't sing, but you get it!

O. That's the one I'm thinking of! Because I have this CD set that my dad gave me, that his dad gave him. His dad was into the Dead and got my dad into them and my dad got me into the Dead. So, I got this three-piece CD set and they are always in my CD player, so I never look at the names of the songs. I don't even know what the actual titles of the songs are because on this specific record collection it's a different version. I just never know the order and they are going back and forth! But when I pulled out the CD recently, one of the songs was "Cryptical," and so that's probably what I'm thinking.

N. Yes. It sounds exactly like what you're thinking, for sure!

O. I was told that. So, that was my branching off and the discoveries of the darker side because I didn't know.

N. The darker side is there for sure!

O. I remember earlier that day when I was in that circle with those people on Shakedown, this other dude who was smoking some weed with us, some dad, he had brought his son.

N. Cool!

O. So, I'm on Shakedown and all the people are pushing food carts and trying to get to the show. People on the sides playing covers and like, different pockets of music. The wild people who pulled me into the circle for a couple of minutes or I get pulled into something else.

Laughter.

O. And then this dude, the dad, was like, "Hey man, we were hanging out earlier." I said, "Oh yeah, Hi!" He had some balloons and asked if I wanted one. I was like, "Nah, I'm good, I've never, I don't really need it. All good."

N. Did you tell him you had never done a balloon before?

O. I think that came out right after that. So, after he had done a balloon, that came out right after. He was like, "What?" And he starts laughing. He said, "Dude, I'll be right back." So he goes and buys me a balloon and says, "I just spent my last five dollars on that balloon for you!"

N. That's epic!

O. Straight up, his last five dollars! So, I was like fuck. Sure, okay! Ya know, I took a tiny little bit and didn't quite do it, and he was no, no. no. He was like, "Come on. Inhale that!"

Laughter.

N. Hit that balloon!

O. So, I did a normal hit off the balloon and it was like, holy shit, and everything just stopped for a second. Everything was waaaaaa, and I started to hear, as soon as I got high off the gas, I was able to hear all the fucking tanks clicking from everywhere.

N. Ccrrrrrrrrrrrrrrrrrr (I make a tank noise).

O. I just realized I had heard that sound all weekend, but so subconsciously, that I didn't know what it was. Until that moment and it pulled me into all of it and I was like holy shit! Everything is clear now!

N. The screaming nitrous tank!

Laughter!!!

O. I was like, OMG, now I know why people love nitrous!

N. Mmmmmhhhhhmmmm!

N. I write in our book about never camping near the nitrous man.

Laughter.

O. Yeah. No way.

N. Because you'll hear it all night long. I had a dude doing a balloon, I was asleep in my tent, and we inadvertently, at the Gorge back in the day seeing um, the Dead, as they were playing with Phil still. We inadvertently camped by the nitrous guy. We didn't know he was there yet. They put you in rows and he was like five cars away on the other row. At four in the morning, I'm sound asleep, in my tent with my earplugs in luckily, and some dude falls on my tent and I thought it was my buddy messing with me at first, but the dude had done a big nitrous balloon and zoned out and fell over on top of me on the outside of my tent.

Laughter.

N. I'm like, "Hey!" Pushing him off, and he's like, "Huh? Whaaaa? Huh? Whaaaat?"

Laughter!

N. By the time I unzipped my tent to look, he was already gone. He was probably embarrassed as hell! He was probably like, "Fuck, fuck…. ah."

O. Yeah dude, it was crazy! I remember coming off of it and almost falling totally, ya know? And then it just spiked my dose too! Ya know?

N. Oh yeah!

O. It's just like, and I was like whoa, this is awesome, it makes sense, but I don't need another one right now.

Laughter.

O. Because before I did it, I saw what people were getting like from it.

N. Yeah.

O. I saw the fucking blue people, ya know! I knew what was going on, but I was like, I might as well!

N. When we were at New Years in SF 2019, Ferd fucking got an entire tank.

O. Oh my god.

N. So, we had our own fucking tank for two and a half days 'til it died.

O. Jesus Christ.

N. We probably had hundreds and hundreds of balloons. We had a party in our hotel with that nitrous tank screeching 'til 4:30 in the morning and no one complained.

O. Wow.

Laughter.

O. Jesus Christ dude. That's why I love it so much, and that's really why I don't but it, cause, I've done it only a couple of times, for that same reason, but.

N. I would never get a balloon at a show unless someone hands me one. Naomi loves them, I'm just not that into them, but if we have our own tank, and I know it's good gas, like we had, it was really good gas, um, then I'll do a bunch because it's fun.

O. Sure, sure.

N. They cut the purity on nitrous now to get more balloons out of it and they mix shit in with it. It's not that strong. People used to be bloody faced at Dead Shows, like they would fall right on their fucking face. Smash in the dirt! Like, bleeding, and they would still be sucking balloons.

Laughter.

O. Yeah, that's what's so crazy.

N. It used to be way stronger. At Irvine there was this whole grass part next to the parking lot and people would just be laying on their backs, like 150 people, all just like (huffing sound), and fishing out. Letting their balloons go. (Balloon, deflating noise).

Laughter.

N. Anyway, so we got a bunch of good shit so far, tell me about.... tell me about your sunrise and we'll wrap this up.

O. So the bridging point from the nitrous experience, to the, because that whole night I was just looking for more, ya know, like where's the music. Someone's got to keep playing right? So, I ended up finding this one dude, and it's getting pretty late, or pretty early. This guy was just ripping! So good. Maybe he wasn't that good. Maybe not.

N. But he was probably ripping, ya know! We know ripping, no matter what it is, ya know?

O. Yeah, he was ripping, so that kind of gave me the upward leap to just stroll through to the sunrise. So, I just kept pacing Shakedown and watching people going to bed, and I kept going. I found this little trail off the beaten path and this little group of people playing music, and the sun was starting to come up really slowly. Ya know, you're like, you make that neural connection that the sky isn't black anymore.

N. You're like, Oh! The earth is still turning. Oh!

O. Yeah! So, I ended up by this little group and uh, it was awesome. They had a mandolin and a fiddle and some guitars and these two just incredibly beautiful women singing. They were sisters. That little crew brought in all these different people. Me and some gnarly dude hopped up on nitrous with a sleeping bag around his head. Just a classic nitrous Dead Head, ya know? Like to a T. He was camping right there if need be!

Laughter.

O. Then this older, like very mystical woman, who was, clearly an old school Head, ya know.

N. Yeah, yeah!

O. We started smoking together and had an instant, okay, cool. You're solid.

N. Yeah, yeah!

O. We started talking and listening to this music, and the sun's slowly coming up. Yeah, she was like this wonderful, just wonderful being. As she was starting to depart, she asked me my name. I told her my name was Owlyn. She fucking went stone cold face. Like wide eyed, like whoa! She said, at every show, she said she had been traveling, following forever, and every show she ever goes to, she finds the presence of an Owl. Whether an Owl comes to her in visions, or she sees one or whatever, it's just part of her experiences, that sequence of Owl sightings. Her owl connection, ya know?

N. Yes, for sure!

O. She said to me that night that she hadn't found one. It was the first night of her entire following to ever not experience that.

N. Wow!

O. And then she met me, and she said, "That's you this time!!!" It was like whoa. That's some shit, ya know?

N. That's incredible. That's the part of the story, that's why I wanted to contact you because it's incredible and I didn't have the specific details and I wanted them directly from you obviously.

O. And the best part of that part is how my story really connected to the sunrise. She left and I was still hanging out. I kept making eye contact with one of the women singing and noted this mental connection with her. And then this other dude trying to hit on her. Trying to get her into his tent and she was like no! She kept looking at me and we were like, you're still singing but eventually we are going to talk to each other, right?

N. Yeah, without even saying it, all eyes, right?

O. Yep, yep. All eyes.

N. Nice.

O. It was her and her sister singing and then, eventually I start to back away and I'm realizing the sun is coming up and it's time for me to leave, ya know? So, she steps out of the jam, ya know!

Laughter.

O. She runs over and follows me. She just runs up and we kind of like linked up arms and we were both like, "Who are you?" to each other. We walked about thirty feet away and we're saying, "What's going on right now? I'm so high." We say a couple more things and she kisses me! It was this magical random, occurrence of connection, ya know? We broke away from the kiss and I was still so high. I was like, I can't believe we just had this mental conversation that actually was true, ya know?

N. Yeah, yeah.

O. And then I gave her, I gave her, I had those little business cards with my art and my number on them and I was giving them to people I met that summer to kind of like meet people and shit. I gave her one and walked away. Like okay, goodbye. Never saw her again. She was at the Colorado shows but we didn't see each other. So, I walk away, and my nose starts bleeding. I'm like, *what the fuck?* So, I felt like she did this to me, but not in a bad way. So, it was really strange, and I was in like complete wonder about it. So, I start walking in the opposite direction of where our camp is, because that was just the way I had been walking with her. I get to this crossroads, where I can walk along the inside, the very end of all the rows. I got pulled into one road. I'm going to walk towards the sunrise to the field way in the back. I'm walking and it's light out now, very light out, and I'm just in a state of bliss thinking about this incredible ride I was just taken on! Never found my friends from the day again, but I just had this really wonderful time and I was really stoked up about the older Head that I met and that woman, but really the experience with the woman who I was smoking with and the Owl situation. That was more of a profound connection.

N. Yeah. That's amazing. I love that story.

O. As I'm walking up this, it seems like forever. As, I get closer I see this little speck sitting on one of those wood picket fences they have. It's the last fence. We were close to the edge of the grounds, and I thought it was some big bird or something. I'm like, "Holy shit! Sunrise and there's something over here!" I walk towards and there is nobody else around. As, I get closer I realize it's a person. I was like, *holy shit, I'm walking towards this person.*

N. No one else is around? This is out on the edge of the whole perimeter, right?

O. Yeah, way out on the edge.. Nothing's going on out there. It's light and probably like six or seven in the morning. So, I get closer I realize it's the bird woman. I don't remember her name, but the same lady who.

N. The same woman that has the owl encounter every time?

O. Yep, yep, yep!

N. Cool.

O. It was the Owl lady, and she just was sitting there. I walk up and stand next to her. She's sitting on the post just overlooking the sunrise over the field and the Gorge.

N. Wow.

O. (*Laughing*)...She was just like, "Oh, well, hello!" She said, "I was waiting to smoke this joint, and I didn't know why, but okay! Want to smoke it with me?" So, I got up on the fence and just sat there. Smoked a big joint and had this moment of, okay, holy shit, what just happened? She was clearly, she's an old school follower. There wasn't too much talking at that time. Just a presence. Being there.

N. Nice.

O. I did tell her it was my first experience and she told me to keep following the music. (*Laughs*) She told me to go to the 2020 eclipse gathering. It was in South America somewhere. Chile actually! She said just get there. Family will take care of you when you get there. Just get there.

N. Wow!

O. Obviously I didn't make it since I moved to Denver to get a tattoo apprenticeship. But we had this follow up connection. I never thought I would see her again after the first encounter and I stumbled into her being the only other person out there watching the sunrise.

N. That is so cool! Fucking amazing. I love that whole story. How it ties back into itself is so cool!

O. It was so special. Yeah! I hope to see her again! Ya know, I probably will.

N. Yeah, you probably will! For sure! Hopefully. Spirits attract in times like that no matter what the situation. I fucking love that. Then you came back. Were Ferd and I up when you got back?

O. I slowly walked back and at this point I'm fully checked out, ya know? You're sleeping still, but as I get closer while I'm walking, I see Ferd walking the other way. It was so funny. Just saying, "What's up buddy?" We both pretty much had no words. Then I walked back to my tent and nodded out, ya know?

Laughter!!!

O. You woke me up a few hours later and we did that slow tear down of the camping stuff and I felt a part of my heart dying. I didn't want to leave!

N. I don't want to leave!

O. That was it, and we drove back!

261.
YES, WE CAN SMOKE ALL THAT!

We got up and packed away the camping gear. Our neighbors for the two-day run were all Canadian. They had a border crossing coming at them, so they gave us all the weed they had not been able to smoke. Four joints and some loose buds. We lit one right away, then another, and to the amazement of our neighbors, we smoked all four of the gifted joints before they even drove off. Wake and bake baby. Wake and bake!

262.
FULL ON RELAPSE.
I'M A DEAD JUNKIE AGAIN.

Dos Equis Beer Pavilion
Dallas, TX
7/2/2019

I love my girl Naomi more than anything, but I wasn't so sure this was the best idea for my relationship with her. Leave for Texas and Colorado for more Dead and Company Tour after already seeing shows in Washington State? I thought it might be a mistake, but it worked out. She's cool like that and I love her for it! I can understand where she's coming from though. Here I am, once again chasing a 30-year-old dream. Going to Dallas and then on to Boulder, broke and just like old times, and I didn't give a fuck where I stayed, I just knew I needed to go.

Ferd and I went last minute (his divorce finalized on Monday, and we left for Dallas six days later) for his 50th birthday celebration. Newly divorced and having just seen the fantastic Gorge shows, he was energized to not let the good feeling go away before tour ended. I agreed with him on that point, and off we went.

263.
NAUGHTY TSA

We had a flight together and got to the security check, late as always. Of course, I got flagged by TSA for a pat down. I have an ounce of weed sealed in my carry on, but they got me on the swabs on the outside of my bag which indicates something different than weed. I didn't have anything else and wasn't sure what was up, but it wasn't a random, we just happened to pick you search.

I soon found out what was really going on when the search person came up and said to step to the secondary area. I was looked at directly in the eyes with a sweet smile by a very well-kept, gay TSA Agent, who gave me the frisking of a lifetime! He touched me with soft, yet firm hands, in every spot you could hide something. He even had me pull up my jeans, so my nuts were moose knuckling my black Levi's, and continued to stare right into my eyes with his creepy little smile, as he rubbed and bumped both sides of my nut sack with his groping hands.

I laughed and asked if that was fun? He didn't reply but also didn't stop with the creepy smile and the direct eye contact. I put my belt and shoes back on and walked away without him finding my weed. I figured I can go through a little TSA grope, long as they don't find my green dope! I hit up the gate, last one to board, and off we went to hot ass Texas.

264.
GUNS IN THE GROCERY STORE!

Ferd and I got to Dallas and of course, they fucked up our minivan pre-order, so we ended up getting an upgrade to a Nissan Pathfinder. Sounds good to us. Plush and the same price. Ferd jumps in to start it up and get the AC going (Texas is hella fuckin-hot), and as I open the back to toss in our skates and backpacks, I realize we have a NY plate, deep in the heart of good ol' Texas. Perhaps not the best thing for two Oregon stoners smoking fatty after fatty on the road, but that's just what we do!

We got our directions straight and hit a grocery store for all the shit we need. Coolers, ice and beer for me, water, and protein snacks for Ferd. We all exist on what we exist on, and I love my beer!

We truly realized we were in Texas when we noticed more than half the people in the store were carrying guns on their hips. Some even had two, one for each hand.

Supplies gotten, we drove for a bit and found the turn to the venue we think we want. It's in the same giant campus that contains the famous Cotton Bowl football stadium, and we promptly got lost in the curving streets that surround that place. I had just broken out the weed we had stashed and finally rolled one! We fired it up and took a hit or two each, and started feeling good about being in Texas!

As we drove around one of the bends that surrounds the Cotton Bowl, we had our first close call with the Texas cops. We rounded the corner and there he was, driving right towards us. Big hat and all. I have no idea how he failed to see us puffing up. This would be a consistent pattern for us until we left Texas. Cops right next to us, a joint on fire, and a huge smoke cloud billowing in the Texas sun, surrounding us in the rental. Maybe the tinted windows saved us? Maybe we just got lucky? Who knows?

He just cruised on past without a glance, and we soon found the proper way into the venue and the parking lot that contained Shakedown. We found a killer parking spot in the shade and started to relax after the red eye flights and the lack of sleep. It was 94 degrees with 87% humidity.

We went skateboarding through the parking lot to check out the scene but had to come back to the AC every 20 minutes or so. Texas humidity is a motherfucker!

We finally grew accustomed to the heat and found a red curb to skate. It is so hot in summertime Texas that the red paint on curbs grinds good without any wax. Texas got Slappy's man!! Fuck yeah! Ferd tried to ollie the corner of a curb and locked, slamming him in the dirt. I fell on my ass slipping out on a slappy. We both ate shit. It was comedy!

We skated around and watched the serious, patched, Texas MC members ride in and park in the "No Parking" spots right up front. The club members put a small blanket/patch with the club logo on their seats. No one goes near the bikes *ever*. The crowd respectfully walked around the bikes by about ten feet. Respect or fear? Doesn't fucking matter! Outlaws demand both equally and you give it to them regardless of the situation.

We fucked off for a while and then went into the show. Super cool venue. Big grass area on a mellow slope. Excellent sound and lots of room to dance! Very much like the last time I saw Grateful Dead shows in Texas in 1985 at Manor Downs, and then the old Southern Star in Houston.

Dead and Company played many of their southern themed tunes which always seem way more appropriate on actual Texas soil! Certain songs just fit the Texas vibe, and with that, we got a tight "Deep Elem Blues" which was all fucking time!! "Deep Elem" is a super gnarly suburb of Dallas that the infamous blues standard of the same name was written about. The crowd got super loud for that one! So many good songs that night!

We got nice breezes as it got dark, and we had an awesome moon-rise as we sat on the grass and shared our weed with the Heads around us. We sat and chilled and smiled after the show. We slowly walked out with the usual herd of people back into the hot Dallas parking lot. It seemed nice and cool inside the outdoor venue for some reason, but when we got back outside to Shakedown it was sweltering again. Texas is a hot wet humid blanket on your head, covering your body, smothering you!

Ferd and I slowly walked back to the car laughing and having a blast. I tell him to toss me the keys as he goes to piss, and when I walked up to our rental, I freaked out for a second because all our windows were wide open, and they were not broken out. I think we've been robbed, or we opened the windows with the remote while we were inside the show dancing, and *then* got robbed! I was not sure which, but I was losing it. First night of the tour and we got jacked for everything except what we have in our pockets and on our backs? Fuck!!!

But no! I was wrong. It was Ferd and I locking the back of the rental and neither of us checking to see that we rolled up the front windows. 20,000 people at the show and no one even noticed, and if they did, they had great karma and just walked on by! "Tragedy narrowly averted," to quote Bobby! Thank you-Texas! Fucking love, you for that!

265.
UNCLE JOHN'S CABIN!

Earlier in the day we met a guy named Sam in the Dallas show parking lot who was hanging out in in the back of his truck in true Texas style. We asked him typical Dead questions about what he listens to, and he said he just likes the old stuff. I quizzed him further and he made a weird song reference that didn't fit with an actual Dead song, and I was like, hmmm?

I remember showing him my new Vans, Off the Wall, Viola Lee Blues rip off shirt and him looking confused. All good though! He was a cool cat, sitting in a lawn chair in the bed of his pickup truck, with a cooler of beer next to him.

Something came up, I got distracted and forgot about it. Then we saw the show, like I said earlier. We came back to the open windowed car (we are lucky idiots) and our parking lot buddy Sam was either back in the back, or *still* in the back of his truck. I low fived him and asked where he sat in the show, and he simply said, "On the back part." Ferd asked him what his favorite songs of the night were, and he said, "I really liked that "Uncle John's Cabin" tonight. I love that song."

Ferd turned away and started laughing as I tried to not crack up and spit out my beer everywhere. We didn't say anything but that's when we knew Ol' Sam never went into the show and that's probably why our wide-open truck didn't get robbed due to our stupidity. So, thanks for that Sam!

And here's to "Uncle John's Cabin" getting played for you again sometime real soon in your future! You're damn lucky Sam! 300 shows and I've never even seen a version of Uncle John's Cabin!

266.
UP THE DRUG CORRIDOR.

On the way to Boulder, we wanted to go to skateparks and waterparks, in no particular order. We got the skateparks, but the waterparks were only open at night for some dumb reason. We are in Texas, right? We had 800 miles to drive and several days to fuck around, so we did, or tried to at least.

Sleeping in a truck stop after we left Dallas at 2 am, we didn't realize that the lights won't turn off with the car still running. That was fucked! All we wanted to do was get a few hours of sleep after being up for over 36 hours. You *must* have your AC on in Texas, even at night. There is absolutely no question about it, and that means leaving the car running. Here we were trying to be discreet, once again smoking out in plain sight and not realizing the whole time that the headlights are totally shining in a busy Texas truck stop.

We got out of there at daybreak and headed north, with Ferd at the wheel and me trying to keep him from speeding into all the little speed trap towns, as we drove up the drug runner's corridor from Dallas. Speed limit 70, then 60, me saying the speed limits out loud so Ferd will slow down. Then 50, then 40, rolling through every dusty half mile long Texas town. Each little hamlet, almost always featuring a radar gun toting cop on the side of the road, hiding behind a row of short squatty trees. Beautiful country. Prime ticket and bust area. We were traveling with caution. It's the way to do it if you want to keep on doing it.

Our drive took us up through the Texas panhandle, a tiny bit of Arkansas, and then into southern Colorado. It's a long drive, but we had amazing weather with beautiful views and stunning vistas in our windshield.

267.
BOULDER IS BANGING!

When you drive into Boulder, Colorado, you see the mountains ring the sides of the town and wrap it in this gorgeous valley. It's an amazing place. I was feeling the Boulder vibe and I was once again starting to feel that Dead show excitement start to build up. It's a strange and fantastic feeling. The anticipation and the excitement surrounding the countdown to it.

I had been calling Pat A, legendary pro snowboarder and Boulder local, to see if we could camp in his yard, but he had gone *real* camping and I sorta lagged on calling early. So, it goes on tour. Quick consensus? Let's see what else is up!

We parked in a grocery store parking lot with a bar next door. I was looking for my old friend Dave Dowd, who has lived in Boulder his whole life. Dave is also a legendary pro snowboarder, and has been seeing Dead Shows in Boulder and Denver since the Folsom Field show in 1980.

I wrote down the name of the bar since it looked very much like the kind of place Dowd would hang out. Moments later, Ferd came out of the store with a 30 pack of Pabst for me! Stoked!

I finally got a hold of Pat A, and I was right! That was Dave Dowd's local bar! Look for his motorcycle parked out front. Pat A had unfortunately lost his number. He said just ask for him at the bar. I love Boulder! I can tell which bar my friend would like to hang out at just by looking at it, and they have 30 packs of Pabst for $10 on sale.

So, we lit a joint, because it's legal, and burned it up right there! Another Colorado plus! Dowd went to the shows, but we never did see each other inside.

A couple of minutes later, Pete Rasato rolled up on his chrome and black Harley with his wife Kate on the back. Pete is an amazing guy, and I see him more and more at shows now that we're older. Pete and Kate have an adult daughter they've brought to shows, and two teenage sons who love skateboarding like I do. It's really cool that we still have a lot in common outside of the Dead. We hung out with them for a bit and made plans to meet up the next day for the show.

We ended up on Pearl St. and it is a lot *less* hippy than it used to be. As with everywhere now, it's been bought up and fixed up. It still has a lot of the early vibe left though. I saw the street jugglers and the fire breathers and even got spare changed, as always.

It was the Fourth of July, and everyone was in town to see the fireworks. Sadly, a huge rainstorm soaked everyone, but the fireworks went on as planned.

Steve hooked up with some chick, as usual, and I slept in the rental on the street. Boulder is chill. I can see why so many of my old friends decided to stay and live there.

268.
CALI BROS!

Duby and Chris are old friends, and at the time, lived in totally different parts of California. Ironically enough, they met up on the same plane, even though neither one planned it or told the other one they were going out to the shows. We picked up Duby and our new friend Chris, in the "always rent white" rental, and off we went.

We rolled and smoked a few fatties on the way out of Denver International on the drive to the hotel to drop our gear off and shower. Duby neglected to tell us the room number when he gave us the key. We only got the floor number. He walked off and none of us thought to ask, so Chris tried every single door on the floor. Several people opened the door and stared out at us with unhappy faces. He tried 50 rooms as we laughed super hard at the fact that we tried so many and not one worked!

Duby finally came back and told us he gave us the wrong key. He opened a pale green room door we had already tried once, and in we went. Another laugh and yet another rent a snore for a short, but comfy place to crash after the show. I was trying with great effort to become *unaccustomed* to the car seat, after sleeping in it three times in four days already on this trip, and a room was the perfect thing for us.

269.

MACHINE GUNS ON SHAKEDOWN STREET.

Folsom Field

Boulder, CO

7/5-6/2019

The day of the first show in northern Colorado was gorgeous. Perfect weather and clear blue sunny skies. We got a spot in a lot on the well-kept campus, amongst old trees and lots of green grass. Joelle and her roommate Andrew had arrived. We'd been looking for them as we walked down through the campus to see what Shakedown was like here at Folsom Field.

The UC Boulder Campus is a military based college and has a heavy-duty security presence. Uniformed military and campus police with fully automatic weapons standing around just making sure all is well. Which it was. The lot was super chill. Everyone was vending and no one seemed to be getting into any trouble. Only saw one poor guy in cuffs. We sat on the grass and did dabs at the top of Shakedown, and only got told once by a cop to, "Knock that shit off and put that stuff away!"

It was summer, hot, and I was getting super sunburned as usual. I kept going back to the car to reapply my screen and grab a few extra cold PBRs. I always have an iced-up cooler on lock! Ya gotta have it! After a few of those round trips, time went by and soon we had to go into the show.

Like I've been saying, it was hot as fuck, so I only wore a *Thrasher* T-shirt, shorts, Jason Jessee style socks, and my Vans. We stood in line for a while, but it wasn't nearly as bad as The Gorge a month earlier.

Ferd and I found our seats in Section 110 in the middle of the stands in the back, and the rest of our crew went down to the floor. We sat in front of these three young Heads who reminded us of us back in the day. Young and free and doing something memorable with this time in their lives!

Ferd met some girls, as always, and they started up a conversation about the Mexico shows. They had been the previous year and we wanted info about what it's like at those shows. They assured us it was the best time, and totally worth it.

Ferd and I high fived as the band hit the stage in the sweet afternoon sunshine. They opened with a killer "Not Fade Away," and were ripping through it when the clouds set in, and the raindrops started. Slowly at first, and then harder and harder. Still in full sunshine at this point, but darkening fast. The whole stadium was rocking and dancing in the warm rain and it was fucking magic. That was quickly changing though. By the time "Not Fade" ended, the clouds had almost covered the blue sky and sunshine.

270.
FROZEN IN THE SUMMERTIME.

Colorado gets fierce storms and one just rolled up on all 30,000 of us by surprise. The sunny summer rain shower turned cold, windy, and extremely rainy all in a half a Dead song. The band obliged the weather gods, and broke into "Cold Rain and Snow" as the second and most appropriate song of the night so far! As they ripped through it, the rain ripped through us. It was gnarly. We got totally and completely drenched in five minutes. The band played through a slightly shorter version of "Cold Rain" and then left the stage after a "Give us a little time," line from Bobby into the mic.

The UC campus has huge, covered, sports practice areas for the winter, and they use those to get people out of the stadium and away from lightning at summer shows. Colorado has some big lightning, that's for sure!

Of course, Ferd and I were at the back of the line, trying to get to the dry areas, and ended up standing there in the downpour shivering, and waiting for the herd to make its way to dry ground.

We finally got under the grandstands and headed to the men's bathroom. Ferd was so cold he dropped his shorts around his ankles at the urinal, grabbed his nuts with both his hands, and said super loud, "My nuts are fucking frozen," as he rubbed them to try to somehow get them back to "normal scrotum temperature." The bathroom was extra crowded. Some laughed, and some turned away from the site. A bare ass, grown man with his pants at his feet holding his *iceticles* in the public men's room of a Boulder Dead show. I was laughing my ass off as he was freezing his balls off!

The rain stopped, the band came back onstage, and they jumped right into the ender of "Cold Rain" without seeming to miss a beat. Dancing dried us off and we had a great rest of the night!

271.
JOELLE AND LAURA.

The plan had been to meet up with my old snowboard friend Joelle and her roommate Andrew. They missed a flight and missed the first night, so we searched for and found them in the afternoon, before the second show. It had been a few years since I had seen her, and I picked her up and gave her a big-huge hug!

Joelle and our late friend Laura, (RIP) both lived in Government Camp, the little town on the side of Mt. Hood. We all snowboarded and partied for years with only vague references about the Dead between us. Years later Laura got terminally ill and had a desire to see as many Dead and Company shows as she could. Joelle got on the bus and Laura and her went to every Dead and Co. and Dead related show they could fit in.

I wish I had been able to see shows with them. Our small group of friends we tour with always has her memory with us wherever we go. We love you, Laura. Say hi to Imbob!

272.
MISSING FLIGHTS AND STARTING FIGHTS.

Ferd got the tickets and some weird plane flight deals, and we geared up quick for the Fall Run on the East Coast. Last minute shit, but we said fuck it and went for it.

The day of my red-eye flight to NYC to catch the first half of the Fall Run Tour was brutal. I was so caught up trimming my summer weed crop, then sealing and sending it ahead, that I started running late to catch my flight. I had to meet Ferd and drop his car off at our friend mechanic Larry's house, just before the flight, but I got lost when a freeway cut through a neighborhood that GPS didn't tell me about. That made me even later and forced Ferd to go to the airport in the car he was supposed to drop off. TC, his roommate, was to drive my car home after dropping us off, but now we had two cars at the airport and only one driver. Perfect start!

My high anxiety about missing my nice sleep filled flight just went up to red again, as I realized that even if I parked in short term and skated through the airport, I would not make my flight. Ferd made it through security with barely enough time, and I drove home ultra pissed-off and ready to bag the whole first half of the fucking tour.

My lady Naomi was still up when I got back and heard all my frustrations. She's the coolest, and just said to try and fix it and went to bed. I spent the next two hours on the phone with the airlines and got a 6 am flight out. I woke her up, and she thought we had just gone to sleep. She said, "You're a fucking asshole." But then she woke up a little, gave me a

333

kiss, said she loved me, and to text her when I arrive. She is the coolest girl ever!

My crazy buddy Red Beard Scott doesn't sleep much, and he was wide awake at 4 am, listening to vinyl from his truly insane record collection. I drove over and he was happy to drop me off at the airport at that ungodly departure time. He also watches my dog! (Thanks man).

273.
RETURN TO MADISON SQUARE GARDEN.

Dead and Company

Madison Square Garden

New York City, NY

10/31 - 11/1/2019

Got through security and didn't get indecently searched by Gay TSA this time. That was nice, once is enough. Slept on the flight as much as I could and landed in Newark. Got a $13 train to Penn Station, NYC, walked up the old familiar yellow stairs and popped out right in front of the infamous Madison Square Garden.

The first thing I noticed besides the sirens, noises and smells, was that the newspaper boxes out front were gone, and a little shop was there in front now. In 1987 at the five-night Fall Garden run, a beat cop swooped up on us smoking out in front of those long-gone newspaper boxes. A guy we had been touring with gave up about a gram when the cop said, "Whoever has the weed, hand it over now." We *all* had weed, but he thought fast and gave the cop the smallest amount any of us had. He knew we all had bags but gave his up because he was almost out.

The cop looked all of us in the eyes, turned and tossed the knotted up little bag behind the bolted down paper boxes where he knew we could still see it, but we could never get to it. The bastard! No one got arrested, but the cop was true New York and fucked with us by doing that. And he knew it! It was probably his best story of the night to tell the boys back at the station. "Hey Frankie, get this! I threw those fuckin-hippies' weed away in plain sight. Yeah, yeah, behind the New York Post boxes, they could see it and everything. But couldn't reach it, ha-ha. They ain't never getting that shit back, ha-ha-ha-ha-ha."

It's funny how a weird little memory like that can come rushing back into your head after so many years of not being there. I found this to be true many times over on this leg of tour. All the places you revisit bring back all the smaller memories to fill in blanks time has slowly faded. Soon all the color floods back in and you remember more and more of your past. It's amazing, fun, refreshing, cozy and comforting. Even if it was a memory of almost getting arrested for weed in NYC.

274.
THE PENNSYLVANIA IS THE SAME!

After I had that little flashback, I went across the street to the ancient Pennsylvania Hotel. I rolled into this old cool spot and met up once again with Duby, Joelle (my fucking tour homies now!), and was introduced to MDOT Dylan.

MDOT Dylan got his name by drunkenly taking a Minnesota Department of Transportation (MDOT) dump truck home–which just happened to have the keys in it–instead of an getting Uber. Seven destroyed parked cars later, he finally pulled over and sat and waited for the cops. They didn't even beat him down. In Portland they would have shot him dead.

Upstairs, Duby showed me how we didn't need a room key. You can just open the door with the entry card by slipping it in the inch-wide crack in the door frame. I made a mental note about that since I often lose room keys, and in we went to our little, new, and humid temporary tiny home!

Ferd was asleep, taking up a whole bed and snoring as always. I made everyone shut up and let him sleep, and we went to get beer. We both had rough all-night flights. Sleep for him, beer for me!

The room we had on the ninth floor contained two small beds and we had six medium size people. The supposed *air conditioner* put out warm air and it was hot as fuck in the room from the humidity. It was 75 degrees and balmy warm on Halloween day.

Joelle immediately stole the cushions off the couch outside the elevator and filled in the gap between the wall and one of the beds and claimed her little Tinkerbell time out spot. I slept on the floor like always. Duby stayed up all night cackling on acid and never slept, and MDOT Dylan and Ferd took the beds.

275.

THE FERD WALL.

No one wants to share a bed with Ferd because he's a sprawler, and moves around all night, and ends up cuddling you or putting his arm over you. It's just plain creepy.

If any of us must share a bed with him, we make what we call a Ferd Wall. You get chair cushions and a blanket and make a wall down the center of the bed. Then you wrap the sheets around yourself on the wall side so he can't slip *under* the wall. He's tricky! He breaks through! At that point though, outside of his constant–from when he falls asleep to when he wakes, no matter what position– snoring, you're pretty Ferd free for the night.

I snore as well, loudly. So does Joelle and so does MDOT Dylan. None of us are innocent of sounding like a dying elk when we sleep, but Ferd always wins!

276.
NEW YORK IS AWESOME!

We cruised out through the Penn's well-worn marble lobby and hit the streets for real NYC pizza slices and beers! Never miss eating pizza in NYC, it is a triple must for everyone! Ten different kinds in five blocks! All different, yet all NYC style and all awesome!

After a few super tall boys and slices, more memories came flooding back. I got my bearings for that part of the city and suddenly I knew my way around again. I finally started to relax. I had been so busy and stressed I had forgotten it was Halloween. I just thought a lot of people in NYC, much like Portland, just dress weird.

I finally put it together in my tired airplane brain and immediately wished I had a costume also. I always dress up on Halloween. It's my favorite holiday but it just didn't happen, so I just rolled with it! I took a little bit of a mushroom and spent my time looking at everyone else's costumes instead!

Tyshawn Jones had just become *Thrasher Magazine's* Skater of the Year, so I went and found the spot where his *Thrasher* cover was shot. I was amazed at how tall the railings are in front of the Garden that Franky Spears ollied up onto. Chest high and a shitty crack in the run up, for his double page *Thrasher* spread. I'm also a skateboard tourist, what can I say!

The shows were insane, and The Garden had not lost one bit of her famous energy. The crowds were sending up huge collective roars outside, just waiting to get in! The hallways were filled with hoots and hollers. The Garden still looks the same, just shinier! Like much of New York does now.

The upper sections were redone and they had TV screens all over the place, but the high-time vibe was still the same. We were in Madison Square Garden and it's on! Let's fucking do this!

We all got seats in far different areas of the Garden, so it was a, go over here, go over there, sort of a show. I like those best! I like to check out every part of the scene! Dance around and be with everyone!

Duby and I hung out way up in the top row smoking out. A guy was sitting next to us, and I offered him a hit. I mentioned Oregon and he said he went to snowboard camp on Mt. Hood as a teenager. Turns out he went to the camp I was Head Coach at, and he was in Dead fan Dave Dowd's coaching group. Jack is his name, and now we see him on tour at every show we attend! Small world made smaller by a wonderful rock and roll group and snowboarding!

Pete and Kate were at these shows, as were Ernest and Kelly. Clark was also there from Portland. I had years of friends from many eras, and we were all back for one thing. The main thing. The music! The glue!

277.

NITROUS OR NOTROUS? WHAT WAS THE QUESTION?

The Nitrous Oxide scene has gone completely crazy on tour in the last few years.

It's super fun for me to do a balloon now and again and I'm not criticizing anyone's party, but this shit has gotten out of hand. Thousands and thousands of balloons get huffed and dropped, and a multicolored discarded balloon carpet soon emerges on the ground under your feet.

The extremely organized crews who sell nitrous are equipped with radios, earphones, and mics. They have a jump on the undercover cops via scouts watching the whole parking lot, and get away plans with designated places to stash the tanks. Sometimes nitrous turf wars erupt like I witnessed in Dallas on Summer 2019 Tour.

Now, I must say, Ferd and I got to know all these guys because we went to a lot of the shows and see them in every Shakedown in every city. We all say what's up, smoke some weed, trade a few balloons for our killer weed, talk about the shows or the drive. Normal tour shit. I'm here, you're here, we're all here. It's just like that.

One of the main crew bosses out there is this big guy who's always super friendly, but it's *extremely* clear he runs the show. His balloon guys sell it in the lot, his money runners bring back the cash from the balloon sellers and his muscle guards the profits someplace off Shakedown.

He walks around and supervises and keeps other sellers out of his turf. In the middle of Shakedown at 3 in the afternoon, him and another quite large nitrous salesman from another crew got into a super-heated shouting match. Face to face, inches apart, yelling about who's turf it is. This isn't normal at a Dead show, and this time no happy hippy was saying, "Hey kind brothers, can't you just get along?" like they normally might. Our big friend leaned right into the gas intruder's face, reached down, opened the valve, and drained his $2,000 tank of nitrous until it was empty and kicked it over. Then he turned and stood up tall, looked the guy straight in the eyes one more time and turned and walked off. He claimed his turf as the deflated nitrous tank rolled away on the slight incline of the parking lot and the evicted gas seller had to go pick up his empty tank with empty pockets.

Dallas was cool about the gas sales and so was Boulder, Colorado. The Halloween 2019 shows at Madison Square Garden the cops didn't do anything. Just stood there and let it happen. Three full city blocks directly in front of the venue became Nitrous Land until 4 am. It was fun and no one had a problem with it.

But when we got to Nassau Coliseum a few days later, things were way fucking different. The cops were out in full force, some undercover and some in uniform making a heavy presence. Here's how shit was going down on Shakedown.

First, the cops let it all start to happen, then, when they know the crews have made some money (the cops confiscate the cash of course, so why not wait till the gas guys make a profit, right?) and start to get comfortable, then the undercover cops come lurking in. We had parked the always rent white rental (white cars get pulled over the least, red, and yellow cars the most. Fact.) one row back from Shakedown like we always do. Ferd and I like to be close to our weed and skateboards.

After the nitrous crews came out and got hustling, the cops started the sting. Suddenly ten nitrous sellers from one crew would be running full speed, all holding balloons with one guy carrying the tank and six fast undercovers right on their asses.

It takes a purchase before they can bust you because nitrous itself isn't illegal. It is illegal to resell without a special license (normally you need to be a doctor or dentist) and certainly not to be sold in kiddie balloons in a dirty Long Island parking lot.

The crews all work in groups in the lot, and all stay in the little section they established. Another crew is selling balloons 50 feet away and so on, all around the lot. The cops know this and try to get a whole crew all at once, because they know they'll all run together to try to get away. One cop goes in and makes a buy, walks a few feet away, and here comes the cop tsunami down on the balloon vendor. A scout yells or whistles and everyone in that crew runs in the preplanned escape route.

Three different sets of crews swarmed by us within 30 minutes. Ten dudes running full speed holding up sagging pants, cradling a tank like a football, opening the valve and draining it, all the while throwing down packs of empty balloons. A sale, nitrous gas, and possession of balloons with intent to fill all adds up to criminal charges. On the other hand, if you drop your balloons and empty your tank before they catch you, all they have is an empty tank. The initial guy who did the sale is always busted, but sometimes the others will get let go because they got rid of the shit quick enough.

Now, that was *not* the case for the third crew that ran by us. They *all* got busted. Ferd and I were standing by the rental and here came another crew, running away. The cops were right up their asses this time. They tackled a few guys to the pavement and grabbed the rest by their necks or arms. One guy got body slammed onto the car right behind our rental, denting the hell out of whoever's hood it was. A big ass cop knocked the wind out of a kid with a tackle then told him, "You're caught, don't resist!" as he held him with his elbows behind his back. The cops took the whole fucking crew in.

As we were driving out of the lot, we saw the crew boss of the busted crew getting cuffed up. It looked to us like he backed his crew and went down with them. That's a solid motherfucker right there. Take the hit with your guys and don't leave them to take the fall.

278.
LOVE MY CONNECTICUT FRIENDS!

Ferd and I usually roll in the always rent white rental at night. It's easier and safer and there's a lot less traffic.

We picked up a white Jeep in Jersey after we picked up our weed and headed up the Turnpike to where I grew up. Bethel, Connecticut. Fourth to eleventh grade. Basically, my real childhood hometown since I lived there longest.

I had met E and Kelly at the Garden shows as I mentioned, had a blast, and now we needed to go up and visit the rest of my old friends!

Ferd and I drove up to Connecticut from Jersey on a gorgeous fall day. Sunny and warm.

Mark and his father Edwin live in the two historic houses on the 18-acre, 300-year-old Rockwell family farm. It's a beautiful setting tucked into the western part of the state. It sits on Rockwell Road, down the street from the town's first school, Anna H. Rockwell School, which just happens to be about a mile down the road from the current Anna H. Rockwell Elementary School.

Mark and his wife Kathleen live in a super cool, rustic cabin on the south end of the property, next to a winding brook. You pass his dad's house and the 1700s barn first, before you get to Mark's spot.

Mark, Kathleen, Kurt, his wife Doreen, E and Kelly were already there. Heather showed up shortly thereafter, and my high school version of *Friends* was right there in front of me.

It's always fun to see old buddies and this time was no exception. We partied, drank and smoked, as we reminisced about all the good times we had in our youth. We talked about shows we saw together and shows we want to see together in the future.

It was super fun to see them and I'm grateful we still have similar things in common all these years later. Thank you rock and roll for keeping us together!

279.
FANTASY SETS ABOUND!

Nassau Coliseum
Uniondale, NY
11/5-6/2019

Nassau gave us two more epic shows with the band stretching out and playing tight!

It is far easier to write about the highlights of a Grateful Dead show than it is to write about the highlights of a Dead and Co. show. The reason for this dilemma is called the *Fantasy Set*.

Grateful Dead sets tended to be reasonably predictable with songs happening in certain parts of the show. First set songs and second set songs, with not a lot of variation. Every three or four shows you're going to get a "Me and My Uncle" in the first set and a "Truckin'" in the second set. "Little Red Rooster" was almost always played in the third to fifth song slot. Anyone ever hear a second set "Rooster?"

These days, the set list is all over the place. Any song can be paired with any other song, and it's all good. We only got weird-exciting groupings of songs occasionally, on a *special* night.

I can't imagine what would have happened if the Grateful Dead did an "Easy Wind"-"Cumberland"-"Casey Jones"-"Here Comes Sunshine"-"Saint Stephen"-"William Tell"-"Eleven"-"Comes a Time"-"Going Down the Road," before the "Drums," in the '80s. Half the crowd would have keeled over drooling and in shock, and the other half would have been tapping every taper in the venue on the shoulder begging, "Can I please get a copy of that?"

Fantasy sets, or voyeur sets, came into play after Jerry had passed. They evolved out of the natural course of the musicians having to ask each other what they wanted to play with each new band incarnation. The Grateful Dead played together so often and were so tight that a set list wasn't needed then. Later, it was. Hence the dawn of the Fantasy Set! Long live the Fantasy Set!

The set list I refer to is an actual combination (in order) of part of the first set, and part of the second, from the first night in Nassau 2019. I didn't even need to make a fantasy set up. Just reading through the set prior to writing this made me want to write this!

Second night was equally epic with the sets touching down on, and roping together the usual, "Help"-"Slip"-"Franklin's." They then did "Dark Star," followed by Coltrane's "A Love Supreme," back into "Dark Star!" What the fuck? Mind blowing song combinations every single night!

This compact, little, six show East Coast Tour was raging! Once you got in the doors and the music started, it blossomed uniquely and fantastically with every performance.

280.
TRASHMORE!

Hampton Coliseum

Hampton, VA

11/8-9/2019

Ferd and I drove all night down to Virginia. We passed over several large, gorgeous, insanely lit up bridges, jamming to Flower Travellin' Band and Djam Karet as the miles clicked by. We arrived just after daybreak, only to find you cannot enter the lot until sometime dumb like 2 pm. We didn't know what to do so I looked up skateparks, even though we just drove all night.

We skated a tiny prefab park which sucked, but then we found the legendary Mt. Thrashmore Vert Ramp. It's fucking gigantic! Ferd and I climbed up and stood on the platform. It was a long drop in, down to the flat. Twelve feet easy. Vert skaters are gnarly! It felt cool to be at Trashmore. Built over a garbage dump in the 1980s, it has been on the skate map ever since.

A legendary skate venue, as we were heading to the final Dead and Company shows at an equally legendary venue. Yes, I'm speaking of The Hampton Coliseum, also known as The Mother Ship. Sadly, after some of the best shows ever, by all types of bands, they would be tearing her down later that year.

281.
NO VENDING, WELL, SOME VENDING.

Hampton had tons of cops, just like Nassau! This time they were checking everyone's vending tags to see if they paid the licensing fees to Dead and Co. to legally sell things on Shakedown. This was a new one to me. I didn't even know you could get a legal vending pass to sell stuff besides photos. They shut a few unpermitted people down, but mainly they just cruised around in cars or on horses making a presence.

Hampton is fun and sits in a nice tree lined parking lot next to a cool little lake. Everyone has played there over the years. We thought it might be a little cooler, but the undercovers soon reared their ugly little heads by busting a few people. That once again shut me down selling any weed openly in the parking lot that day. I still did some weed trades and got a shirt for my lady back home, but it was nothing but a bust if you tried any harder than that.

Dead and Company let the place go to the wrecking ball in true and proper fashion, with sizzling shows to say farewell to one of the best. A ripping "Bertha" opened, and the place was on its feet for the rest of the night!

An 11-minute "Good Lovin'," a 15-minute "Shakedown," and a 14-minute "They Love Each Other," and those are just three songs from an eight song first set! They played almost 80 minutes in that set alone! That's why I went back on tour! To *see* shows just like this and not *miss* shows just like this! The second set was equally stellar! Give it a listen or three!

282.
SKATE AND ANNOY.

After the last show, I was walking through Shakedown with my skateboard in my hand and a clearly wasted guy says, "Hey bro, lemme do a kick flip bro," through eyes that were almost shut. I said, "All right" because sometimes the person will fool you and snap a big old popped and proper kick-flip. But not this guy. He did one and only half flipped it. One turned into five, which turned into ten. He ate shit twice, was drunkenly determined and soon was at fifteen tries on his way to twenty. He kept half flipping my brand-new Real deck onto the grip tape on a sidewalk so rough you could barely ride on it. He zung out twice and shark bit (when a skateboard smashes you on the shin with its nose or tail) a girl on the shin. She was pissed. He was unaware and undeterred. I was getting annoyed. He tried twice more and then he fell on his drunk ass.

I grabbed my hammered-on board, took off in the parking lot and didn't turn back to look at him or even say anything. I had only been riding that board for a week. He fucked up the nose and tail in 20 flip attempts, and it looked like I had been riding it for a month. Flipping fool.

I was a little bit stressed out by this, and the fact that I had to fly all night and switch planes with five minutes to spare in Denver. Just as I was feeling most stressed, I saw a green sticker with white letters on a vending table on Shakedown that read, *One show at a time*! It was ironic, perfectly timed, and it brought my spirits up right when I needed it most. That's one of the cool things about the Dead scene. Something as small as a Dead sticker with a few perfectly combined words on it, can make your whole day brighten up and magically make all the stress go away.

Ferd and I drove in relative silence. I think he was still a little high on acid and I was just plain burnt out. Not a lot to say after so many days of traveling together. Just mellow thoughts of the last six shows we just saw! Sometimes that's the best way to end a part of a tour. High five and say see you back home.

283.

A SKATEBOARD FOR A PILLOW.

I walked towards the revolving doors, as the always rent white rental drove away for the last time on this tour. Ferd was going to Jersey to see his folks. My head revolved into the ghost town that is Norfolk International at 1 am. No one around, only a few lone workers pushing a broom or a vacuum. I got a spot in a dark corner on a hard floor and got a few hours of uncomfortable sleep before I headed to Denver and then on to Portland.

My flight out of Norfolk was smooth and uneventful and I slept even more. When we got to Denver, another plane was clogging up our arrival gate and we had to wait on the tarmac for a while. All I wanted to do was catch my connector to Portland, and after we finally deplaned, I remembered how big Denver Airport really is. It's fucking huge! I was in B concourse at the very end gate. I speed walked all the way, hustling. Then I had to take a train to C concourse, then go to the last gate at the end of C. But I read the flight wrong and I was at the end of C 1-30, not C 30-60, which is where I needed to be. I stopped to look at the departure board again and my flight wasn't even on the board now. I'm dead tired, haven't smoked any weed and my body was killing me from sleeping on floors and in cars.

I decided if I'm going to make it, I needed to skate to my gate and fast. I tossed down my board and started pushing. I had soft Bones wheels and took off on the polished marble floors. Those floors are super-fast! I was zig zagging around all the other travelers, hauling ass. It wasn't that crowded, but still enough where I had a few close, close calls. My wheels rolled from marble floor to carpet floor to people mover, clack, clack, clack, and back full speed.

I didn't hit anyone until right before my actual gate. I came off the carpet, stopped pushing and slowed down just as a guy with a baseball hat turned hard right in front of me, headed for the bathroom. I hit him with a good amount of forward momentum, and I went flying as my board rammed his roller bag. I slid about four or five feet on the marble, jumped up, and helped him up. Myself and his bag took most of it. I said, "Sorry," and he said, "It's okay, I'm late too. Just go man." And I did.

I made the plane, sweating and with high anxiety, but at least I made it. Bad thing is my knee didn't survive. It's already bone on bone and worn out, but when I rammed into the guy, I tweaked it and it turned into a fat cantaloupe, not a knee anymore.

I arrived in Portland, and Red Beard's wife Elizabeth picked me up with two beers and a bowl waiting for me in the car. I was stoked to be home and glad my friends had time to come get me, because I'd be limping around for the next month.

284.
DRIVING WITH DUBY!

New Year's Eve
Chase Center
San Francisco, CA
12/30-31/2019

I drove to Duby's weed farm way the fuck out in the sticks, east of Stockton. I didn't get paid before I left because my weed trimming job wasn't finished, so I once again took off on a Dead trip on a wing and a prayer. No money and barely enough gas.

I had $74 when I left Portland. Two cases of Pabst, weed, bread, cheese, meat, and a topped off tank. I took my lawn mower gas can, which was half full, in case I ran out along the way. I figured I could survive on that for four days, and away I went, heading south for my first New Year's Eve with the Dead since The Other Ones show with Jimmy Herring on guitar in 2002. That '02 NYE, incidentally, was the first time Ferd and I saw a Dead gig together! We had been in the same stadiums back in the early '90s, but we hadn't become friends yet.

Duby's lovey dog Tilda woke me up on the floor by licking my face and dripping the water she just drank all over my head. It was light out now and I could see how cool it was there in central California. It sort of looks like the set from *M*A*S*H* and you're kind of expecting Hawkeye to come driving up the dirt road in a green jeep. Crazy landscape. Hilly with stunted, awkwardly growing oaks, eucalyptus trees and lots of short scrub grass.

We packed up the tail gating gear and headed down to San Francisco. Joelle and Andrew missed yet another flight and had to catch a two-part flight that went from Minnesota to Arizona before they got to San Francisco, and they missed the entire first show. Again!

Duby had gotten us the tickets on his credit card, so now it was up to him to resell them. It took a bit of time, since you're forced to deal with suck ass online tickets, but some Head was happy to have them!

It seemed like Joelle and I were having a race to see how many flights we could miss trying to be on this tour, but she finally prevailed and missed more flights than me between the shows in NYC and San Francisco.

285.
FLIPPER AIN'T A DOLPHIN.

The show was epic, and it sounded good in the Chase Center. A new building with awesome acoustics is always a good sign.

The new Chase Center is super, super steep in the upper seats. Duby and I had long snowboard careers riding crazy mountain runs, dropping cliffs, and it seemed steep to *us*.

We were in Section 223, Row 10 and a young couple was sitting with an older guy in the row in front of us. The older guy hung out for a few songs until intermission. The three of them talked for a while and then he got up to walk down the aisle to the lobby. He tripped on the seat back in front of him and went face first over the seats and down. He fell forward and did three full body flips, totally stretched out flat like he was planking. He bounced down 16 rows of seats and ended up sitting upright on a short staircase. It made the most horrible sound. That limp body thud. No one likes hearing that. We thought he was dead.

But, no! He sat there for 20 minutes as a medical team checked him out. He moved his arms and legs, and rotated his head and neck, and eventually stood up. He ended up walking away to a big round of applause from a whole lot of concerned and worried Dead Heads. Had he been lower down in the section, he very easily could have tumbled right over the edge and down into the crowd below.

Hey, Fall Guy! If you ever read this, I hope you're okay and have no lasting injuries or pain. Since your fall is forever burned into my brain from seeing it happen while I was on mushrooms, your spectacular tumble got you into this book!

286.

NITROUS TANKS A SCREAMING!

Ferd and Natalie showed up with a full tank of nitrous, straight from a dentist's office, and we stuck it in the trunk for the after party.

Andrew and Joelle had to reroute through Phoenix and finally met up with us at the hotel after the show they sadly missed. We had the nitrous tank and about a dozen people, and we stormed the hotel room with our noisy gas party. Nitrous tanks are loud-as-fuck. There is no disguising the shrill sound of a tank filling up a balloon. It's like a little jet engine and that sound goes through walls, doors, and windows equally well.

The hotel had a little walkway outside our windows, and we had them open to let the weed smoke out. I went down to the car in the basement parking garage for more beer and could still hear the tank screaming from inside our room!

A guy we saw checking in said he could hear it in his room on the third floor, so I said he might as well come in and join the party, and he did! Him and his friends became our friends and we all ended up seeing Phil together at TXR on January 1st. This drunken, smokey, noise fest went on until about 4 am, and no one complained at all. The hotel was sold out. There were only a few rooms with Dead Heads and the rest were total civilians, and we still got no complaints. I was amazed!

287.
NEW YEAR'S EVE AND THE NAMING OF LSANDREW!

We slept in until about ten the next morning. New Year's Eve-day! The weather was absolutely perfect, so we went to Haight St., had pizza, beers, and went to the fantastic Amoeba Music store. We stopped in front of the Grateful Dead's old house at 710 Ashbury and did the Grateful Dead tourist thing.

We took a few pics but spent most of our time trying to convince Chris to stay for the NYE show. He promised his wife he would be home, and he was not being swayed by us. We kept telling him, "How bad can it be? It's just a divorce." Funny shit like that to ease the fact that he had to go home. We eventually parted ways with him, until the next time.

Then we absorbed the epic day, and walked along the end of Golden Gate Park down by Kezar Stadium in the perfect San Francisco winter sunshine. We had the full tailgating package in the car (grill, full cooler, spices, table, chairs, and a nitrous tank) and Duby had stopped at the store to get some prime cuts to grill up outside the Chase Center.

We ended up parking right in front on the Chase side of the street. One of the three Shakedowns (several small parking lots at the Chase so Shakedown gets spread out) was right across from us. We took out the lawn chairs and the full cooking package. Duby got his grill on and Ferd started filling up balloons for everyone! It was a lazy, hazy feast in the warm San Francisco winter, and it fueled us up for the rest of the night.

We had to move the car to off street parking at 6 pm or get towed. We drove it all the way down to the pier parking lot almost under the Bay Bridge.

Duby had a vile of liquid LSD and Andrew was ready to do some. Duby (over?) poured a few drops onto Andrew's hand, and he licked it right up without even blinking. It was several hits, not just one. Thus, the dawn of Andrew's new nickname, LSanDrew!

We had a little time before we had to head in since the show was starting later than normal. This allowed us to celebrate New Year's Eve in a more relaxed manner. Little did we know what was coming.

We did our usual fucking around, trying to get it together before we went inside. An act that has been constantly repeated over and over throughout the years. The nitrous tank that never stops giving had thrown its anchor in our water as well. Hard to motivate if you can't walk.

LSanDrew had gotten a lot less vocal, which is not his style, at all. I looked at him for a moment and I could tell that his acid trip was coming on strong, and it was going to be a heavy one. I worked on getting my own shit together and noticed LSanDrew had gotten into the back seat of the always rent white rental, and was hunched up holding his knees like he was cold. He was also staring into the back of the headrest, like it contained some magic clue about the origins of man or some other fascinating universe altering message.

I asked Joelle to get him going, since we did have a show to see. She opened the door and he sort of scrunched himself up even more. Joelle had to coax him out of the car, telling him the show is going to start. He got out, Joelle goes back to getting her show stuff sorted, and the next thing we know LSanDrew is back in the backseat of the car, scrunched up and staring at the back of the headrest again. This time he did not want to get out and he looked a little scared. Joelle started giving him shit (they share a house, so she knows how to get him going) saying, "Get out of the fucking car and don't fucking get back in!" He finally got out, with huge saucer eyes, and Duby quickly locked the doors so he couldn't do it another time. Something truly fantastic must have been playing on the back of the headrest, but only LSanDrew will ever know what it was!

We had a six-block walk to the Chase and LSanDrew kept slowing down or just stopping. We would notice he wasn't with us, and would turn around to find him standing there on the sidewalk looking around. Joelle would go back and retrieve him and a block later he would do it again. This happened three times, and on the fourth time he sat down on a ledge in front of a building, and didn't want to get back up. It's clear he was way too high and had already started to hallucinate. Joelle went and sat with him for a few minutes and told him we needed to go inside now.

Somehow that got through his overwhelmed head, and he got up and walked the rest of the distance with us. It took a bit to get in through the usual crowd and it was clear LSanDrew was on a different dimensional level than we were. At this point it's the three of us. Joelle, LSanDrew and myself. We got our tickets ripped and headed in. Joelle and I looked left and right to find our seats on the directories on the wall and LSanDrew disappeared. Just like that. High as fuck and already gone. Two minutes in. This was the beginning of an adventure that lasted all night.

LSanDrew ended up abandoning his cell phone on the floor in the lobby because the government was *inside* it. Therefore, we couldn't call him to find him.

Joelle and I found some short-lived seats and after four or five songs we got separated as well. I went up to the mid-section in the back and danced behind the guy with the burgundy top hat and wheelchair, his girl who sells beer and water on Shakedown, and my man with glasses and the wild dreads who always sells posters. I see them at all the shows and even though I barely know them, they always have a good vibe. It's just like that at a Dead show. I had a little space to chill, and it sounded great in that area.

I found LSanDrew at set break for a minute, looking wild eyed and not making a lot of sense. I was standing with Alan Stein in the beer line. We turned around and, once again, he was gone.

288.
ON TOWARDS MIDNIGHT!

The show was epic! Right away we got "Midnight Hour" as a "Now you have to wait 'til the midnight hour" show opener. Then we were treated to two more sets after the first! The "Eyes" was one of the best Dead and Company versions I've seen, and I'd seen a lot during the past half year.

Just before twelve, Trixie Garcia and Sunshine Kesey took off from a secret runway in the audience and flew #55, a bright red *Steal Your Face* and *Skeleton* adorned biplane around the inside of the arena. Bill Walton was on stage dressed as a giant shimmering Father Time! Wavy Gravy was dressed as a diminutive ancient Baby New Year. An entire chorus line of dancers dressed in 1920s outfits danced across the whole stage. Thousands of balloons came down from the ceiling precisely at midnight, and the band dropped into a mellow but stellar "Sugar Magnolia."

We got twenty-four songs total and spent hours and hours inside the show celebrating another New Year with all our friends, just like so many times before. I love the magic. I cannot escape its gravitational pull and I have no desire to try to resist, at all. Take me with you. I'm in!

And then it was over and I'm suddenly out. Outside, that is, and news of LSanDrew's government infiltrated and subsequently abandoned phone is revealed to all. Now it's up to us to find it for him.

289.
ACID AND NITROUS REGROUP.

Joelle called LSanDrew's phone after the show and someone, somehow was able to answer it. I barely convinced a guard to let me back inside to retrieve it, only to have been told the wrong gate number. I went back out empty handed, and Joelle convinced the same guard to let her back in. She finally found the kind person waiting with the infiltrated phone and she was clearly *not* an agent of the government.

We regrouped with a laugh and walked the long walk all the way down to the last parking lot, right by were the ferry goes across the water to Oakland. Of course, the never-ending nitrous tank is lonely and has been missing us, so we do the proper thing and bring it right back into our party!

It's now about 2 am and we're watching the people in line to get on the ferry to go across the bay. No one is ready to drive, so we just stay put. I have two bottles of Champagne and the cooler is still half full of beer, so we're good! We all do a toast, and we wish each other a good 2020. Little did we know what was coming.

Duby was dosed, high as fuck and being mischievous. Joelle was playing the stereo with Kendrick Lamar and Ice Cube mixed in with Dead songs. Duby would scream out, "DJ Tink on the ones and twos!" His new name for Joelle and her music choices, which he coined a month before in NYC.

Ferd was filling balloons in the back seat. No one wanted to be the balloon filler. It sucks! Everyone just wanted to huff the gas. Duby and I got a little thing going, were we kept handing Ferd balloons to fill so he didn't have time to get out of the car. This allowed us to do balloons freely and we kept giving him compliments and thanks to keep him in there filling. Nice balloon bro! Thanks man!

290.
DAMN YOU DUBY!

Pretty quickly it was 4 am and we figured we should probably split before the cops came to kick us out. Duby kept calling me security all night, so I may as well be. I saw the cops circling, so we slowly packed it in. I was the least high, but still high, so I got the job of driving. Duby on the other hand, was still high as fuck and being even more mischievous than before. I got the whole area clean and got everyone in the car, including the frosty topped nitrous tank.

It's cold, so we put up the windows and attempted to leave. I rolled about 20 feet and Duby opened the screamer valve on the nitrous tank, filling up the inside of the car with gas while I'm trying to drive. Everyone cracks up! I hit the brakes, jump out, and air out the car. As I'm doing this, Duby is yelling, "Security!" at me at the top of his lungs. I got the car aired out, get back in and go. I got about 50 feet this time and here comes the screamer valve, wide open again. I hit the brakes and jump out. Everyone was cracking up like they were listening to Mitch Hedberg, but I had to drive us, no matter what. I needed some cooperation, and it wasn't forthcoming. I was threatening to put the tank in the trunk and that got Duby to chill. He still wanted a balloon for the ride, after all!

Picture four people in a little white rental, three with full, multicolored balloons stuck to their faces, and me trying to herd this bunch of cats full of laughing gas.

I start driving and it's 4:30 by now. Someone on nitrous in the back seat has directions to the hotel and is guiding me. They said go right and I did, and I end up going the wrong way up a one way. It's NYE in San Francisco! Cops are all over the fucking place and my wasted friends are sending me up wrong way streets.

I U-turned quickly, and got back on the right track and back to the hotel, somehow unscathed. Tank off. We crashed as the sun was coming up.

291.
A BIG NEW YEAR'S DAY PHIL SURPRISE!

Phil Lesh,

TXR

Marin, CA

1/1/2020

We were torched the next day and Duby thankfully got the room another night, so we didn't have to get up.

Once we finally did get it together, we went to the airport, then over to TXR in Marin. We heard a cover band was playing that afternoon. We walked up the road past the car lots and went inside. The band was good.

Joelle bought us a round of drinks. We saw our new friends from the nitrous party in our room sitting at a big table. They invited us to sit with them and we did. I started grooving on the band. Then I realized that the singer sounded a lot like Phil. I listened more and the bass sounded exactly like Phil, and no one sounds like Phil, except Phil!

I looked through the glass of the patio and there he was. Big as life! Hi Phil! We had no idea he was set to play. Completely blind-sided and I was so stoked! Phil is my all-time favorite, and I will never sway from that opinion. I hadn't seen Phil perform for two years since he last played Portland, and now I'm here with a beer and fries listening to Phil for free on his own patio! Sometimes things line up perfectly, and this was one of those special sometimes.

292.
OUR FIRST $6000 DEAD SHOW.

Moon Palace

Cancun, Mexico

1/15-20/2020

We all got tickets to PITS. We met Josh and Sally the Minnesota farmers, via Joelle, and our crew was complete. I brought an ounce of weed and some shrooms because this is an epic place to see a show, and I hate finding my shit in Mexico. Party on!

Lizards, Iguanas, friendly feral cats, and weird raccoons live and walk around on the grounds. The lizards are the best and sit and sun themselves all day!

Naomi and I both wore my old Dead clothes from the '80s and '90s. What didn't fit me, fit her. Most of it still fits me though. Am I shrinking now?

Ferd was sending it on the stationary surfer wave ride, then Duby stepped up and dropped some style on us, with his smooth slasher runs. My swollen knee said, "No way Jose," in very clear and painful terms, so I was sidelined and relegated to action camera man.

293.

FIRST NIGHT IN THE SAND!

We all went in as the sun was setting on night one. "Not Fade Away" opener! Sounded epic to us! The sand was warm, and the small waves crept up at us from the calm ocean. We even had a little soft rain during the show. It was a wonderful night.

I found a full LA Kush vape pen Layin' in the Sand at Playin' in the Sand. That thankfully kept me in smoke after mine ran out!

They had awesome sound in this gorgeous beach venue, but my knee was quickly blown out from walking in the shifting sand. I didn't care though. I was in the tropics at a Dead and Company show. That's all that mattered.

It was a giant booze party all day and night. Drunk ass people everywhere! Us included! Waiters and waitresses walked around with unlimited trays of beers and mixed drinks. Open bars are everywhere.

It went like this. Beers at the airport. Beers on the bus. Beers at check in, beers on the room shuttle, beers in the room! The pull-out, hard alcohol bars built into the cabinet next to the mini fridge just added to the booze fest. It never stopped unless we were sleeping.

In the always hungover mornings, I would share a joint with our neighbor, musician Alex Myth, as we looked at the lizards and talked about the song selections from the night before, all the while painfully squinting behind sunglasses!

You're always waiting for something. Food, concert, wrist bands, so they keep you well lubed with booze. Waiting in line I told the story about the "Uncle John's Cabin" guy in Texas and cracked a bunch of people up! Everyone was in a good mood! Mexico is amazing and tropical shows rule!

294.
WHERE ARE THE FINGERS?

Naomi and I were walking around the hotel pool area before the second show and headed down the beach towards the event. Lots and lots of Heads milling about taking the long walk and slowly heading in. It was a normal crowd of Dead Heads, but something was missing. It took me a little while to put my finger on it. And that was the key. I finally realized that we hadn't seen any miracle fingers anyplace at this show. Not even one! It was funny that it was completely absent.

Clearly the reason for it was the hotel and ticket package you had to buy to be on the property, but still, it was strange. To me, it sure was weird not to see the usual 200 people walking around with an "I Need a Miracle" sign in one hand and the traditional index finger pointing to the sky on the other hand.

I made a point of this to Naomi, so she put her finger up and started asking for one, which made us and everyone else laugh, since we were already inside the hotel grounds. It was strange to have something you're totally accustomed to seeing at a Dead show, not be there. You have this sense that something's wrong or out of place when it actually is out of place because it's not even in the place! A few certain elements are always on Dead Tour. When one of the most prominent ones is not there, you notice!

295.
WRIST ON. WRIST OFF.

The show promotors give you wristbands that act as your ticket into the show. It also works as the key to your hotel room door. I was skeptical of the wrist band right away and I was right to be worried. We got to our room and Naomi's wrist band worked to open the door, but mine did not. I went the next morning and had it reprogrammed. It opened the door fine after that.

That afternoon we went up to the gates to figure out the pink wristband game they play for line placement now. While we were standing there, a CID badge wearing guy asked to check our wristbands and scanned them. Me, and about six others, all made jokes about no reentry and that now we won't get in. We laughed it off after he assured us that would *not* happen.

Duby and I got in the line on the beach to get in early and we were up towards the front. Naomi, Joelle and LSanDrew had gotten lost looking for a bathroom and getting more drinks. Boozy times! The line started moving and they had not come back yet. We had excellent line placement and Duby and I were excited to get up close. It sounds killer up close, and you can see them play and you might get in the video of the show later. That's always a fun bonus!

I stuck with Duby until the turnstiles, but I was forced to wait for the others, so I stepped out of line while Duby kept going to get that good spot up front. I was getting a little freaked out because they weren't back and the good line spot we held for two hours just drifted away. Now half the long line was past us and inside before us.

They finally showed up two fisting beers, which made up for the lagging. We made our way through the maze and up to the electronic ticket/wristband check. Everyone went in before me and got a green light, but when I put my wristband up the light turned red. They tell me it's cool, they can fix it. A CID person brought me around the corner to a ticket booth and guess who is standing there also? Duby! He was way up front, and his wristband didn't work either.

He was pissed off and had every right to be. Almost the entire crowd was inside now, and getting to the front was no easy task if you didn't do it early. There was also another guy who was standing with us when the CID guy "checked" our wristbands earlier in the day, and his went red also. It took over 20 minutes to make them work correctly.

Later, when I stumbled back to my room at 2 am, that shitty wristband key did *not* work on my room door anymore. I was under the impression I would be stress free on this all-inclusive stay. Damn-you wrist band!

296.
SILENCING THE SNORES.

We drank all day in the booze tsunami and ended up losing each other around one of the pools sometime after 2 am. Naomi and I wobbled back to the room and passed out. Fuck you, wristband!

We met Joelle, LSanDrew and Duby in the Sunrise lobby the next morning (Ferd was off with Natasha), and we all went to Gondola for breakfast. Joelle ordered drinks and beers for everyone and proceeded to tell us of the previous night's adventures trying to sleep in a room full of partyers.

This was the first of 14 shows in the last half year where I was *not* sharing a room with my crew, and I knew there would be some funny shit going down that I would miss out on. As I've mentioned before, we all snore except Duby, and it drives him nuts. Ferd snores from moment of sleep to moment of awakening, and the rest of us snore off and on throughout the night. Duby has taken to bringing wet towels to bed with him. He then waits until he can't stand the snoring anymore and puts a wet, rolled-up towel in the snoring culprit's mouth, to shut them the fuck up!

His other trick is to lay a wet folded towel over the person's face. It's super funny to see the person react to the towel treatment while fully asleep! Pushing it off, but still passed out. Duby immediately puts it right back on their face, or plugs them right back up if they spit it out of their mouth.

He also splashes water on you, mainly on your face to make you roll over and shut up. It's hilarious to watch if you're still awake, but it fucking sucks if it's you getting the water treatment!

297.
AQUA PHONES!

Back to breakfast. We all go through the giant food buffet, sit back down, and Joelle orders more drinks. She tells us she saw LSanDrew sit up in bed the night before and reach for his water bottle. He felt around for it, but he was clearly blacked out. Instead, he picked up his cell phone and the light went on, illuminating his face. He brought the phone up to his mouth and tried to take a sip from it as if it was his water glass.

Joelle starts laughing at this point in the retelling (she'll start to tell a story and must stop because she's laughing too hard to go on), and says he looked really confused and wrinkled up his brow, and then brought the phone back up to his mouth to make another sip attempt. This time tipping it back more to try to get some out of it like it was almost empty.

LSanDrew was laughing and asked in his sandpaper versus cigarettes voice if he really did that? Joelle assured him, in her way, that he indeed, did do that. But LSanDrew is witty and quick, and he got the last laugh by saying, "That's why I wasn't thirsty when I woke up!"

She said his confused look stayed on his face and he lay back down and went back to sleep. It's always crazy times with my group of friends. You don't even have to be awake to be having fun! It never seems to end, and I hope it never will!

298.

GO BIG DUBY.
BOOM BOOM ROOM SERVICE!

Duby thinks ahead. Always. It's a trait he's had forever. He looked up Cancun head shops to find a dab rig. He found the good, pimp hotels and so many other things. But the best one is his love affair with 24-hour unlimited room service. At the Moon Palace you can call and order whatever you want, and they'll bring it from any of the restaurants. The only downside is it takes a while. Duby figured it was two hours out from order time to delivery to the room and started in on a master plan of ordering for us for the week.

We would all do a dab or smoke a joint and then go do something fun. Normally, the wave pool or the main pools and beach chairs. We would spend two or three hours doing that and by the time we got back to Duby's room, a giant feast would be awaiting us. Four strip steaks and salads, six orders of tortilla soup, sixteen tacos, four orders of ceviche, twenty-four chicken wings, and best of all, a dozen different deserts including fantastic cheesecakes and exotic chocolates for us to drool over. After Duby got his timing down, food was always waiting after whatever we did for the rest of the trip. Feast on! We ate it all!

299.
CID SWOOPING MY SHROOMS!

The last show was in the afternoon instead of at night. The crowd was non-existent, and we walked right up to the gate to go in. I was worried about my wristband not working for me after the first night's bullshit, so I wasn't even thinking about what was in my pockets.

The yellow shirt security guy poked at my pocket and asked what was in it. I showed him my glasses and my little baggy of Tums with folded up paper in it. He sent me to the CID security and the guy asked me what was in the little pieces of paper. I told him weed because I thought he would say okay and let me go in. It actually had two micro doses of mushrooms folded up in small pieces of paper to keep them separate. The guard asked me again what was in the papers, and I told him weed. Then he started to open them up and asked again what was in them. I told him mushrooms, and at that point I figured I was going to jail. He says, "So, you lied to me twice!" The guy asks another security guy to "run a scan on this" and I stand there waiting to see if I'm going down in Mexico for next to nothing. He opens one piece of paper up, sees that it is in fact mushrooms, then takes both doses and keeps them. He says, "I'm keeping both of these since you lied to me twice. I would have let you keep one if you hadn't lied to me twice, but now I'm keeping both. You can have your Tums back." I was pissed, but I wasn't going to a Mexican jail on a mushroom charge, so I didn't bitch.

I walked into the show and then I got mad. This was my last show, we paid insane amounts of money for it, and the guy treated me like I was 15, not 55. The fact that he told me it was okay to have them if I had told him the truth was even more maddening. If that's the case, then it needs to say in the CID guidelines for the show, *just be honest and tell security what drugs you have when they ask, and they'll let you right in to the show.* But it did *not* say that in any of the rules.

So, Mr. Security, why do you need to be such a hard guy? You signed on for a three-month CID job in lovely Cancun, Mexico. You get paid well, you have a nice room at the resort, epic weather, a huge variety of awesome food, multiple pools to access, beautiful beaches and tons and tons of new hot girls every fucking day! And you still need to flex your muscle and be uncool.

The Dead audience is the most mellow ever. You had no reason to be that way. Yet, you were. Why man? All your coworkers (who were awesome) were in good moods. Five of them were standing there just past the entrance, and one guy made a very funny joke about one of my tattoos. We all laughed and the bad mood you put me in lifted. Not sure why you were so salty though man. You got it really good down there.

300.
LAST DAY IN THE SAND.

The final day was epic, and the band played to us, the sun, and the ocean all afternoon. Naomi and I got up close and swayed together in the breeze.

"Playin' in the Band" for the opener of the last day of Playin' in the Sand seemed appropriate, and the jam in the middle was rolling and flowing like the waves in the ocean on our left!

A dream like "Uncle John's" floated out of "Playin'" and had the whole crowd grooving back and forth in unison. "Dark Star" suddenly morphs out of "Uncle John's," and it's off to that special place in your head where the music endorphins release, and you're tripping without having to trip! "Dark Star" has that power to send you places! "Dark Star" filled the gap left by my confiscated mushrooms! During this gorgeous version the music *was* the high!

Naomi likes acid *and* mushrooms and she had chosen the former this afternoon. The effects were clearly showing as she danced barefoot in her sundress, being wonderful, beautiful, and tan!

When Dead and Company open the first set with "Playin'" and end it seven songs later with "Terrapin," you know you're in fantasy set land and you still get to wonder how they can top the first set? How about "Scarlet," "Fire," "He's Gone," "China," "Rider?" And then "Althea" after "Drums" and "Space?" Not so much a topper of the first set, but an equally exciting song combination!

"Althea" after "Space" was a rare and unexpected treat and it took me by surprise. I like hearing it deep in the second. "Althea" is not just for first sets anymore!

We slowly walked out after an ironic "U.S. Blues" encore. After three fantastic shows, and all the sunshine I could handle, I was not missing January in Oregon, and I was not feeling the blues for the U.S. I love Mexico and I could Play in the Sand there forever!

301.
THE SEASON OF WHAT NOW?

At this stage in my life, I was light years away from where I started seeing shows, to where I ended up seeing shows. I always thought Jerry would live for a long, long time. I could not have imagined it would be so different now. Who would have thought a modern-day pop star would ask to play guitar in the Dead after hearing a studio version of "Althea?" If some acid fueled, self-proclaimed soothsayer had said to me this would be the future of the Dead way back when, I would have politely said, "You're way too high bro."

But it really did happen, and it has morphed into something truly incredible. If you break it down, it's not the same. It never will be the same and it never should be the same. That's been the backbone of the whole deal the entire time anyway, right? Never do it the same way twice. Even if it's half the old band and half a new band.

It still catches and holds onto the real vibe that we all love so much and remember in our heads so vividly. And that is what our hearts and our heads need, and we still have it today, so I'm running with it!

302.
MORE SHOWS? NOPE!

2020 started out as a thrilling year to look forward to in terms of following Dead and Company. I was anticipating being on the road and hearing and seeing all the gigs they had scheduled to play.

We saw a most incredible show to ring in the New Year at The Chase, and then had a trip of a lifetime to see the Playing in the Sand shows in Cancun, Mexico. New Orleans Jazz Fest for our first time, was on the horizon for May 2nd. I was excited. I hadn't been to NOLA since 2000 with Far-L. The Summer Tour had been announced with sixteen shows around the Midwest and East Coast, and the *Farmer's Almanac* predicted good summer weather. It was looking perfect!

It took Naomi and I a little time to decide if we could do NOLA. We finally decided we would go after much pushing and prodding from Joelle and LSanDrew. We decided to fly into another city to save money, and then rent a car and drive a few hours to Jazz Fest. Joelle already had a super cool house rented for us. Ferd, Duby and Brandy, Duby's girl, had already confirmed, and it was a go as far as we were concerned. Same rad crew. Another show. Another new city. More Dead and Co!

303.
FUCKING CORONA VIRUS!

Then the whole world went to shit! It started as a minor warning. A virus is going around in China and it's spreading. That was all we heard at first. Then came the report of the deaths associated with this virus. They called it a Corona Virus. The virus that wears the crown. The King of all Virus!

King Corona was unjust, unmerciful, and unrelenting. Killing across the globe with seemingly no regard for race or creed, sparing some, but taking thousands and thousands of others in a swift and dramatic way. Separating families from dying loved ones because you couldn't share the same air in the same room with them, or you would also be joining them.

All the restaurants, bars, schools, banks, and everything else except essentials like gasoline and groceries, shut down. Unemployment hit high marks not seen since the great depression. Then they said don't go out. Don't interact with others. Limit yourself to your immediate family. Stay Home. Save Lives. Wear a Mask.

The streets in every city were empty. Business after business shut their doors and put up permanently closed signs. Everyone was told to wear a mask and stay a safe social distance of six feet or more away from one another. Normal life skidded to an abrupt halt and a new way of living was force fed to us by mother nature.

304.
A FEW MONTHS LATER.

I'm writing this section in April 2020. The new pandemic took hold about three months ago and quickly got way out of hand. I've barely seen any of my tour friends for months now. We cancelled our plans as the events we were scheduled to attend were cancelled. Duby moved back to Portland from the M*A*S*H set in NorCal during this time, and Ferd lives in Portland, so we had a little interaction with each other. Mainly to discuss when we could go back on tour. Or if we could ever go back on tour?

We had no idea how things would eventually turn out. Will we ever be able to get together in large groups again? Will all the current band members remain unaffected by King Corona? If a year or two goes by, will they even want to tour anymore? Three of six of the band members are no longer spring chickens. All of this has been discussed and mulled over for weeks and weeks now, with no solution or cure in sight. Nothing on the horizon so far. Nothing, except hope! Right now, that's the only thing keeping our "Ship of Fools" from sinking. Pure, positive hope for the future.

We can get there! I want to see you all on "The Golden Road" once again. Let's see how it turns out.

305.
TWO YEARS LATER

Now it's December 2021 and this book is finally done! Shows started back up with Billy and the Kids, and then Bobby and Wolf Bros. at Red Rocks on two different occasions in early summer! Playing In the Sand was announced and sold out immediately! Then they added another PITS and it sold out just as fast!

Just as everyone dropped a million billion bucks on those shows, they announced a 31-show Summer Tour of mainly Southern, Midwest and East Coast shows. As soon as vaccinations went up and sickness went down, Dead and Company Tour was back on in grand form, but I couldn't go yet.

This being my first book, it took me far longer to finish than I predicted. Tour started in Raleigh, and I was *not* on the bus! I was proofing and formatting and learning how to book it! Two days before the Phoenix show I had enough done to go promote Tour Head. I hopped a plane to Arizona, and OG Mt. Hood homie, Ethan *RatBoy* Ball, picked up Ferd, Joelle, and me. It was on again for the last five shows of the 2021 Fall Tour!

Phoenix, Chula Vista, and three nights at the amazing Hollywood Bowl, culminating with the Halloween show! Exceptionally cool costumes abounded! Our adventure was crazy and fun as always, but that's a story for another time. I'll just say it started with three missed plane flights by all of us who flew, and it went comedically sideways from there, like Dead Tour always has, always does, and always will!

Long live your passions for this music we all love! Thanks for coming on this road trip with my friends and me!

Here's to years!

See you on tour!

-Nordy 2022

Me with Grateful Dead ticket. Welches OR. Summer 1995. (Selfie)

**Jeff Evans. Front row during set break. 101 degrees. Eugene OR.
Summer 1994. (Unknown)**

Here's what I did with my life after Dead Tour. Timberline,
Mt Hood OR. Summer 1998 (Patrick Lennox Wright)

My dear friends Farrell and Laurie Timlake.
Fare Thee Well, Los Angeles CA. Summer 2015 (Selfie)

Scott Miller. I saw my first show with him in 1981.
Hollywood CA. Fall 2021 (Selfie)

Joelle Hicks with the late Laura Merriman. On Tour until the end! RIP.
Denver CO. Summer 2017. (Unknown)

**Owlyn Madrone at his first show ever, after catching the vapors!
Gorge. George, Washington. Summer 2019 (Selfie)**

**Steven Ferdinand half naked and dancing it up for his
50th Birthday show! Denver CO. Summer 2019 (Nordy)**

**Ferd, Duby, Joelle, me and MDOT Dylan.
New York City NY. Fall 2019 (Unknown)**

**Pete and Kate Rasato. Madison Square Garden.
New York City NY. Fall 2019 (Nordy)**

Mark Rockwell and me. Bethel CT. 2019 (Nordy)

Kurt, Doreen, Kelly, Heather, Ernest and me.
Bethel CT. Fall 2019 (Mark Rockwell)

Ferd and me doing nitrous on New Year's Eve. San Francisco CA. Winter 2019 (Nate Duby)

The inside of the Dead and Company New Year's Eve show at midnight! San Francisco, CA. Winter 2020 (Nordy)

Marque at the check in at the Playin in the Sand shows in Mexico. Playa Del Carmen, Mexico. Winter 2020 (Nordy)

Josh and Sally, Naomi and Joelle. Minnesota homies! Playa Del Carmen, Mexico. Winter 2020 (Nordy)

**Nate Duby on his magic Unicorn. PITS. Moon Palace, Mexico.
Winter 2020 (Nordy)**

**The infamous LSanDrew on a roll! Moon Palace, Mexico.
Winter 2020 (Nordy)**

**Joelle and Naomi loving life! Moon Palace, Mexico.
Winter 2020 (Nordy)**

**Me and my lovely lady Naomi, relaxing on the sandy beach post PITS.
Tulum, Mexico. Winter 2020 (Nordy)**

MY TOUR HEAD FRIENDS: WHERE ARE THEY NOW?

Well, I know where they are! I had to ask them to fill in my memory gaps here and there for this book.

Amy.

Amy is my younger sister who has always had a wonderful sense of appreciation for great rock and roll! Eric Clapton is her Jerry! She is married to Jim and has two children.

Scott Ernest aka E.

Scott lives in Bethel, Connecticut and is the national manager for a large shipping company. We went to Halloween 2019 at Madison Square Garden together and I visit him in Connecticut when I can. Scott has two adult children.

Dan Stein.

Dan lives in Eugene Oregon. He is the Top Dog at a large organic produce farm he has been tending for many years.

Cultivation is his passion! Dan's fantastic sarcastic humor always kept us laughing going down the road.

Mark Rockwell.

Mark is married to his wife Kathleen. He lives on the historic 300-year-old Rockwell Family Farm on Rockwell Road. He owns a fine craftsmanship company and is restoring the original historic 1700s built, Rockwell School House as of the writing of this book.

George Jurdy.

George lives in Old Town Portland, Oregon. He has been a Repo Man among *many* other jobs over the last 40 years. He still attends shows when he can.

Scott Miller aka ML.

Scott lives in a gated community in Tijuana, Mexico and is a skip tracer for a repossession and debt collection company. Scott has the best memory of anyone in this book and I thank him greatly for his contributions.

Kurt Ogrinc.

Kurt has two grown children, a boy and a girl and lives with his wife Doreen in Connecticut. He is an internet tech by trade. Kurt is one of my biggest musical influences in my lifetime.

Pete Rasato.

Pete is married to his wife Kate. They have of a daughter and two sons and live in Colorado. Pete has been a schoolteacher, and a youth mentor for over 30 years. I see him at Dead and Company shows now, more than ever.

Alan Petrasek.

Alan lives outside of Sacramento, California. His wife Stana is a recognized artist. He has two adult children and one grandchild. He wore a Jerry Garcia tie and ran a successful insurance agency for 20 years. He is now semi-retired and free to ride his Harleys. His son-in-law, Zack Bowden, has played drums on tours for Phil Lesh, Jackie Green and Steve Kimock, among other notables.

Farrell Timlake aka FAR-L.

Far lives in the peninsulas of Washington State and raises goats for his boutique soap business on Grateful Goat Farms. He is also Vice President of Marketing at

White Rabbit Cannabis Franchise Company. Farrell has two adult children.

Laurie Timlake.

Laurie is Far-L's wife. She works with him processing and shipping out the goat soap to pretty faces in shiny places and is an internet marketer. Far-L, Laurie and I kept up the Dead tradition, seeing as many Dead or Dead related shows as we could in the Northwest during the last fifteen years.

Mike Simpson aka EZ Mike.

Mike is a legendary music producer. He, along with John King are known as the Dust Brothers. They have worked with the best artists in the world and have created multiple gold and platinum records including the incredible *Paul's Boutique* by The Beastie Boys.

Sue Higgins.

I saw a lot of fantastic shows with Sue! She lives in Seattle and has two grown children with Farrell Timlake.

Melissa S.

Melissa was a college student at Pitzer when we met in line for tickets in 1982. Meeting her brought me back to the Dead Heads I needed! I believe she lives in Oakland, California. She is probably/most likely a doctor.

Craig Benson.

Craig lives in Redding, California. He has been in restaurant and hotel management for the last 40 years. He is still seeing shows and I hope to see a few with him again! Always a good time!

Kip Bailey.

Kip lives in Redding. He has worked at the logging mills and various other jobs in his area his entire life. Still seeing shows and I hope to see a few again with him as well.

Jeff Evans.

Jeff is married and still lives in Portland, Oregon. He is an avid live music collector and a human archive of Grateful Dead concert knowledge.

He has been a mail-carrier for more than 30 years. Jeff contributed much to this book!

Dave Stotts.

Dave is a multitalented photographer working in multiple mediums at any given time. He's been a Photographer Pass holder at Grateful Dead, JGB and Dead and CO. shows for decades. He lives in Oceanside, California and is one of my favorite tour friends to this day!

He now has a top-secret job working with government manatees. Don't tell anyone.

Memphis Chris.

Chris was an entrepreneurial Tour Head and a smooth hustler from Tennessee. Chris was one of the most pivotal people I ever encountered in Grateful Dead life, and I only hung out with him for *sixteen* days. Last seen in Berkeley, California.

Willie Waldman.

Willy is one of my favorite Grateful Dead Tour friends of all time! He is a Grammy Award winning horn player who had already played with many famous people in Memphis prior to us meeting.

He went on to play on some of the world's greatest recordings by artists such as Sublime, Snoop Dogg and Tupac Shakur and has performed with Phil Lesh and Ratdog. He is now in supergroup Banyan and leads the fully improvisational Willie Waldman Project.

Candy.

The Acid Queen! Candy lived wherever the wind took her and sometimes Memphis. She was always epic to be around. Our trips were extensive, and exceptionally memorable! Last seen in Memphis, Tennessee.

SF Paul.

We were the skateboard boys! We met through Candy. Paul was young, fun and a hard partier. Last seen in Providence, Rhode Island.

Clark Caswell.

Clark lives in Portland. He got sober 25 years ago and now runs his own treatment center for people suffering from drug addiction. Clark and I see the same Dead and Company shows now all the time now!

Naomi Yospe.

Naomi and I met in Portland in 1987 and attended the same shows, we just didn't drive together. We dated a bit then and stayed friends over the years. We got together again in 2010. We have been together since. I love you baby! Thank you!

Big Rick.

Big Rick was a tour staple who lived in Portland for a year, then went back on permanent Grateful Dead Tour. Big Rick was one of the fun ones to attend a show with. Never a dull moment! Last seen in Los Angeles.

VW Mike.

Mike had the best running Volkswagens ever! He is a licensed VW mechanic, and it was a pleasure to ride with him. Last seen in Portland, Oregon.

Chris Feeney.

Chris went on trips with VW Mike and was always a fun and funny person to travel with. Last seen in Portland, Oregon.

Kelly P.

Lives in Connecticut and is a nurse practitioner. She attends East Coast Dead and Company shows with Scott Ernest regularly these days, so we get to reconnect occasionally!

Heather R.

Lives in Connecticut and manages a bank. Our youth was a wonderful, special time in life to me. I still see her at Mark Rockwell's reunions when I go on East Coast runs.

Glenn M.

Among my best musical influences and one of my first real stoner buddies. BMX for him and skateboards for me. Last seen in Bethel, Connecticut.

Bill and Sharon.

Reed college grads who loved the Grateful Dead. We saw many shows together and trimmed mountains of weed at the yellow grow house. Last seen in Portland, Oregon.

Owlyn Madrone.

An avid and ripping skateboarder and tattoo artist living in Colorado, Owlyn is a young vibrant Head who is always welcome to roll with us!

Steven Ferdinand aka Ferd.

A renowned chef who has worked all over the world. Ferd lives in Portland, Oregon and consults for the restaurant industry when he isn't on Dead and Company Tour.

Nate Duby.

A successful legal Cannabis cultivation mogul. You don't get to know where he was last seen. He hits shows when the farm allows. And yeah, that's his real name.

Joelle Hicks aka Tink.

A Minneapolis hair stylist of the highest caliber. Shows are not the same without Tink! A member of our modern-day Dead and Company Tour crew for life!

LSanDrew

A fine carpenter when his hand works. He lives in Minnesota and hits shows when he can.

Chris.

A family man who lives in California. We never know when he'll show up, but I'll always have a cold Pabst for him.

Ellen Lipinski.

A television and movie Lead Artist in charge of creating and painting sets. If you see the big Jerry's head banner in the hit movie *Wild*, know that Ellen painted that!

Taylor Bradley.

A death metal head/Dead Head from Memphis/Portland and a semi-historian in the music world. His musical taste spans every genre.

Pauly Reyes.

Paul is a longtime cultivation and distribution pioneer. An expert skier and my OG favorite mountain companion, Pauly has a family and grows figs in Oregon.

Randall Scandal Standridge.

Scandal is a musician, chef, and a hell raiser! Our friendship started on Mt. Hood in Oregon. We have had insane adventures in the snow and at the strip bars, over the years! Scandal needs to write his own book!

TOUR VEHICLES.

Mom's car.

Dad's company car.

Blue Pinto Wagon.

Alan's VW Bug.

Farrell's Blue Truck.

Dan's Toyota Tercel.

Farrell's White Truck.

Brown Pinto Hatchback.

Chris's Green Volkswagen Van.

Willie's Red Dodge Van.

E's Green Monte Carlo

Green Tortoise.

VW Mike's Bug and VW Van.

George's Blue Volvo.

Mark's Toyota Celica.

White Audi.

Farrell's Audi #1 and #2.

White BMW.

White Jaguar.

Farrell's BMW.

Gold Honda Civic.

White Jeep.

White rental cars.

Skateboards, Subways, Trains, Planes, Buses, Crutches, and my Thumb.

PHOTO CREDITS.
(IN NO ORDER)
HUGE THANKS TO:

Alan Petrasek

Mark Rockwell

Scott Miller

George Jurdy

Ray Krebs

Farrell Timlake

Dave Stotts

Heather Ross

Nathan Duby

Joelle Hicks

Owlyn Madrone

Patrick Lennox Wright

Meaghan Gentry

Tim Lannon (RIP)

Donna Nordwall (RIP)

Bertha Klein (RIP)

ACKNOWLEDGEMENTS.

The author would like to express his thanks to the following:

Ron and Donna Nordwall.

Amy Nordwall-Ewan. Jim Ewan.

George and Bertha Klein.

Diana Klein-Dworshak.

Stan and Kevin Sexton.

The Kiely and Klein families.

Harry and Ellen Nordwall.

The extended Nordwall family.

My families on both sides who always treated the little spastic hyper me, with love and affection.

Special thanks to Jeff Johnson and Chandler Vinar for encouraging me to write down my crazy stories I would tell after work, while we drank Dickel Whiskey and Rainier Beer like Pigpen did! Here it is! Cheers!

ABOUT THE AUTHOR.

Nordy was born in Minnesota. He has been a contributing writer for Thrasher Skateboard Magazine and Snowboarder Magazine, among others. From youthful Grateful Dead tour head to professional snowboarder, to award winning content producer, to ordained reverend, to writer, Nordy has been on one hell of a bizarre psychedelic rollercoaster ride during his crazy life.

He lives in Oregon. Tour Head is his first book.